Property of:

_____

A PROFESSIONAL'S HANDBOOK ON GROUTING, CONCRETE REPAIR, AND WATERPROOFING FOR: Contractors
Architects
Engineers
Specifiers
Owners

FIVE STAR PRODUCTS, INC.
425 Stillson Road, Fairfield, CT 06430

FIVE STAR PRODUCTS, INC.
425 Stillson Road
Fairfield, CT 06430

Library of Congress
Catalog Card Number 87-082917

The following are registered trademarks of FIVE STAR PRODUCTS, INC. or affiliated companies:

FIVE STAR® GROUT and device
FIVE STAR® INSTANT GROUT
FIVE STAR® SPECIAL GROUT 100
FIVE STAR® SPECIAL GROUT 110
FIVE STAR® SPECIAL GROUT 120
FIVE STAR® SPECIAL GROUT 130
FIVE STAR® SPECIAL GROUT 150
FIVE STAR® SPECIAL GROUT 160
FIVE STAR® SPECIAL GROUT 200
FIVE STAR® SPECIAL GROUT 400
FIVE STAR® SPECIAL GROUT 550
FIVE STAR® EPOXY GROUT
FIVE STAR ET® EPOXY GROUT
FIVE STAR® RAPID EPOXY GROUT
FIVE STAR® SPEED EPOXY GROUT
FIVE STAR® HIGHWAY PATCH
FIVE STAR MAGPHOS™
FIVE STAR® CONCRETE PATCH
FIVE STAR STRUCTURAL CONCRETE™
FIVE STAR STRUCTURAL CONCRETE™ V/O
KEMBLOK®
NBEC®
DEVOIDER®
PERMANENT LIFE AGGREGATE®
PLA®
SEACON®
SUMMERSET®
WCM® and device.
NOMIX™ Cement
PostSet™

The tables, data, and other information in this book have been obtained from many sources, including professional architects, engineers, contractors, subcontractors, manufacturers, government organizations, trade associations and suppliers of building materials. The publisher has made every reasonable effort to make this book accurate and authoritative, but does not warrant, and assumes no liability for, the accuracy or completeness of the text or its fitness for any particular purpose. It is the responsibility of the users to apply their professional knowledge for the use of the information contained in this book, to consult the original source, publisher or manufacturer for additional information when appropriate, and, if they themselves are not professional experts in the field, to consult with **FIVE STAR PRODUCTS, INC.** when appropriate.

TABLE OF CONTENTS

SECTION II - NONSHRINK EPOXY GROUTS

SECTION III - CONCRETE REPAIR

SECTION IV - CEMENTITIOUS WATERPROOFING SYSTEMS

COMMON CONVERSION FACTORS

LENGTH

1 inch	=	.0833 ft.	=	2.54 cm
1 foot	=	.333 yd.	=	.3048 m
1 mile	=	5280 ft.	=	1.609 km
1 meter	=	39.37 in.	=	3.281 ft.

AREA

pi	=	3.14159		
Circular inch	=	.7854 sq. in.		
Square inch	=	6.452 sq. cm.		
Square feet	=	144 sq. in.	=	.111 sq. yd.
Square yard	=	9 sq. ft.	=	.8361 sq. m
Square mile	=	640 acres	=	2.590 sq. km

VOLUME

Cubic inch	=	16.39 cc		
Cubic foot	=	1728 cu. in.	=	7.481 gal.
Cubic yard	=	27 cu. ft.	=	0.7646 cbm
U.S. gallon	=	231 cu. in.	=	3.785 liter
U.S. gallon	=	128 fl. oz.		
U.S. fl. oz.	=	29.57 cc		
Imperial gal.	=	1.20 U.S. gal.		
Imperial fl.oz.	=	.961 U.S. fl. oz.		

WEIGHT

1 lb. water	=	27.6 cu. in.	=	.1198 gal.
1 cu. ft. water	=	62.43 lbs.		
1 gallon water	=	8.345 lbs.		

WATER/CEMENT RATIO

Multiply W/C by 11.3 to obtain gallons per bag.

WEIGHT

1 ounce	=	28.35 g		
1 pound	=	16 oz.	=	.4536 kg
1 short ton	=	2000 lbs.	=	907.2 kg

TEMPERATURE

$$°C = \frac{°F - 32}{1.8}; \qquad °F = 1.8 \times °C + 32$$

METRIC CONVERSIONS

MULTIPLY:	BY:	TO GET:
inch	× 25.4 (exact)	= millimeter (mm)
square inch	× 6.452	= square centimeter (cm²)
cubic foot	× 0.02832	= cubic meter (m³)
pound per cubic foot	× 16.02	= kilogram per cubic meter (kg/m³)
pound per cubic yard	× 0.5933	= kilogram per cubic meter (kg/m³)
ounce (U.S. fluid)	× 29.57	= cubic centimeter (cm³) (milliliter)
quart (U.S. fluid)	× 0.9464	= cubic decimeter (dm³) (liter)
pound (avoirdupois)	× 0.4536	= kilogram (kg)
ton	× 0.9072	= megagram (Mg) (metric ton)
psi	× 6.895	= kilopascal (kPa)
psi	× 0.006895	= megapascal (MPa)
horsepower	× 745.7	= watt (W)
square centimeter per gram (cm²/g)	× 0.1 (exact)	= square meter per kilogram (m²/kg)
calorie per gram	× 4.184 (exact)	= kilojoule per kilogram (kJ/kg)
pound-force (lbf)	× 4.448	= newton (N)
pound-force (lbf)	× 0.004448	= kilonewton (kN)
temperature, degree Fahrenheit (°F)	(°F-32)/1.8	= temperature, degree Celsius (°C)
temperature interval, degree Fahrenheit (°F)	°F/1.8	= temperature interval, degree Celsius (°C)

PREFACE

This Handbook was developed for FIVE STAR PRODUCTS, INC. by U. S. GROUT CORPORATION, FIVE STAR HIGHWAY PRODUCTS, INC., and FIVE STAR WATERPROOFING PRODUCTS DIVISION as an aid to the owners, architects, engineers, and contractors involved in the selection, specification and placement of the materials described herein.

Since the day of its inception, the grouting industry has never had a definition of NONSHRINK. The earliest products were not NONSHRINK, which led to the expansion of the industry when other organizations realized they could make shrinking products and sell them as NONSHRINK grout.

The American Society for Testing and Materials (ASTM) and the American Concrete Institute (ACI) have tried for many years to establish test methods, standards, and specifications to correct this problem. The nature of these organizations is that the work that comes out of the committees must be on a consensus basis, which means that the manufacturers of the so-called "shrinking NONSHRINK grouts" must be accommodated.

Throughout the Handbook, when the word NONSHRINK is used, it means that once the grout is in place, there is no plastic or hardened *vertical* shrinkage at any time.

The Handbook will cover grouting, concrete repair and waterproofing materials used in the construction and building industry - their properties, manufacture, handling, placement and specification.

At the back of each section are documents describing the products discussed in that section.

This Handbook contains what are considered to be the standard procedures used throughout the construction industry at the time of the writing of this Handbook. Some of the recommendations occurring in this Handbook are subject to variations for unusual design or field conditions. The user should contact the manufacturer when unusual conditions occur.

There are some companies, such as FIVE STAR PRODUCTS, INC., who are constantly doing research and development work in this field. It is recommended that individuals working in this area keep in touch with such organizations in order to be current with the latest developments. An example of this is a recently developed, patented way of placing concrete without mixing. NOMIX CORPORATION of Fairfield, Connecticut handles this development. For further information regarding this major development, please contact FIVE STAR PRODUCTS, INC.

We wish to acknowledge the assistance of all the owners, architects, engineers and contractors, who, with their great wealth of experience, were of major assistance to us in the development of this Handbook. This information was compiled by the engineers and technical personnel of FIVE STAR PRODUCTS, INC.'s Engineering and Technical Center located in Fairfield, Connecticut.

SECTION I
NONSHRINK CEMENTITIOUS GROUT
INTRODUCTION

This section of the Handbook deals with NONSHRINK, cementitious, precision grouts used for structural and equipment setting purposes and other applications which require NONSHRINK capabilities. See Section II for precision, NONSHRINK epoxy grouts for areas of dynamic loading or chemical attack.

Selecting a NONSHRINK grout, whether it be a cement-based or an epoxy-based grout, will be determined by many factors. Under large, heavy, vibrating machinery where dynamic loads are present, or in chemical attack areas, one would normally expect to use a NONSHRINK epoxy grout. In most other applications, one would normally expect to use a cement-based grout.

The cost of grouting is a small portion of the total expense of a construction project, and the material cost of the grout is minor when compared to the labor cost for installation. Often, too little attention has been given in the engineering stage to the selection and specification of the grout. An increase in the degree of sophistication of machinery and the need for alignment has caused the choice of grouting materials to become a critical issue.

The need for this precision has led to the development of a NONSHRINK grout. The proper selection and specification of the appropriate type of NONSHRINK grout will save much time and effort as well as liability.

To meet the need to evaluate precision, the ASTM studied this matter for many years and selected a test procedure and developed a standard now known as ASTM C 827-87 (Standard Test Method for Change in Height at Early Ages of Cylindrical Specimens from Cementitious Mixtures) to measure the volume change of grouts. This is presently the only approved ASTM standard for measuring volume change of grouts.

See following photograph of test equipment.

ASTM C-827

ASTM C-827 test equipment

"NONSHRINK GROUT" is generic terminology used with the assumption that there is one commonly understood definition. This is not the case. The phrase has been used indiscriminately. In order to discuss the subject of NONSHRINK grout, a definition is required, and practical considerations must be understood.

FIVE STAR PRODUCTS' major breakthrough in NONSHRINK grouts assured the designer and owner that the grout used would perform to expectations. A grout that does not shrink in the plastic state will bond to a clean baseplate, and if it is dimensionally stable in the hardened state, it will retain that bond. Conversely, when grouts shrink in the plastic state, no bond develops, causing loss of EBA *(Effective Bearing Area)*. Additionally, when materials shrink in the hardened state, there is a further loss of EBA.

In precision NONSHRINK grouting, the critical dimension is the vertical dimension. In this Handbook, when the word NONSHRINK is used, it means that once the grout is placed, there is no plastic or hardened vertical shrinkage at any time. A NONSHRINK grout should completely and permanently fill a space and provide high Effective Bearing Area (EBA). To achieve this high EBA, it is essential that no vertical shrinkage occur. Shrinkage in the plastic and/or hardened state reduces or eliminates EBA. It is essential that the reader recognize the importance of the NONSHRINK property and its correlation to EBA so that equipment and bases are properly supported.

Certain grouts which attempt to compensate for plastic shrinkage by expanding in the hardened state will require an extended period of wet cure. Trying to correct for plastic shrinkage by this method results in a very dangerous condition which is very difficult to control. This hardened expansion usually results in a tremendous force which often warps or misaligns baseplates. The material will often self-destruct and lose its structural integrity.

Thus, to grout completely and permanently a designated space, the grout must be NONSHRINK in the plastic state and dimensionally stable after hardening, with no expansion in the hardened state.

In addition to NONSHRINK requirements, other physical properties such as workability, versatility, reliability and durability must be considered. Specific applications may require sulfate resistance, high temperature exposure, high early strength, low heat of hydration, or other special requirements. No *single* type of grout can supply the requirements of the *variety* of applications encountered. Engineers and specifiers should have various types of cementitious grouts available for selection to meet constantly varying construction requirements.

Some of the advantages of cement-based grouts are their economy, ease of installation, and the wide variety of conditions under which they can be used.

Cement-based grouts usually contain hydraulic cement, sand, and other ingredients which attempt to compensate for plastic and/or hardened shrinkage and are mixed with potable water. In the past, added ingredients were: iron aggregate, aluminum powder and various cementitious materials. Such ingredients were either marginally successful or totally unsuccessful. In the mid 1960's, U. S. GROUT CORPORATION introduced a major breakthrough in technology which resulted in grouts that are truly NONSHRINK. These products exhibit controlled expansion in the plastic state at various temperatures (unlike aluminum powder grouts) and are dimensionally stable in the hardened state (unlike iron grouts and grouts containing shrinkage-compensating cements). Some countries have now banned the use of aluminum powder and have generally phased out the use of iron grouts.

A NONSHRINK grout should be NONSHRINK when tested by appropriate ASTM standards. Effective Bearing Area should be the ultimate criteria for acceptance.

The intent of this section of the Handbook is to review the proper selection, specification and use of all types of NONSHRINK grouts. The Handbook will serve as an aid to those who must determine which type of grout to use, how to properly specify grouts and how to design for a specific application.

CHAPTER 1
SELECTING A CEMENTITIOUS
NONSHRINK GROUT

In the grouting industry, there are two basic categories of cementitious grout. There are the NONSHRINK cement-based grouts and other miscellaneous grouts which would include aluminum powder grouts, iron grouts, dry pack grouts, fiber grouts, expansive cement grouts, and field proportioned grouts.

A NONSHRINK grout is a grout that does not shrink in the plastic state, is dimensionally stable in the hardened state, and bonds permanently to a clean baseplate. Therefore, to grout completely and permanently a designated space, the grout must be NONSHRINK in the plastic state and dimensionally stable after hardening.

Air-releasing (non-metallic) grout is considered the most popular precision grouting material on the market today. It was developed in the mid-1960's as a replacement for the self-destructing iron grouts. It has been extremely useful because it may be used for critical and non-critical applications. For twenty years, air-releasing (non-metallic) grout has been supporting the most sensitive machinery, both vibrating and stationary, and has been used as the primary grout for nuclear power plants which have the most demanding specifications. This non-metallic grout contains PLA which has the property of controlling the release of minute air bubbles without changing the chemistry of the cement, and totally eliminates plastic shrinkage. It develops very high effective bearing area and long term vertical dimensional stability through the use of DEVOIDER. Products utilizing PLA and DEVOIDER are known as FIVE STAR GROUTS.

Metallic powder grouts were developed many years ago. The only metallic powder grouts still in limited use are aluminum powder grouts. Aluminum powder grouts are seldom specified, and the manufacturers, due to a poor history, seldom will identify their grouts as aluminum powder grouts and are unwilling to identify, in their literature and on their prepackaged product, that they contain aluminum powder. The use of the word "non-ferrous" or the absence of the word "non-metallic" is a general indication of an aluminum powder grout. The volume change of aluminum powder grouts is unpredictable due to the minute quantity, distribution, and fineness of the aluminum powder used, the variations in the alkali content of the cement, and the variations in temperature at time of placement. In addition, aluminum powder grouts provide no mechanism to correct shrinkage in the hardened state. Therefore, aluminum powder grouts should never be used in critical applications as NONSHRINK grout since they are unreliable and uncontrollable. When submitted for use, aluminum powder grouts should be used only for non-critical applications and the designer should specify that an engineer closely supervise the mixing and placement. It should be noted that the cost of this supervision makes the use of aluminum powder grouts very expensive.

The iron grouts originally depended on oxidation of the iron filings to create expansion after hardening, which may cause machinery misalignment. This is uncontrollable and often results in the breaking out of the grout. This method is seldom used today because of its failure to perform satisfactorily due to the high plastic shrinkage, drying shrinkage, and breaking out. In an attempt to correct the problems evident in iron grouts, some manufacturers have introduced new products in which the iron is coated against oxidation and therefore provides no shrinkage correction in either the plastic or hardened state.

There are combinations of coated irons and expansive cements, but like the above, they are not NONSHRINK.

Dry pack grout (a mixture of sand/cement with only enough potable water to make a stiff mix) was used for many decades before the development of precision NONSHRINK grouts. At the time, this was the only known way to reduce the shrinkage of cement-based grouts to an acceptable level. This method is seldom used today because of the high installation cost and its failure to perform adequately.

Fiber grouts are still in the development stage. The fibers have no relationship to the NONSHRINK properties of a grout. They are merely installed in the grout to hold the mortar together. There are many types of fibers, the most commonly known are glass, metal or plastic fibers. There has been no advantage found in the use of these materials in a grouting application. However, there is still considerable talk by the manufacturers of fibers about their potential use. At present, fiber grouts are in the category of exotic materials and offer no advantages.

Expansive cement grouts are used for non-critical applications because of the probability of causing misalignment of machinery due to their expansion in the hardened state and their high drying shrinkage. The expansive cement grouts generally exhibit plastic shrinkage. Upon drying, they exhibit even greater drying shrinkage than sand/cement grouts. In the expansive grout category, there are also gypsum products which are purported to be used for grouting. However, their durability, bond, and other properties are not up to standards and have not been accepted for permanent installations.

Field proportioned grouts can be made up of sand/cement and various additional components, but they are almost impossible to control because of the lack of proper proportioning in the field, and the use of the shrinkage eliminating ingredient is often one that is not in the NONSHRINK category.

There are two products, PLA and SEACON, which can be used with proper supervision in the field to make a field proportioned NONSHRINK grout. They are available from FIVE STAR PRODUCTS, INC. However, this method is not recommended unless the project requires an enormous quantity of grout and the supervisor is well trained in grout blending and placement.

In selecting and specifying a cement-based grout, there are many options for the specifier to consider. The specifier can select a fast-setting grout, a high temperature resistant grout, a highly chemical or sulfate resistant grout, a special colored grout for grouting stonework, or a low heat of hydration grout where deep pours are being used.

Each of these grouts is available in various consistencies for placement, including a pumpable consistency. In general, the selection can be made by using the following Grout Selection Chart. Once the appropriate grout has been determined, the literature in the back of this section should be referred to in order to ensure that the grout selected meets these requirements.

If the grouting application is not covered in this Grout Selection Chart or the manufacturer's literature, you should contact **FIVE STAR PRODUCTS, INC.** for the product that meets your specific requirement.

FIVE STAR PRODUCTS is well known for its ability to formulate grouts for special purposes. The Engineering and Technical Center people are constantly developing new products and properties and also keep up technical exchanges of data and developments worldwide.

NONSHRINK CEMENTITIOUS GROUT SELECTION CHART

All Grouts Must Offer The Following Properties:

- Precision Nonshrink
- High EBA (Effective Bearing Area)[1]
- Contain DEVOIDER[2]

ENTER

Impact, Vibration, Chemical Resistance, High Live Loads	**No**	Use Cement-Based Grouts

Yes

See Section II —
Epoxy Grouts

CONDITION:

Special Grouting	**No**	FIVE STAR GROUT

Yes

CONDITION:

Tight Clearances	**Yes**	FIVE STAR SPECIAL GROUT 100
Large Volume Placements for Difficult and Limited Access Areas	**Yes**	FIVE STAR SPECIAL GROUT 110
Salt Water Attack Areas	**Yes**	FIVE STAR SPECIAL GROUT 120
Grout for Limestone, Marble and Granite	**Yes**	FIVE STAR SPECIAL GROUT 130
Sulfate Attack Areas Deep Placements	**Yes**	FIVE STAR SPECIAL GROUT 150
Radiation Shielding	**Yes**	FIVE STAR SPECIAL GROUT 160
High Operating Temperatures	**Yes**	FIVE STAR SPECIAL GROUT 200
Small Annular Spaces Cable Grouting	**Yes**	FIVE STAR SPECIAL GROUT 400
Hot Weather Grouting Sulfate Attack Areas	**Yes**	FIVE STAR SPECIAL GROUT 550
4 Hour Start-Up Selective Chemical Resistance	**Yes**	FIVE STAR INSTANT GROUT

[1] EBA: Effective Bearing Area — percent final face area of grout in direct contact with bearing plate.

[2] ALL FIVE STAR GROUTS contain DEVOIDER which offers the unique advantage of preventing cavities; overcoming plastic shrinkage; keeping the grout tightly against the plate for permanent support; producing the highest Effective Bearing Area.

CHAPTER 2
PERFORMANCE PROPERTIES AND TESTS

There are five basic physical performance properties that are of interest to the owner, architect, engineer, and contractor concerning NONSHRINK grout. In order of importance they are: vertical volume change/EBA, compressive strength, workability, reliability, durability and creep.

In this portion of the Handbook, different test methods, their technical applicability, and usefulness in evaluating performance requirements will be discussed.

A. VERTICAL VOLUME CHANGE/EBA

Vertical volume change is a vital performance property with respect to NONSHRINK grouts. Unfortunately, until recently there was little agreement on how and when to measure vertical volume change.

Horizontal length change is of little interest in grouting, except from the standpoint of extremely long pours where expansion and contraction joints are used.

Another procedure used in the past, which is not applicable to grout, was curing specimens in water. Procedures using this method are not applicable to grout because grout is almost never placed or cured under water or in a non-evaporating condition. Curing under water can make a cementitious grout temporarily swell, but shrinkage will take place on removal of the water.

A grout that has no vertical volume shrinkage in the plastic or hardened state will have a high Effective Bearing Area (EBA).

Since the word NONSHRINK means that once grout is in place, there is no plastic or hardened vertical shrinkage at any time, test methods have to be carefully selected to measure these properties.

The only approved ASTM standard for measuring vertical volume change for grouts is ASTM C 827-87 (Standard Test Method for Change in Height at Early Ages of Cylindrical Specimens from Cementitious Mixtures). This test measures the plastic volume change from the time of mixing and may be extended to cover the hardened volume change as well.

ASTM C 827 has a number of advantages. The results from this method are statistically reliable and can be reproduced consistently, assuring that the data generated is sound and can be used to make a judgment about the material's ability to perform. This test procedure may be continued for long term (28 day) results with great accuracy, negating the need for other test methods.

 Designation: C 827 – 87

AMERICAN SOCIETY FOR TESTING AND MATERIALS
1916 Race St., Philadelphia. Pa. 19103
Reprinted from the Annual Book of ASTM Standards. Copyright ASTM
If not listed in the current combined index, will appear in the next edition.

Standard Test Method for

CHANGE IN HEIGHT AT EARLY AGES OF CYLINDRICAL SPECIMENS FROM CEMENTITIOUS MIXTURES[1]

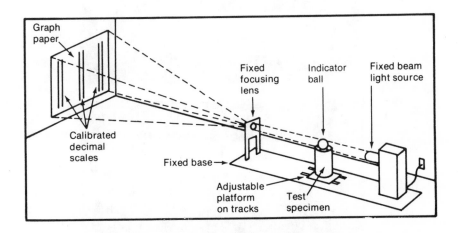

There is a test still being evaluated by ASTM to measure the hardened vertical volume change under a non-evaporating condition. This test is presently known as the Corps of Engineers Specification for Nonshrink Grout CRD-C-621 (formerly CRD-C-588), but has not reached the point of exhibiting enough reliability, consistency, or acceptance to become an ASTM standard. It should only be used in conjunction with ASTM C 827.

To be considered NONSHRINK, the vertical volume must not go below the original placement volume.

B. COMPRESSIVE STRENGTH

This property is adequately defined and understood. Since grout is generally placed in depths of two to three inches, the standard test method uses 2″ cubes which should be restrained to simulate a grouting application.

Compressive strength is determined by using the applicable portions of ASTM C 109 (Test Method for Compressive Strength of Hydraulic Cement Mortars) for cement-based grouts.

See following photograph of mold used in the test method.

The generally accepted minimum compressive strength for cement-based grout is 5,000 psi in 28 days.

C. WORKABILITY

The workability of a grout is of critical importance to the achievement of a high quality installation. Field forces face problems which are often unknown to the specifier. For many years, some grout manufacturers have been promoting fluid consistency, which is measured within approximately 30 seconds after mixing, and have not been promoting the concept of workability, which involves consistency, working time, and placement versatility.

Consistency is defined as the relative mobility or ability of freshly mixed material to flow. Working time may be defined as that length of time during which the grout maintains its ability to be placed and move under the equipment without development of "cold joints." A grout should maintain this ability for not less than 45 minutes. Placement versatility is critical because many jobs require different placement methods, i.e., pouring, pumping, troweling.

Selecting a grout by evaluating only one of the following properties: consistency, working time or placement versatility, will usually lead to placement problems. Eliminating any one of these three properties will often result in a shrinking grout, a grout with large cavities, and very low, if any, effective bearing area. This is exclusive of the cost of replacement of defective grouting jobs. By carefully reviewing each different workability property and the behavior of the grout in relation to these properties, a grout can be selected that will provide proper workability to achieve the highest effective bearing area with the lowest possible in-place cost.

CONSISTENCY

Consistency determinations are generally made immediately after mixing. Grout cannot be placed in the 30 to 60 seconds after mixing that it takes to perform a consistency determination. It is important that the grout remain workable for a minimum of 45 minutes after mixing to permit it to move under the equipment and to avoid "cold joints" which may develop during delays.

It is desirable to use placement aids such as vibrators, pumps or plungers to facilitate placement rather than over-watering the grout. While fluid grouts may be used where tight clearances exist, it should be borne in mind that the use of excess water to make a grout fluid will often increase the shrinkage, cause segregation, decrease strength, and result in reduced Effective Bearing Area.

Flow cones and flow tables are useful only in determining descriptive terms for grout. A grout described as "fluid" because it passes through a 1/2 inch opening in the allotted time, but which has a short working life and exhibits segregation, will not produce an acceptable installation.

A grout should provide variable consistencies so that placement methods such as troweling, flowing, pumping and plunging may be used.

WORKING TIME

Many manufacturers have developed grouts which stiffen rapidly (some in as short as 15 minutes) in an effort to minimize plastic shrinkage inherent in their grouts. This rapid stiffening causes quick loss of consistency which may cause the contractor to rush the job, creating problems with poor workmanship, entrapped air, and a lower effective bearing area. In addition, quick stiffening of these grouts will often result in the grout setting in the mixer, pumps, and hoses, causing blockages, cold joints, and large cavities during placement, thus resulting in little or no effective bearing area.

Therefore, working time must be determined prior to selecting a grout to ensure the contractor has adequate time to properly place the grout by the most reliable and economical method. Working time can be determined by performing tests for consistency repeatedly on the grout mix over an extended period of time. Unfortunately, many manufacturers are reporting only the initial consistency (30 seconds after mixing) of the grout. This does not relate to field conditions. The longer working time a grout has, the better the grouting job will be. For normal grouting, it is recommended that the grout have a useful working life of 45 minutes.

PLACEMENT VERSATILITY

It is very important for the contractor to have the maximum flexibility to place the grout using the most economical and reliable method that will result in the highest effective bearing area, without compromising the in-place properties of the grout. Some manufacturers offer only grouts that have a fluid and self-leveling consistency. Fluid grouting will require additional forming, watertight forms, and other extra installation procedures. Fluid grouting is not recommended except where extremely tight clearances exist. Many grouts which are sold as fluid grouts cannot be pumped, vibrated, or pushed into place because of their short working times. It is essential in selecting a grout that placement versatility be given major consideration. On most grouting projects, any grout used should be able to be pumped, vibrated, pushed into place or poured without segregation or loss in working time. The money that a fluid grout saves in placing is almost always lost in forming and clean up.

It is important that a contractor have flexibility to place grout using any method that will result in the highest Effective Bearing Area. Fluid-only consistency grouts with early stiffening properties deny the contractor any choice in placement method.

Grout should have the versatility to be plunged, poured, pumped, or vibrated. Strapping or chaining used to be used but has been found to cause entrapped air and is therefore not recommended.

The grout which provides the most placement versatility will allow the contractor to achieve the best possible installation at the lowest cost and should be the one specified. The advantages and disadvantages of grout being placed using a variety of methods is discussed further in this section.

EXAMPLES

The importance of three fundamental placement properties is exhibited in the following chart. Grout A, like many fluid grouts, has an initial high level of workability by being fluid, but stiffens quickly, thus losing all placeability in just over 10 minutes. The quick loss of consistency demonstrates poor placeability, since it results in an inability to place the grout before initial stiffening occurs.

The contractor will find he has to place the grout over an extremely short period of time before stiffening occurs. Frequently, this type of rapid installation of a fluid grout under normal grouting conditions results in trapped air, air bubbles forming under the baseplate, along with problems of blockages and voids caused by a non-continuous and incomplete grouting job due to the rapid loss of consistency. (In addition, many fluid grouts exhibit problems of segregation, lower strengths and high drying shrinkage caused by a high water-to-cement ratio or the addition of water reducing agents and other chemical admixtures.)

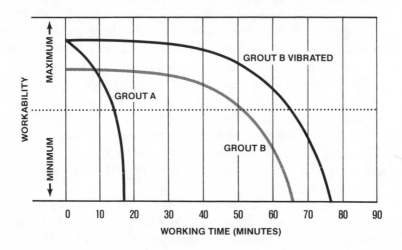

Long working time allows the contractor to place the grout at a proper pace to limit blockages, voids, and cold joints to produce the highest effective bearing area possible.

In summary, workability of the grout is to be determined by considering the available ranges of consistency, length of working time, and the placement versatility of the grout. FIVE STAR PRODUCTS, INC. provides grouts which are non-sag, trowelable, flowable, fluid, and can be vibrated, pumped or plunged into place. They provide long working times to ensure the highest quality of workmanship at the lowest possible cost, and highest effective bearing area without blockages, segregation, low strengths and other undesirable properties found in other grouts. For special applications such as very tight clearances and pumping over long distances, FIVE STAR PRODUCTS offers FIVE STAR SPECIAL GROUTS which possess an enhanced placeability property to solve the most difficult placement problems.

D. SEGREGATION

Segregation is the separation of aggregates of various sizes and densities from a mix. This is often caused by using excess water or fluid mixes. This will often result in grouts exhibiting shrinkage, low strength, and poor durability. Segregation can readily be measured by taking the material and pouring it directly into an ASTM C 827 light test container. After running of the light test to determine the shrinkage or expansion, the material in the container is allowed to harden. After hardening, the container is split in half lengthwise and segregation can be visually determined. Grouts with large particle sizes, or with heavy aggregate, are prone to segregation. A grout which segregates should never be used for NONSHRINK grouting. Most fluid and iron grouts exhibit considerable segregation. When segregation occurs, there is usually a total loss of EBA. (See paragraph H, Miscellaneous Properties and Tests, shown on the following pages.)

C-827 cylinder broken in half, showing
extreme segregation.

The consistency, working time, placement versatility, and segregation must be checked on every grout, before specifying or approving a contract, in order to ensure a good grouting installation.

E. RELIABILITY

The reliability of a material to behave in a predictable manner during placement is critical. Major concerns for cement-based grouts during placement are the unpredictable working time due to rapid stiffening and unpredictable volume changes due to some uncontrollable reactions resulting from such products as aluminum powder, which become exaggerated with temperature changes.

All grouts must be prepackaged to ensure their uniformity and reliability. This can only be accomplished by factory blending under controlled conditions.

The reliability of a grout is dependent on the manufacturer controlling the quality of the materials used in the grout, the manufacturing and blending procedures, the packaging, storage, handling and shipping, as well as the assurance of an approved Quality Control Program. This is discussed in the following Chapters 3, 4, and 5. For all equipment and other critical applications, it is essential that a NONSHRINK grout should have at least a ten year proven history of use.

F.   DURABILITY

Durability refers to the ability of a material to remain in service over a long period of time with little or no maintenance. With cement-based grouts, this means materials that have volume change in the hardened state, either positive or negative, should be avoided. Additives such as iron filings, either catalyzed or noncatalyzed, should not be allowed as they may cause the material to expand uncontrollably in the hardened state and cause cracking or raveling as shown in the following photograph. More importantly, expansion in the hardened state may cause misalignment.

Another material to be avoided is shrinkage-compensating cement which may also expand in the hardened state in the presence of water required for hydration.

Metallic and expansive cement grouts which expand after set often cause machinery to move out of alignment. If this occurs, the cost to the industry, exclusive of production downtime, is many thousand times the cost of the original grout.

For the engineer to ensure the maximum durability of cement-based grout, he should carefully evaluate the properties needed for each application. Consideration should be given to whether the job requires: flowable grout because of tight clearances; slow setting cement because of installation problems; high saltwater resistance; low alkali, nonstaining grout (white) for limestone or marble mortars or special coloring; hot weather grouting; very high sulfate resistance; high temperature resistance; impact or chemical resistant grout; an instant grout for immediate machinery start up. This entire selection of grouts is available from **FIVE STAR PRODUCTS, INC.** The engineer can also avail himself of pump grade grouts for each of the above categories in order to reduce installation costs and increase performance on large grouting jobs. Durability of epoxy grouts is discussed in Section II.

G. CREEP

The phenomenon of creep occurs in all materials. Creep is defined as deformation under the action of a constant load. Cementitious grouts may fail under certain circumstances if creep is not kept to a minimum.

The tendency of grouts to creep makes it very important that engineers, specifiers and contractors know in advance what the creep tendencies of the cementitious grout are. When selecting a cementitious grout, the creep tendencies must be known. Short term tests from which data has been extrapolated should be ignored. Creep is too important a factor under machinery and in post-tensioning, pre-tensioning and in other similar areas. A creep test should be of at least one year's duration, with all data actual, not extrapolated. An acceptable test for creep appears on pages II.16 and II.17 and is about to be approved by the ASTM. A photograph of the creep assembly follows.

To ensure that creep will remain within an acceptable range, two main rules should be followed:
1. Select a cementitious grout for which long term data are available, such as **FIVE STAR GROUT.**

-21-

2. Design such that the total of dead load (weight of equipment) plus live load (bolt torque load) does not exceed 500 psi.

H. MISCELLANEOUS PROPERTIES AND TESTS

There has been considerable discussion in recent years about bleeding of grouts. This is defined as water that accumulates on the surface of the grout due to settlement of the particles.

A truly NONSHRINK grout must not shrink in the plastic state or in the hardened state. NONSHRINK grout should also be required to expand slightly during the plastic state to ensure all spaces and voids are completely filled. In addition, this will ensure complete contact with the plate and eliminate excess water underneath the plate. Slight plastic expansion will also cause ejection of excess water from the grout when restrained by the plate. Ejection of this excess water will actually result in a lower water to cement ratio in the grout and, thus, a higher quality product.

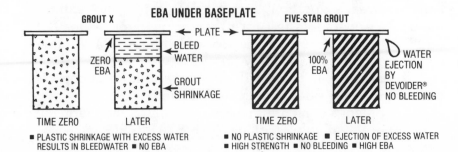

-22-

The ejection of this excess water is not to be confused with bleeding. Bleeding is the result of sedimentation. Water ejection can be demonstrated by pouring the grout into a glass container, screeding off at the top level of the container, placing a plate over the container, and noticing the water being ejected. If the grout shrinks below the top edge of the container, bleeding may result and there would be no possibility of water ejection. In addition, if the grout shows shrinkage, there will be no possible bond to the plate.

The significance of any water which may occur on the surface of the grout has to be evaluated on whether or not plastic shrinkage occurs. The advantage of slight plastic expansion and the resulting ejection of water will eliminate a potential problem of excess surface water which may occur in a grout under a baseplate.

If there is any doubt about the NONSHRINK capabilities of a grout when it arrives in the field, the cylinder plate test, as discussed in the Field Quality Assurance Program, should be used.

An unscientific test which is being promoted by some grout manufacturers is called the "plate test." In this test, a grout is placed under a steel plate which is intended to simulate a baseplate. However, contrary to standard field practices, the bottom of the plate is greased or waxed. After the grout is placed and hardened, the plate is then tapped with a rod to determine if there are any voids, and the plate is removed to inspect the surface of the grout.

This test makes no measurements whatsoever on whether the grout has shrunk vertically. A soupy sand/cement mix can be placed under the plate and may show a smooth surface with no voids, and yet it will have shrunk considerably down from the underside of the plate.

The tapping of the plate with a rod, contrary to what some manufacturers wish to believe, cannot discover voids under a plate. Recently, one of the foremost acoustical consulting firms was asked to evaluate this tapping procedure. After a test program, they stated unequivocally that tapping a baseplate with a rod would not determine voids under the plate.

They also found that very expensive sonic equipment would not determine if there were voids. The type of metal, thickness of the metal, consistency of the grout, spacing of the anchor bolts, tightness of the anchor bolts, and many other factors affect the sounding.

The baseplate test described above is unacceptable as a NONSHRINK grout test or as a test to determine voids. The failure to take vertical measurements invalidates the test. Further, the greasing or waxing of the plate is contrary to all recommended practices and prevents the grout from bonding to the plate which is critical for a NONSHRINK grout.

The cylinder test program covered in the next chapter is a test that *is* recommended for evaluating the NONSHRINK properties of a grout in the field.

CHAPTER 3
QUALITY ASSURANCE PROGRAMS FOR MANUFACTURER AND FIELD

Quality Assurance programs should be required for all grout manufacturers, and are required for many critical installations. There are two categories of Quality Assurance programs: manufacturer and field.

QUALITY ASSURANCE PROGRAM - MANUFACTURER

The grout manufacturer must maintain records of all the cements, sands, aggregates, and chemicals used. All containers of raw materials and finished product should have a code marking so that the source of all materials can be traced and verified as meeting the manufacturer's standards. The manufacturer should regularly take samples from the plant and verify them in his own test laboratory as meeting his requirements, including NONSHRINK properties. The manufacturer must maintain test records on production runs and should retain them for at least one year. Shipping tickets should be maintained at the plant and at the main office for all shipments.

Cement-based products stored beyond six months should not be shipped without the manufacturer's certification that the products meet the manufacturer's standards. The manufacturer should furnish written certification when required stating that the material is in accordance with the project and manufacturer's specifications.

The manufacturer should have instructions for normal placement conditions printed on the outside of the bag. These instructions should include the maximum/minimum mixing water limits in quarts per bag.

```
FIVE STAR GROUT

PRODUCTION PROCEDURES

QUALITY ASSURANCE PROGRAM

QA AUDIT CHECKLIST




                          FIVE STAR PRODUCTS, INC.
                          Fairfield, CT  06430
```

The manufacturer should have posted instructions for manufacturing the material at the plant. The accuracy of the weighing scales at the plant must be checked every six months, as required in a good Quality Assurance program.

The manufacturer should provide access to his production facilities by the engineer upon receipt of adequate notice for the auditing of the Quality Assurance Program. If a manufacturer cannot comply with this Quality Assurance Program verification, his products should not be approved.

All FIVE STAR GROUTS are manufactured in accordance with the most rigid quality control procedures. The FIVE STAR GROUT system is tailored around the Quality Assurance Program meeting the requirements of 10 CFR 50 Appendix B, Quality Assurance Criteria for Nuclear Power Plants as required by the Nuclear Regulatory Commission. Nuclear power plants have the highest standard of quality control in the United States. FIVE STAR GROUTS are supplied to 91% of the nuclear plants.

Certification of the performance of FIVE STAR GROUTS is available within 30 days after manufacture, due to the 28 day requirement of most test methods.

QUALITY ASSURANCE PROGRAM - FIELD

The engineer should establish in his specifications a Field Quality Assurance Program to ascertain that the grout he has specified meets his standards. This can be done by verifying the printed instructions on the bag and also performing a simple field test.

A random sample bag should be taken from the first shipment to the job site, opened, and mixed in accordance with instructions. Two standard 6 x 12 inch test cylinders should be filled with the grout mixture, screeded off and one immediately covered with a clean steel baseplate with two anchor bolt holes in it. The second cylinder is then immediately placed on top of the plate to simulate the restraining action of the machinery or columns.

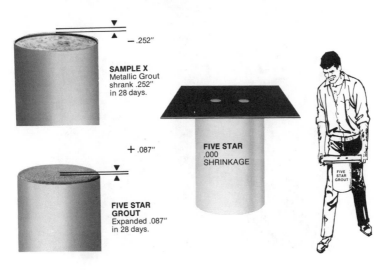

SAMPLE X
Metallic Grout
shrank .252"
in 28 days.

— .252"

+ .087"

FIVE STAR
GROUT
Expanded .087"
in 28 days.

FIVE STAR
.000
SHRINKAGE

Within 24 hours, the top cylinder, which is unrestrained, should show grout expanding higher than the screeded surface. The lower cylinder will show water ejection taking place under the baseplate, thus verifying there is no bleeding. At the end of 14 days, the top cylinder is to be removed and the baseplate with the cylinder below is to be carefully lifted in a vertical direction. If the cylinder bonds to the baseplate, the engineer is assured that the grout is NON-SHRINK. If the grout does not bond to the baseplate, the grout should be rejected.

FIVE STAR GROUT

GROUT "X"

In addition to this, cube specimens should be made in accordance with ASTM C 109, with a restraining plate placed over the molds to simulate the grouting application. These cubes should be cured under the same conditions as the actual grout and should be tested for compressive strength in accordance with ASTM C 109.

CHAPTER 4
ESTIMATING AND PURCHASING
OF CEMENTITIOUS GROUTS

ESTIMATING

Estimating the quantity of nonshrink grout required is easily done by calculating the grouting volume (length x width x average depth), converting to cubic feet, and then adding five percent for waste on large placements and ten percent waste for small placements.

Care should be taken to ensure that the published grout yield per unit is adjusted to a cubic foot basis. Many manufacturers market their grouts in units of unusual weights and volumes.

In estimating the quantity of grout which is sold in units other than one cubic foot, divide the manufacturer's yield into the number 1 to determine the actual number of units required for one cubic foot.

For example, a manufacturer has a yield in a 55 pound unit of .42 cubic feet.

$$\frac{1 \text{ cubic foot}}{.42} = 2.38 \text{ units per cubic foot}$$

For grouts that are not packaged in cubic foot units, care must be taken to proportionally increase the freight cost and the field handling cost. For example, if it takes 131 pounds of grout, as in the above example, to yield one cubic foot, the shipping cost would be 31 percent higher than a grout which yields one cubic foot per 100 pounds. In addition, if it takes 2.38 - 55 pound units to yield one cubic foot, the field handling cost should be increased approximately 2.4 times.

PURCHASING

Unfortunately, grouts are not all sold in cubic foot packages. Cement-based grouts are sold in 50, 55, 60 and 100 pound bags, one-half cubic foot bags and cubic foot bags. To ensure that all prices are directly comparable, all requests for quotation should be made in cubic foot units. Grouts must not be compared, bid, or purchased on a weight basis because there is no relationship to the volume. The customary unit of volume is the cubic foot. Requesting quotations in cubic foot units ensures direct price comparisons.

CEMENT BASED GROUTS

CEMENT-BASED GROUTS
ALL PATENTED * ALL PRECISION NONSHRINK * PERMA-
NENT ALIGNMENT * INDUSTRY'S HIGHEST EFFECTIVE
BEARING AREA * 45 MINUTE WORKING TIME * CHEMI-
CAL RESISTANT * HIGH TEMPERATURE RESISTANT *
NONMETALLIC * STABLE * PERMANENT * 4 HOURS -
4000 psi * RAPID STRENGTH GAIN * FLOW * TROWEL *
VIBRATE * PUMP * HIGH STRENGTH * HIGH BOND *
MANUFACTURED AND AVAILABLE WORLDWIDE

NONSHRINK CEMENTITIOUS GROUT
ESTIMATING SHEET

From Premeasured Units

		FIVE STAR	PRODUCT "X"
A.	Cost per Bag or Unit	_____	_____
B.	Yield per Bag or Unit (Cubic feet/bag or unit	_____	_____
C.	Cost per Cubic Foot (A divided by B)	_____	_____
D.	Total Cubic Feet Required (From field estimates)	_____	_____
E.	Total Material Cost (C x D)	_____	_____

CAUTION: INCLUDE A SURCHARGE FOR HAN-DLING BAGS THAT ARE NOT CUBIC FOOT BAGS AND FOR THE EXTRA FREIGHT CHARGES FOR SMALLER BAGS AS DESCRIBED IN THE PREVIOUS ESTIMATING SECTION.

CONVERSION TABLES
COST OF NONSHRINK GROUT PER CUBIC FOOT

Instructions:

1. Determine cost of grout per 100 lbs. (Not all grouts are supplied in 100 lb. bags.)
2. Determine cubic foot yield per 100 lbs. (stated in manufacturer's literature).
3. The intersection of the cost per 100 lbs. and the cubic foot yield per 100 lbs. in the body of the table is the cost per cubic foot of grout.

COST PER 100 LBS.	CUBIC FOOT YIELD PER 100 LBS.								FIVE STAR GROUT
	0.70	0.75	0.78	0.80	0.85	0.90	0.95	0.97	1.00
$16.00	22.86	21.33	20.51	20.00	18.82	17.78	16.84	16.49	16.00
$17.00	24.29	22.67	21.79	21.25	20.00	18.89	17.89	17.53	17.00
$18.00	25.71	24.00	23.08	22.50	21.18	20.00	18.95	18.56	18.00
$19.00	27.14	25.33	24.36	23.75	22.35	21.11	19.99	19.59	19.00
$20.00	28.57	26.67	25.64	25.00	23.53	22.22	21.05	20.62	20.00
$21.00	30.00	28.00	26.92	26.25	24.71	23.33	22.11	21.65	21.00
$22.00	31.43	29.33	28.21	27.50	25.88	24.44	23.16	22.68	22.00
$23.00	32.86	30.67	29.49	28.75	27.06	25.55	24.21	23.71	23.00
$24.00	34.29	32.00	30.77	30.00	28.24	26.67	25.26	24.74	24.00
$25.00	35.71	33.33	32.05	31.25	29.41	27.78	26.32	25.77	25.00
$26.00	37.14	34.67	33.33	32.50	30.59	28.89	27.37	26.80	26.00
$27.00	38.57	36.00	34.62	33.75	31.76	30.00	28.42	27.84	27.00
$28.00	40.00	37.33	35.90	35.00	32.94	31.11	29.47	28.87	28.00
$29.00	41.43	38.67	37.18	36.25	34.12	32.22	30.53	29.90	29.00
$30.00	42.86	40.00	38.46	37.50	35.29	33.33	31.58	30.93	30.00
$35.00	50.00	46.67	44.87	43.75	41.18	38.89	36.84	36.08	35.00
$40.00	57.14	53.33	55.28	50.00	47.06	44.44	42.11	41.24	40.00
$45.00	64.29	60.00	57.69	56.25	52.94	50.00	47.37	46.39	45.00
$50.00	71.43	66.67	64.10	62.50	58.82	55.56	52.63	51.55	50.00

To determine the comparative cost per cubic foot, use the above table. For comparative purposes, the Purchasing Agent should multiply the number of units per cubic foot by the delivered price per unit (which includes the manufacturer's quotation, plus tax and freight).

CHAPTER 5
CEMENTITIOUS GROUT DELIVERY
AND STORAGE PROCEDURES

A. DELIVERY CONDITION

Nonshrink cement-based grout should be shipped from the plants palletized, shrink-wrapped, and delivered to the site in sound, dry packages. It should be stored in a dry area in accordance with ACI instructions. The temperature should be approximately 70°F, but not below 40°F, and not above 90°F.

B. STORAGE DAMAGE

Any material which becomes damp or otherwise defective should be immediately removed from the site.

C. STORAGE TIME

The total job storage time of cement-based NON-SHRINK FIVE STAR GROUT should be limited to six months, or the manufacturer's recommended storage limit, whichever is less. For critical applications, it is recommended that a sample be sent to the manufacturer if the material has been stored for more than six months, for verification of the properties.

CHAPTER 6
CEMENTITIOUS GROUT
PLACEMENT PROCEDURES

INTRODUCTION

It is critical that proper placement procedures be followed in placing **NONSHRINK** grout. If they are not, the grout cannot be expected to perform as specified. This section of the Handbook details the procedures to be followed to ensure proper grout placement.

The selection of a grouting method best suited to the intended application should be the primary concern of the Engineer/Contractor. The size and number of plates to be grouted, the number and location of obstructions, anchor bolts, clearances, etc. should all be considered in determining which grouting method will produce the desired results.

Selecting a grout which can be placed in a wide range of consistencies, depending on installation requirements, will greatly simplify overall grouting for the project while providing the flexibility to satisfy each individual application.

Additionally, there are a large number of tools available to the contractor to facilitate the placement of the grout. The cost and complexity of the tools range from 2 x 4's nailed together to form a plunger, (see below)

"Typical Plunger"

to simple pumps,(see below)

to highly sophisticated systems costing thousands of dollars. One of the most valuable tools is a small, high frequency, round-tipped pencil vibrator (see below).

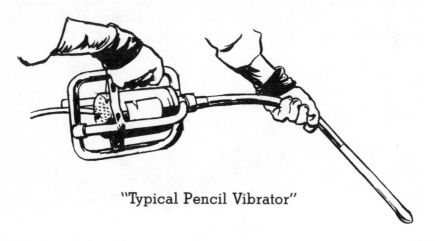

"Typical Pencil Vibrator"

This tool, like the plunger and pump, improves the quality of the placement of the grout, cuts down on labor costs, and has one additional advantage: rapid placement with resulting higher strengths.

A typical 2 ft. x 2 ft. baseplate with a 2 to 3 inch clearance underneath is best suited for a non-sag (trowelable) mix. The use of a flowable or fluid grout, unless absolutely required because of inaccessibility, is not desirable.

Using the minimum amount of potable water to place cement-based grouts prevents numerous problems and increases strengths. Additionally, when the use of flowable or fluid consistencies is required, it is essential that special forms be constructed to retain the mix. The forms must be watertight or leakage will occur.

On the 2 ft. x 2 ft. baseplate described above, it would take a carpenter from one-half hour to one hour to build the forms. On a larger application, it can often take a day or more for a team. The extra costs and loss of time should be carefully considered.

Once the flowable or fluid grout is in place and solidified, the forms must be removed, resulting in additional costs. In addition, the savings in placement time resulting from pouring fluid grouts will seldom compensate for the additional cost of watertight forms. A good rule of thumb is not to use a fluid grout unless there are very tight clearances. Usually, a pencil vibrator can accomplish what a fluid consistency accomplishes without high water content.

With the normal clearances found in grouting, great care must be taken with fluid grouts, since with their very loose, fast, and self-leveling consistency, they will almost always fall below the plate, thus causing air to be entrapped and reducing the EBA. NONSHRINK grout should always be placed in a controllable consistency, without segregation, and in a continuous wave, so that the top of the grout never loses contact with the plate.

A typical example of when a fluid grout will not produce the desired results is a condition in which a baseplate contains shear keys as shown in the following sketch. Voids will occur at shear keys in dead corners on the front and rear sides of the shear keys perpendicular to the grout flow. The voids develop because fluid grout traps air in the corners, and the air has no way of being vented. The result is a significant loss of EBA due to air entrapment.

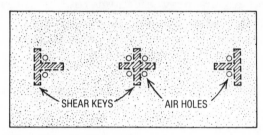

Baseplate with Shear Keys

Pumping the grout into place is a much better and a more efficient means of grouting this type of baseplate. Using the pump nozzle, the grout flow can be directed to ensure that the area is completely filled, and no voids are left behind.

Pumping the grout into place is the ideal method for many types of grouting applications. This is discussed in detail in the section on placement procedures. Pumping creates the necessary surge to drive out the air voids that cannot be accomplished by flowing a grout.

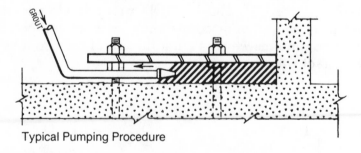

Typical Pumping Procedure

INSTALLATION

CAUTION: Most grouts are not recommended for placement under a wide range of temperatures. Consult manufacturer's written instructions for placement temperature limitations.

A. GENERAL

   1. The general application procedures outlined herein are for use under normal conditions. If grouting is to be done when ambient and mix temperatures are not between 40°F and 90°F, follow additional recommendations outlined in the Hot Weather Grouting and Cold Weather Grouting parts of this section. Temperatures below 70°F tend to slow the set of grout, and temperatures above 70°F tend to accelerate the set of grout.

      If it is desirable that the set times and strength gains are to be maintained at near the 70 degree rate, the applicable hot weather or cold weather section should be reviewed for guidance. If other unusual or difficult conditions exist (chemical attack, high working temperatures, low clearances, shear keys, etc.), the contractor should contact the owner's engineer and the grout manufacturer's Technical Service Department.

   2. All necessary tools and materials should be as close as possible to the area being grouted. Mortar box, mortar mixer (with moving blades), wheelbarrow, shovel, hoe, water measuring container and grout should be within easy reach.

In compliance with 1987 government regulations, the following warning is suggested for all cementitious products: *WARNING: Contains cementitious materials and silica sand. May cause irritation. In case of contact with eyes, immediately flush with plenty of water for at least 15 minutes. Call a physician. Wash skin thoroughly after handling. Keep product out of reach of children.*

Take these simple precautions to avoid skin contact with cement powder or freshly mixed grout or mortar:

- *Wear rubber boots high enough to keep out cement products. Tops of boots should be tight to protect feet.*
- *Wear rubber gloves to protect hands.*
- *Wear long pants tucked in boots to protect legs.*
- *Wear knee pads when finishing concrete to protect knees.*
- *Wear long-sleeved shirts buttoned at the wrists and neck to protect upper body and arms.*
- *Wear tight-fitting goggles when handling cement products to protect eyes.*
- *Do not breathe in the fine dust when opening or dumping bags.*

---

3. Placing nonshrink grout is not a difficult process if the engineer and contractor are aware that a wide variety of methods is available to them. Four commonly-used methods will be discussed, but these are not the only methods available. Most other placement techniques are take-offs of these four methods. The following will discuss the advantages and disadvantages of each of the four methods so the engineer and contractor can choose the methods best suited to their applications.

   a. *Non-Sag* (Trowelable)

   Only a backboard is required with the non-sag method, so carpentry expense is saved, and additional time is saved because forms do not have to be built or stripped. On small accessible placements, this method can be very economical. However, on large, difficult placements, grouting with a non-sag mix is time-consuming, requires skilled labor, and may be impossible.

b. *Flowable*

Flowable grout placement requires the use of forms and a headbox. The cost of building the forms and headbox will often offset the cost savings in placing a flowable grout. A flowable grout has a looser consistency than non-sag grout but is stiffer than fluid grout, thus avoiding excess air being whipped into it during the mixing process and being trapped under the plate. Watertight forms are required for flowable grout as well as for fluid grout.

This particular method can be used for the majority of applications. If a grout is made fluid by adding more water than is required, segregation can take place, as well as the ever present danger of considerable bubbling at the surface, often caused by the use of some flowing agents.

c. *Fluid*

Fluid grout should only be used in situations where there are very tight clearances. Some manufacturers have promoted the use of fluid consistencies to speed grout placement when they have very short working times. With most grouts, fluid consistencies lead to greater shrinkage, air bubbles, air entrapment, and segregation. Much skill and experience is needed with this method to prevent the entrapment of air. In some cases fluid grouts may exhibit close to 100 percent of bubbles on the surface of the grout under the plate.

This eliminates any possibility of full support or high EBA. Its use in areas with tight clearances is sometimes desirable but should be limited to special cases. Fluid grouts should be carefully checked for increased plastic shrinkage and the possibility of early setting and segregation. FIVE STAR SPECIAL GROUT 100 has a unique formulation eliminating these problems.

d. *Pumping*

Pumping should be used on all large or multiple grout installations, particularly if shear keys or other obstructions exist, or if grout must be placed over great distances, or if venting air is impossible. Pumping the grout in place is a desirable placement method to grout many applications with cement-based grouts. It is fast, and will consistently achieve good results. It takes a little longer to set up the pumping equipment for grouting, but once the equipment is familiar to the workmen, the pumping method results in generally superior installations. Less water will be used than with a fluid grout. Consideration must be given to the working time of the grout when pumping.

The manufacturer should be contacted for recommendations as to the special grout to be used to avoid the setting of the grout while it is in the lines and equipment. Pumping will result in fewer air bubbles and considerably more grout can be placed by the same number of people in a single day.

As grout installers become more experienced with pumping, this technique will continue to increase in popularity due to high performance characteristics.

4. The manufacturer must be consulted for recommendations on what grout should be used and how it should be placed. Due to the great number of variables on job sites, the final decision must remain with the installer. The specifier can make the contractor's job easier by specifying a grout that provides flexibility in placement. To select a cement-based grout that can be placed by only one method is to invite mistakes and increase the cost of grouting.

5. The placement procedures used for grouts are just as critical as selecting the proper grout. The leading grout manufacturers maintain extensive technical service staffs to assist you in selecting the proper grout and the applicable placement procedures.

6. The following parts will discuss surface preparation, forming, mixing, placement, finishing, curing, and hot and cold weather grouting for cement-based products.

B. SURFACE PREPARATION
   1. *CONCRETE*
      a. The concrete on which the grout will bear should have attained its design strength before grouting.
      b. Concrete should be sound and all surfaces to be in contact with the grout should be entirely free of oil, grease, laitance, curing compounds, and other deleterious substances.

c. Roughen the surfaces by chipping, sand-blasting or other mechanical means to assure bond of the grout to the existing concrete.

"People Mover - Preparation for Grouting"

d. Particular care should be given to the quality of the concrete foundation. When concrete foundations contain limestone aggregate, efflorescence may occur on the surface and it is sometimes necessary to seal the concrete before grouting or poor bond to the concrete will be obtained.

2. *FOUNDATION PLATES*
   a. All metal surfaces of equipment bases which are to be in direct contact with the grout should be thoroughly cleaned to bare metal immediately before grouting. NONSHRINK cement-based grout will not bond to grease, oil, paint, primers or epoxy coatings that are sometimes on the underside or contact surface of the baseplate. These materials should be removed immediately prior to or as close as possible to grouting time.
   b. Leveling and alignment of foundation plates should be performed according to the recommendations of the equipment manufacturer and/or project specifications.

The leveled foundation plates should provide a minimum of two inches clearance for plates less than three feet wide. An additional one inch clearance should be provided for each additional three feet in width. For pours with clearances in excess of three inches, contact the grout manufacturer for detailed procedures.

Grout placements deeper than three inches can be accomplished by adding clean, washed pea gravel to the mix, and/or using cold water, with the manufacturer's approval. The manufacturer should be contacted for the size and amount of aggregate recommended for deep pours. The added aggregate will act as a heat sink and reduce the temperature rise. This result can sometimes be achieved with reinforcing steel placed throughout the grout.

For shallow pours or deep pours, special grouts are available to meet special field conditions.

For long pours, expansion joints should be provided in the grout, in addition to considering the possibility of the use of mesh or rebars in the long direction.

c. Shims, wedges, blocks and leveling nuts as shown in the following sketch are used to hold up the equipment during alignment and installation of grout and may be removed if the engineer so desires.

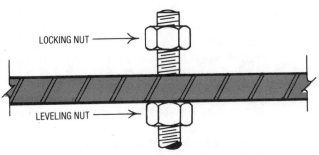

"Locking and Leveling Nuts"

If they are to be removed, the shims should be protected from bonding with the grout with a piece of plastic or some other nondeleterious material.

3. *ANCHOR BOLTS*

   a. Equipment manufacturers or design engineers often require anchor bolts to be grouted. All surfaces should be thoroughly cleaned of oil, grease, and other deleterious substances. All excess water must be removed from the holes. Any compressor used to blow out water or other substances from the surfaces in contact with the grout should be equipped with an oil trap in the air line to prevent oil from being blown onto the contact surfaces and affecting the bond of the grout.

   b. Since the grout used under the equipment is NONSHRINK, there should be no need to tighten down the anchor bolts after the grout has reached its design strength. If the bolts have slack in them, the grout should be removed because there is a good possibility the NONSHRINK grout did not perform properly beneath the plate. If the nuts and bolts are tight, further tightening of the nuts could cause the bolts to stretch beyond their yield point.

4. *WETTING*

   As a result of studies by the American Concrete Institute and the Portland Cement Association on whether concrete substrates should be soaked with water or dry at the time of placement of cementitious repair materials, the following procedure should be followed. With a dry substrate in hot weather, the grout may lose water too rapidly for proper hydration to take place. Conversely, if the substrate is too wet, cement may be washed from the bonding surface. Therefore, it is generally recommended that the substrate be moistened and any excess (visible accumulation) of water be removed. Under unusual circumstances, the manufacturer of the grout material should be contacted for guidance.

Covering concrete with continuously wet burlap or flannel rags, or running a fine hose spray will usually give satisfactory results.

All excess water must always be removed prior to grouting.

5. *GROUT REMOVAL*

    Surfaces from which the grout is to be removed after placing should be treated with a bond breaking material.

C. FORMING

    1. *WHEN TO USE FORMS*

        Forms are not always required! Non-sag grout should be packed against a backboard. Since the consistency of cement-based NONSHRINK grout can be varied, use the following table to determine if forms are needed.

Size of Baseplate	Obstructions	Method/Mix	Forms
Small (less than 2' x 2')	None	Non-Sag Stiff Plastic	No
Medium to large (greater than 2' x 2')	None	Loose Plastic Flowable	Yes
Medium to large (greater than 2' x 2')	Some	Flowable, Pump Vibration*	Yes
Large	Many	Pump	Yes

Vibration is preferable to adding more water to obtain placeability.

    2. *FORM STRENGTH*

        All forms should be built of materials of adequate strength, securely anchored and shored to withstand the forces developed by plunging or vibrating the grout into place.

    3. *SEALING AND WAXING FORMS*

        Forms should be tight against existing concrete and vertical wood surfaces, and joints should be sealed with tape. Form oil, heavy wax or other approved release agents should be used for easy form removal.

4. *AIR RELIEF HOLES*

With some baseplate designs, air relief holes are mandatory. Baseplates with a skirt around the perimeter should have relief holes (minimum 1/8" diameter) in each corner. If the plate is bisected with stiffening members, then relief holes should be provided at the intersections with the skirt. (*See Figure A for minimum required air relief holes.*)

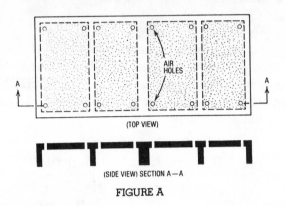

(TOP VIEW)

(SIDE VIEW) SECTION A—A

FIGURE A

5. *SHOULDERS*

Grout should always be cut back to the bottom outer edge of the baseplate and tapered to the existing concrete as shown in the following sketch.

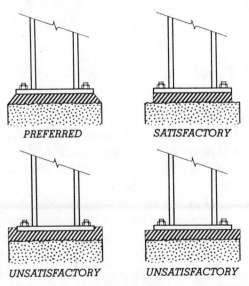

PREFERRED

SATISFACTORY

UNSATISFACTORY

UNSATISFACTORY

FIGURE B

D. MIXING
  1. *FOLLOW DIRECTIONS*
       Grout should be mixed according to the proce-
  dures recommended by the manufacturer. Grout,
  like all mortars, should be mixed in a mortar mixer
  (with moving blades), not a concrete mixer,
  wherever possible. Mixing by hand will take three
  to five times longer, use considerably more labor,
  and still not obtain the same results as with a mortar
  mixer (with moving blades). A mortar mixer (with
  moving blades) more thoroughly blends the potable
  water into the mix.
       Hand mixing will often result in lower
  strengths, lumpiness, segregation, and less flowability. If the mix is to be flowable, it should always
  be mixed in a mixer and the mixer run until the surface water has disappeared and desired consistency
  is reached. *Carefully read all mixing information
  on the package and the latest literature.*
  If in doubt about mixing procedures, call the manufacturer. All leading grout manufacturers recommend the use of a mortar mixer (with moving
  blades).
  2. *MIXER TYPE*
       If a mechanical mixer is used, it should be a
  mortar mixer with moving blades (see following il-
  lustration) inside the drum as opposed to a concrete
  mixer with fins on a rotating drum.

"Typical Mortar Mixer"

The drum and blades should be thoroughly cleaned and rinsed and excess water removed before placing the desired mix water in the drum. Concrete mixers, vertical shaft mixers, or propeller mixers may be used when a mortar mixer (with moving blades) is not available. These other types of mixers are not as efficient and may cause segregation, bubbling and improper wetting.

3. *CONSISTENCY*

The consistency of cement-based grout will vary with the amount of water added. Use this flexibility. Always start with the minimum water (potable) as printed on the manufacturer's bag, and add additional potable water to obtain the desired consistency.

Do not exceed the manufacturer's printed maximum recommended water. Under rare circumstances, a false set may occur which may be corrected by remixing (without the addition of more water). Never retemper mix (add more potable water after initial stiffening). Mixing should be not less than three minutes nor more than five.

The larger the volume of grout, the less water will be needed for the same consistency.

4. *CLEANING*

All equipment and tools should be cleaned with water. Adding an abrasive material such as gravel to the water when cleaning a mortar mixer is helpful.

E. PLACING

1. *GENERAL*

On receipt of the first shipment of grout to a job site, the grouting contractor should immediately perform the NONSHRINK Quality Assurance Field Cylinder Test described in Chapter 3 of this Handbook.

a. *Check Temperature Conditions*

Determine if the ambient and mix temperature will be between 40°F and 90°F. Procedures for hot weather, cold weather, and other grouting conditions are covered in other parts of this section. Be sure to check concrete and steel plate temperatures.

b. *Working Time*

Working time varies with temperature, as well as the type of cement used and other components of the mix. Cement-based grouts have a shorter working time in warm weather and a longer working time in cooler weather. Grouts with working times of less than 15 minutes will usually result in high waste and poor performance and should not be used.

Check placement temperature to estimate the time available to place grout. A simple procedure is to mix the grout to the desired consistency and fill a styrofoam drinking cup to check the working time available under job conditions.

SUMMERSET, manufactured by FIVE STAR PRODUCTS, INC., is used to provide additional working time when required.

c. *Transporting Grout*

Use a pump, wheelbarrows, or buckets to transport grout to placement site.

d. *Elimination of Voids*

The placement of grout should proceed in a manner that will assure the filling of all spaces and intimate contact of the grout with contact surfaces. Be sure to check the need for grout holes.

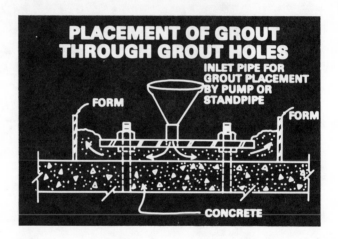

PLACEMENT OF GROUT THROUGH GROUT HOLES

INLET PIPE FOR GROUT PLACEMENT BY PUMP OR STANDPIPE

FORM

FORM

CONCRETE

e. *Continuous Grouting*

Grout placement should be rapid and continuous so as to avoid cold joints under the baseplate. Cement-based grouts should not be placed in layers. All grouting should take place from one side to the other to avoid trapping air.

If it is necessary to place grout through grout placement holes in the baseplate, it is essential that the grout be placed from one hole continuously until the grout has passed the second hole. Grouting may then continue at the next grout placement hole. Pumping is usually the desired procedure in this case.

2. NON-SAG (TROWELABLE) GROUTING

A trowelable mix is used in small applications with high accessibility. Its non-sag ability eliminates the costly job of forming. (See Figure C.)

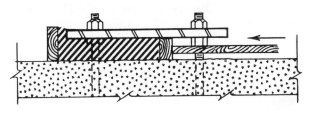

FIGURE C

3. FLOWABLE GROUTING

When hydraulic head pressure is used to flow grout in place, the level of grout in the head box must never fall below the top of the baseplate, because air will be trapped.

The head box should be filled to the maximum height and worked (plunged or vibrated) down to the top of the baseplate. This procedure is repeated until the grout moves completely under the baseplate, pushing air out in front of it, and rising above the bottom of the baseplate on the far side. (See Figure D.)

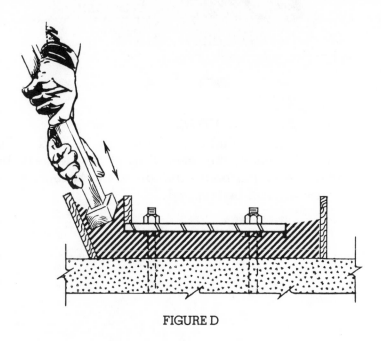

FIGURE D

4. *PUMPING GROUT*

Pumping should be used on all large or multiple grout installations, particularly if shear keys or other obstructions exist, or if grout must be placed over great distances, or if venting air is impossible. When grout is pumped into place, grouting is started at the far end of the space to be grouted.

As the grout is pumped in, the nozzle should be backed out slowly so that it always remains within the grout, preventing air entrapment. (See Figure E.)

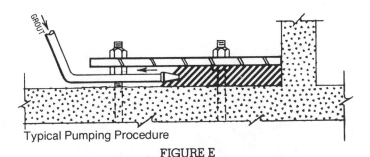

Typical Pumping Procedure

FIGURE E

Selecting the appropriate pump to get the grout properly in place is critical. The pump should be a positive displacement type such as a diaphragm or piston pump and not a screw pump. The size of the job will dictate the size of the pump to be used. Pumps vary in size from small pumps that deliver 10 to 15 cubic feet/hour to large compressor-driven pumps that can deliver several hundred cubic feet/ hour. The pump, the hose, and the nozzle should first be rinsed with water.

"Pumping Grout in Oil Refinery"

A "pig" (cleansing plug) should then be washed through the line to ensure that the line is clear, followed by a slurry of FIVE STAR GROUT. This will ensure that neither water nor cement are removed from the grout during pumping, and that the pump and hose will not clog.

"Pumping Cementitious Grout"

For large pumping installations, the manufacturer's pump grade formulation should be used. The grout manufacturer should be consulted for specific recommendations.

F. FINISHING

Just before the cement-based grout has reached its final set (the grout can be cut with a steel trowel and will stand up without support), the forms must be removed and all the grout that is above the underside of the baseplate must be cut back to the lower edge of the baseplate.

A 45 degree angle cutback is preferred. (See Figure F below.) If this is not done, any movement from temperature or vibration will crack the grout. This also enables the user to verify that the grout is **NONSHRINK** and tight under the plate. The grout should then be finished off with a wood float or brush finish. At no time should cement-based grouts extend upward along the side of a baseplate or machinery foundation. This will result in cracking of the grout due to sudden temperature change in the baseplate or machinery foundation. Sometimes, when anchor bolts are close to the edge of the baseplate, a vertical crack may occur in the grout due to temperature changes. This will not affect the vertical support of the machinery. It can be cosmetically corrected by coating the crack with a mixture of the grout.

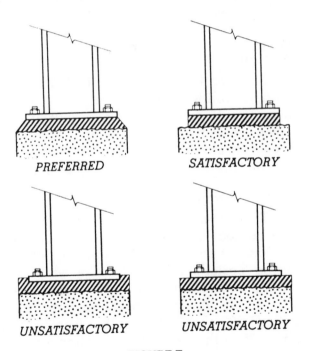

FIGURE F

G. CURING

1. *FOLLOW DIRECTIONS*

Grout should be cured according to the manufacturer's recommendations in their latest literature, specifications, and on the packages. For any unusual conditions, call the manufacturer for guidance.

2. *FORMS*

Begin curing immediately after form removal, cutback, and finishing.

3. *TEMPERATURE*

The temperature of the foundation plate, supporting concrete foundation, and the grout should be maintained between 40°F and 90°F during grouting, and for a minimum of 24 hours thereafter. Machinery and baseplates will cool at low temperatures or heat up at hot temperatures or in the sun more rapidly than the grout. These conditions should be avoided during the curing period.

4. *WETTING*

The grout should be protected from extreme drying conditions by covering all exposed grout surfaces with *continually* wetted burlap, or flannel rags or sealed with polyethylene for a minimum of three days at 70°F for regular grouts. Special grouts may require more or less curing depending on the grout.

5. *CURING COMPOUNDS*

To prevent rapid surface drying and crazing, the exposed surfaces of the grout should be coated with curing compound immediately after the moist curing period. Two coats of a white pigmented curing compound meeting the moisture loss requirements of Corps of Engineers Specification CRD-C 302 should be applied (see Technical Bulletin #25 at the back of this section for details).

H. HOT WEATHER SUPPLEMENTAL INSTRUCTIONS FOR CEMENT-BASED GROUTS

High temperature conditions when placing cement-based grouts reduce working time, increase the rate of strength gain and increase the importance of curing due to rapid evaporation of water from the grout. Refer to previous sections for all basic preparations for grouting.

FIVE STAR PRODUCTS, INC. offers special hot weather grouts which can be mixed and placed under high temperature conditions.

1. *PRECONDITIONING TEMPERATURE*

For 24 hours prior to grouting, NONSHRINK grout should be stored in a cool, dry area with the temperature as close to 70°F as possible.

2. *WETTING*

When any cement-based grouts are used, concrete should be soaked for 24 hours prior to grouting. One hour before grouting, ice water or cold spray should be used to cool concrete, steel and forms in order to bring materials in contact with grout to temperatures below 90°F. Excess surface water must be removed just prior to grouting.

3. *SHADING*

Concrete, steel and forms should be shaded from direct sunlight beginning 24 hours prior to placing grout. The shading device should not be removed until four days after placement or until the cement-based grout is adequately cured.

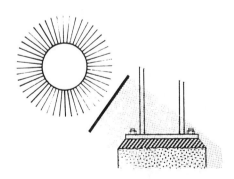

4. *MIXING*

       Cement-based grout should be added to the appropriate amount of cold potable water needed to produce the desired consistency. If the water supply is run through a hose lying in the sun, it must be flushed to remove the heated water. If further cooling is needed, the water may be run into a drum containing ice. Ice should not be added directly to the grout.

5. *TIME OF PLACEMENT*

       During hot weather, it is desirable to place the grout in late afternoon or early evening when the temperature is dropping. This allows heat development to take place during the coolest part of the day.

6. *CURING*

       The grout should be protected from extreme drying conditions for a minimum of three days. The method needed to protect the grout will depend on temperature and humidity, with low humidity and strong winds being the worst conditions. The most desirable methods for protecting the grout during hot weather include wet burlap, a soaker hose and ponding after final set.

       The chart on the following page gives curing instructions for different temperature and humidity conditions. If strong winds inhibit the ability of a given curing method to keep the grout moist, a wind break must be erected until wind is no longer a problem or curing is finished.

MINIMUM CURING RECOMMENDATIONS
For Regular NONSHRINK Cement-Based
Grout During Hot Weather

HUMIDITY	TEMPERATURE		
	70–90°F*	90–100°F*	Over 100°F*
High 70-100%	3 Day Wet Burlap	3 Day Soaker Hose	3 Day Soaker Hose with Sun Shading
Medium 40-70%	3 Day Wet Burlap	3 Day Soaker Hose	3 Day Soaker Hose; 3 Day Ponding with Sun Shading
Low below 40%	3 Day Wet Burlap	3 Day Soaker Hose	3 Day Ponding with Sun Shading

Discontinue curing in evening at end of curing period.

It should be noted that the above curing periods are minimum recommendations. It is recommended that under extreme conditions, the curing period be extended. Discontinue moist curing only during the evening hours *at end of curing period* to take advantage of the cooler temperatures. Rapid drying during a hot period may cause surface dusting and cracking.

To prevent rapid surface drying and crazing, the exposed surfaces of the grout should be coated with curing compound immediately *after the moist curing period*. Two coats of a white pigmented curing compound meeting the moisture loss requirements of Corps of Engineers Specification CRD-C 302 should be applied (see Technical Bulletin #25 at the end of this section for details).

I. COLD WEATHER SUPPLEMENTAL INSTRUCTIONS FOR CEMENT-BASED GROUTS

Low temperatures delay the set, increase working time and delay the strength development of cement-based products. These conditions should be compensated for by the simple procedures recommended below.

FIVE STAR PRODUCTS, INC. offers special cold weather grouts which can be mixed and placed under cold temperature conditions.

Since no hydration will take place when the grout is at freezing temperatures, grout must not be allowed to freeze before it reaches 1,000 psi. However, once it has reached this strength, it may be subjected to freezing temperatures. Hydration will continue when the temperature of the grout rises above freezing. This hydration will be slower than that obtained if the grout can be cured at 70°F by some exterior source of heat. Grouts that depend on rusting or other chemical reactions, such as iron grouts and aluminum powders, should never be used in cold weather because the reaction is slowed or completely stopped. All FIVE STAR GROUTS have been formulated to perform satisfactorily in cold weather. Refer to the previous chapters for all basic preparations for grouting.

1. PRECONDITIONING

Packaged grout should be kept in storage as close to 70°F as possible until just prior to use. Mixing water should be heated to approximately 70°F before use.

2. HEATING FOUNDATION AND BASEPLATES

The baseplates and foundations must be raised to a temperature above freezing. Often, in cold weather, baseplates and foundations will exhibit a temperature 5 to 10 degrees cooler than the surrounding air. The closer the temperature of the baseplate, grout, and foundations can be raised to 70°F and maintained at this temperature, the more rapidly the grout will develop its early strength. It is mandatory that the concrete in the foundations or in precast sections be completely free of frost during grouting and early curing. This heating can be done with infrared heaters directed to all contact surfaces, or by supplying external heat in a method approved by the engineer.

(See following photograph for a typical solution to the problem.)

"Tented, Heated Enclosure for Cold Weather Grouting"

3. TIME OF PLACEMENT

During cold weather, it is desirable to place the grout early in the day to take advantage of rising temperatures to aid in preventing freezing.

4. CURING

The ACI states that if a cement-based material reaches 500 psi compressive strength, it will resist freezing. However, a better procedure is to be sure the grout has attained a compressive strength of 1,000 psi before removing the heat.

As soon as the forms have been removed and cut back is completed, the exposed surfaces of the grout should be given two coats of a white pigmented curing compound meeting the moisture loss requirements of Corps of Engineers Specification CRD-C 302 (see Technical Bulletin #25 at the back of this section for details).

a. Space Heating

If space heaters are used to maintain ambient temperature above 70°F, FIVE STAR GROUT will develop well over 1,000 psi in 24 hours. After this time, heat can be removed and grout will cure at a slower rate than normal. If freezing conditions occur, hydration will stop but no damage should be done to the grout. Space heaters should be vented to the outside to prevent carbonation.

b. Infrared Heaters

Infrared heaters have been used in grouting precast garages at temperatures around 20°F throughout the day. This can be accomplished by covering the area to be grouted with tarpaulins and subjecting the precast section near the grout to infrared heating for 24 hours. Grout may be placed after this time and the infrared heat continued for another 24 hours so that the temperature around the grouted section is maintianed at 70°F. This procedure enables continuous erection and can be applied to other winter grouting installations.

c. Freeze Protection

If the temperature cannot be brought up to 70°F, the grout should be maintained at a minimum of 40°F. The protection must continue until 1,000 psi has been reached before removal. After this time, freezing conditions are not likely to structurally damage the grout. However, to obtain higher working load capabilities, the grout should be further protected until it has reached its design strength. The design strength may be tested by leaving cube specimens at the job site and breaking the cubes periodically.

CHAPTER 7
TYPICAL CEMENTITIOUS GROUTING APPLICATIONS

Several typical grouting applications have been selected: A 2' x 2' baseplate, a 6' x 10' baseplate with shear keys, a waffle baseplate, and embedded anchors and tie rods, and precast, prestressed applications are discussed.

In each of these types of installations, the advantages and disadvantages of different placement methods are reviewed.

The following basic rules must be kept in mind:

1. Use the minimum water possible in all placements and do not exceed manufacturer's recommended maximum.

2. Fluid grouts and their required watertight formwork should only be used when absolutely necessary. The use of watertight formwork should be evaluated, considering its increased cost and possible delays in construction time.

3. If, when using any placement method, the grout extends up the side of the baseplate, it must be cut back to the lower level of the baseplate. This will avoid cracking of the grout due to possible movement of the baseplate caused by temperature changes, vibration, or other unknown causes.

4. When grout is placed in depths of over three inches, consideration should be given to extending the grout with clean pea gravel. Conditions may vary. Contact the manufacturer for further information.

5. Consider the use of grout holes and air relief holes on inaccessible plates.

6. Equipment anchors must be kept a reasonable distance from the edge of the plate to avoid vertical cracking of the grout.

7. Improper curing, over-finishing, or steel troweling of the grout may result in hairline cracking of the surface.
8. The manufacturer should be consulted for any situation which needs clarification relative to grouting.

Contractors often must patch spalled or honeycombed concrete. For large areas or major repairs, FIVE STAR STRUCTURAL CONCRETE, as discussed in Section III, should be used. For small, minor repairs, FIVE STAR GROUTS, which are already on the site, may be used. The surface must be free of all oil, grease, laitance, curing compounds and other deleterious substances. The surfaces should be roughened by chipping, sand-blasting, or other mechanical means to assure the bond of the grout to the existing concrete. Contact the grout manufacturer for any unusual applications. For additional information on structural concrete repair, see Section III.

The following applications were selected as typical situations. They are meant to be guidelines in selecting grouting procedures. Every project is subject to many variables which could require modifications in the selected method. The manufacturer can be of great assistance in this area and should be consulted for any needed clarification.

TYPICAL GROUTING APPLICATIONS
Nonshrink Cement-Based Grouts
2' x 2' BASEPLATE

A typical 2' x 2' baseplate is easily grouted with any one of the methods listed below. The decision of which method to use hinges first on performance, and second on economics.

PLACEMENT METHOD	ADVANTAGES	DISADVANTAGES
NON-SAG (Trowelable)	* No Forms * High Strength * Time Saving	* Not economical if a Large Number of Plates are Encountered
FLOWABLE	* Fast Placement	* Forms Must Be Built * Construction Delay * Increased Overall Costs
FLUID	* Fast Placement * Tight Clearances	* Watertight Forms Required * Skill required in Placement * Air Entrapment During Mixing * Segregation * Construction Delay * High Costs
PUMPING	* Fastest Method * Little Air Entrapment * Considerable Economy When Large Number of Plates are Encountered	* Forms Must be Built * Rental of Equipment * Skilled Personnel

The Non-Sag (trowelable) method is the best choice when a few plain plates need to be grouted. Both the flowable and fluid placement methods have many disadvantages which outweigh their speed of placement. In addition, fluid grouts may exhibit very high drying shrinkage and segregation. If a large number of plates are encountered, pumping the grout should be considered because of economy and high performance.

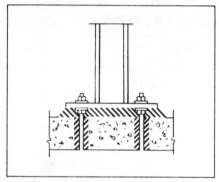

STRUCTURAL COLUMNS, AND BEARING PLATES, POLES AND ANCHORS.
FIVE STAR GROUT can be dry packed, rammed, trowelled, poured, or pumped, indoors or out.

TYPICAL GROUTING APPLICATIONS
Nonshrink Cement-Based Grouts
6' x 10' Baseplate With Shear Keys

Often a baseplate with obstructions is encountered. In this example, the obstructions are three shear keys under a 6' x 10' baseplate.

PLACEMENT METHOD	ADVANTAGES	DISADVANTAGES
NON-SAG (Trowelable)	* No Forms * High Strength	* Labor Intensive * Skilled Labor Required * Difficult Placement
FLOWABLE	* Little Skill	* Forms Must Be Built Required
FLUID	* Speed of Placement	* Watertight Forms Required * Skill Required in Placement * Air Entrapped During Mixing * Low EBA * Segregation * Reduced Strength * High Costs
PUMPING	* Fastest Method * Highest EBA * Lowest Cost	* Forms Must Be Built * Rental of Equipment * Skilled Personnel

The selection of the Non-Sag method would not be the most economical procedure, and there would be difficulty in obtaining a high performance placement.

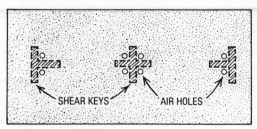

Baseplate with Shear Keys

The flowable placement method is worth considering under these conditions. Due to its many disadvantages, the fluid method should be avoided. Pumping is the fastest, best performing, and most economical method under this type of plate.

TYPICAL GROUTING
APPLICATIONS
Waffle Baseplate

A waffle plate, or a plate with a skirt around the perimeter, is often encountered in grouting applications. Waffle plates are one of the most difficult types of plates to grout successfully. It is assumed that there are adequate grout holes in the 6' x 10' plate. With this application and similar obstructions, close supervision and air relief holes will be required.

PLACEMENT METHOD	ADVANTAGES	DISADVANTAGES
Non-Sag (Trowelable)	* No Forms	* Labor Intensive * Highly Skilled Labor Required * Vibration Required * Air Entrapment
FLOWABLE	* Fast Placement	* Forms Required * Vibration Recommended
FLUID	* Speed of Placement	* Watertight Forms Required * High Costs * Skill Required * Air Entrapped During Mixing * Low EBA * Segregation * Reduced Strength
PUMPING	* Fastest Method	* Forms Must Be Built * Rental of Equipment * Skilled personnel

The Non-Sag (trowelable) method should not be used because of the high possibility of entrapped air under the plate. The flowable method may be used provided great care is exercised in making sure the grout rises through the air relief holes. The use of a vibrator is recommended. The fluid method should not be used because of the high risk of the self-leveling grout falling below any one of the many waffle areas, and losing contact with the plate during placement, thereby entrapping air and reducing the EBA.

Pumping is the fastest, best performing, and most economical method under this type of plate.

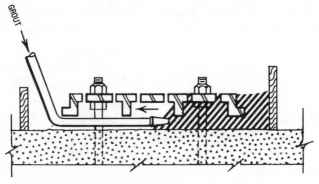

Typical Pumping Application

TYPICAL GROUTING APPLICATIONS
Nonshrink Cement-Based Grouts
Embedded Anchors and Bolts

In anchoring bolts or anchors in concrete, it is important to remember that a NONSHRINK grout must be used in order to ensure adequate anchoring strength to the embedded item. When the bolt diameter is one inch or less, the hole diameter should be a minimum of two inches. When the bolt's diameter is greater than one inch, the hole diameter should be at least twice the bolt diameter. The bar should be embedded adequately so that the embedded item will pass its yield point before pullout or prior to the grout pulling out of the surrounding concrete. In the back of this section are load factors and formulas for designing anchors.

PLACEMENT METHOD	ADVANTAGES	DISADVANTAGES
NON-SAG (Trowelable)	* No Forms	* Labor Intensive * Highly Skilled Labor Required * Vibration Required * Air Entrapment
FLOWABLE	* Little Skill Required * Fast Placement * Good for Moderate Embedments with Adequate Annular Spaces	* Cannot Be Used Horizontally Unless Pumped
FLUID	* For Tight Clearances and Deep Embedments	* Segregation * Reduced Strength
PUMPING	* Good Method of Placement for a Large Number of Bolts	* Rental of Equipment * Skilled Personnel

The Non-Sag (trowelable) placement method is a good procedure for shallow anchorages. The grout can often be placed in the hole before the anchor and then the anchor inserted and vibrated to ensure proper coverage. Flowable grout is good for long, deep holes with adequate clearances. It is recommended that it be pumped wherever possible.

If the clearances between the anchor and the surrounding walls are so tight that only a fluid grout can be placed, there is a good possibility of segregation, reduced strength, and failure to develop the design loads. It is recommended that the hole be enlarged in accordance with the formulas on pages I.41–43 and then the grout can be placed by either the flowable or pumping method.

Special grouts are formulated for each of the above applications, including cable grouting. Machinery anchor bolts can be placed before or after the grout is placed in any of the above applications, provided the bolt is vibrated before the grout sets. "J" hooks, nuts, or bends in the bolts are not required when **FIVE STAR GROUT** is used as the anchoring grout.

Drilling the anchor bolt hole in the field after the machinery arrives at the site provides considerable advantages. Many times, machinery manufacturers, for various reasons, have to change the anchoring locations, and setting anchors accurately in the field prior to the arrival of machinery is extremely expensive. When the machinery arrives, the anchor bolt locations can be readily determined, the anchor bolt holes quickly drilled, and then a plain bar, deformed bar, or completely threaded bar may be used as the anchor, if threaded to receive the locking nut.

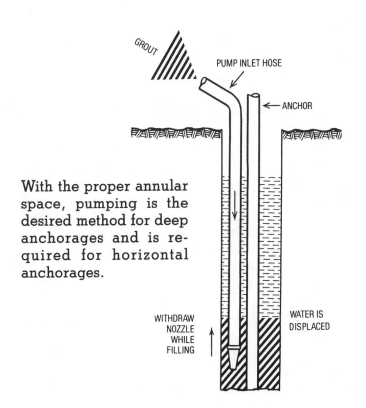

GROUT

PUMP INLET HOSE

ANCHOR

With the proper annular space, pumping is the desired method for deep anchorages and is required for horizontal anchorages.

WITHDRAW
NOZZLE
WHILE
FILLING

WATER IS
DISPLACED

TYPICAL GROUTING
APPLICATIONS
Nonshrink Cement-Based Grouts
Precast or Prestressed Work

The grouting of horizontal and vertical joints between precast or prestressed panels may be performed by one of the following methods.

PLACEMENT METHOD	ADVANTAGES	DISADVANTAGES
NON-SAG (Trowelable)	* No Forms * High Strength * Time Saving	NONE
FLOWABLE	* Fast Placement	* Forms Must Be Built * Construction Delay * Increased Overall Costs
FLUID		(same as above)
PUMPING	* Fastest Method for Large Volume of Joints or Bearing Pads	* Rental of Equipment * Hand Pumps for Small Jobs * Machine Pumps for Large Projects

Limestone or marble mortar joints should be grouted with **NONSHRINK FIVE STAR SPECIAL GROUT 130** to avoid the staining action of gray cements.

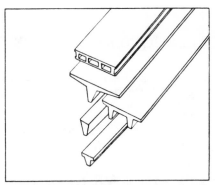

FIVE STAR GROUT can be used for grouting precast walls and floors, bearings and joints, prestressed cables, and patching of spalled concrete under any weather conditions.

"Equipment Mounted on Barge
for Grouting Precast Section on Bridge"

CHAPTER 8
TYPICAL INSTALLATIONS BY INDUSTRY

The following pages depict installations where various types of FIVE STAR GROUT have been used. The installations encompass many industries and many types of equipment. Grout type, performance, and installation will vary with industry and equipment. For these reasons it is imperative that engineers, architects and owners discuss their specific requirements with FIVE STAR PRODUCTS' Engineering and Technical Center.

"Hydroelectric Plants"

MINING & METALS INDUSTRY
APPLICATIONS

METALS INDUSTRY

Acid Pumps
Ball Mills
Car Scales
Clarifiers
Coilers
Continuous Casting
  Equipment
Crushers
Descaling Pumps
Engines (steam, gas,
  diesel)
Expanders
  (i.e., pipe mill)
FRP Tanks
Fan Housings
Forges
Gantry Cranes
  Rail Beds
Gear Boxes
Large Lathes
Large DC Motors
Main Mill Housings
Manipulator Rail Beds
  and Raceways
Manipulators
Milling Machines
Mill Tables
Mold Shake-Out Electric
  Equipment
Shapers
Shearing Equipment
Slab Pushers, Pilers
Spindle Carriers
Stamping Machines
Steel Making Vessels
  (AOD/BOF/Q-BOP)
Straighteners

Structural Support Plates
Tension Reels
Transfer Car Rail Beds

MINING INDUSTRY

Clarifiers
Compressors & Engines
Conveyor Support &
Drive Equipment
Crane Raceways
Crushers & Vibrators
FRP Tanks
Fan Housings
Furnaces
Gear Boxes
Centrifuges
Granulators
Hammermills
Kilns
Pumps
Rod and Ball Mills
Starter Bolts

"Ore Grinding Mills"

PETROCHEMICAL, CHEMICAL, PIPELINE INDUSTRY APPLICATIONS

Catalytic Cracking Units
Pressure Vessels
Compressors
Turbines
Tank Supports
Pipe Supports
Structural Columns
Chemical Pumps
Clarifiers
Engines
FRP Tanks
Processing Machinery
Refrigeration Units
Flood Pumps
Valve Supports

"Petrochemical Plants"

PULP & PAPER INDUSTRY
APPLICATIONS

Paper Machines
Power Plants
Auxiliary Equipment
Pumps
Barkers
Boilers
Calenders
Chippers
Compressors
Dryers
Hoods
Turbines
Fourdrinier Sections
Winders
Patching
Clarifiers
FRP Tanks
Fan Housings

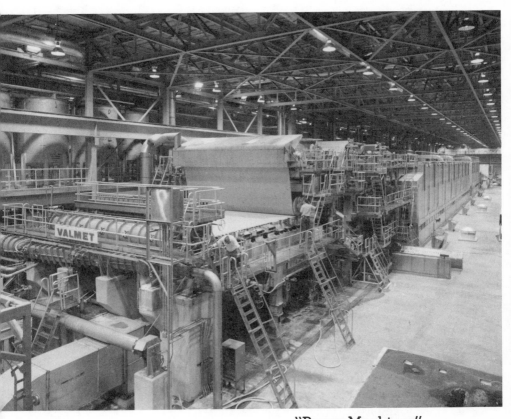

"Paper Machines"

POWER INDUSTRY

Turbines
Generators
Compressors
Pumps
Reactor Supports
Coal Pulverizers/Crushers
Coal Handling Equipment
Pipe Hanger Supports
Transmission Tower
Scrubbers
Cooling Towers
Auxiliary Equipment
Rock Anchors
Radiation Shielding
Penetration Closures
Reactor Foundations
Structural Columns

"Nuclear Power Plants"

PRECISION APPLICATIONS
IN OTHER INDUSTRIES

Anchor Bolts
Clarifiers
Compressors
Concrete Patchwork
Conveyor Support
Crane Raceways
Crushers
Dowels
Engines (steam, gas, diesel)
Precoat Panels
Prestressed Cables
Bridge Seats
Robot Welders
Solid Waste Shredders
Hammermills

Fan Housings
Kilns
Lathes
Mill Tables
Pumps
Structural Steel Columns
Valve Supports
Vessels - Tanks
Vibrators
Radar Tracking Facilities
Bearing Plates
Grillages
Refrigeration Units
Molding Equipment
Pipe Supports
Banbury Mixers

"Robot Automobile Welder"

"Master Automobile Body Gauge"

"Fossil Fuel Power Plants"

"Grouting Precast Building Panel."

"Close-up of Grout Pumping Operation."

"Foundations for High-Rise Steel Office Building."

"Grouting a Refinery Compressor."

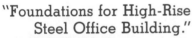

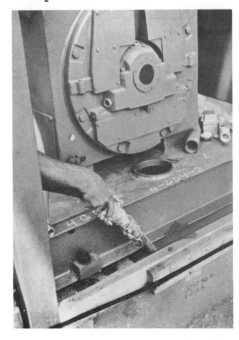

CHAPTER 9
CEMENTITIOUS GROUT SPECIFICATIONS

The purpose of a specification is to ensure that the type and performance of materials, techniques, and equipment used by a contractor meet the requirements established by the designer and the owner. The proper grout should be clearly specified for the particular application.

In specifying a NONSHRINK grout, the specifier faces a particularly difficult situation. Manufacturers today can and are marketing products claiming that they are NONSHRINK or nonmetallic, and they may or may not meet either of these requirements or be NONSHRINK when tested according to pre-approved national test standards such as ASTM C 827-87 (Standard Test Method for Change in Height at Early Ages of Cylindrical Specimens from Cementitious Mixtures). There is no prosecution of this misrepresentation by the various federal, state or local governments. When a manufacturer has not had a ten to twenty year history of satisfactory performance, the specifier should specifically ask for or obtain independent verification that the products he desires to specify are NONSHRINK and are supplied by companies with many years of experience and rigorous quality control, and require that the manufacturer mark on all packages and literature that they warranty that their products have been tested under the appropriate ASTM standards and show 0.0% shrinkage.

The contractor is in a difficult position if the specifications do not, first, name a grout, or second, clearly state the type of grout and performance of grout desired for a particular application. Specifications must not be unclear, vague, obsolete, or otherwise fail to define the level of performance required.

The designer is also in a particularly difficult situation if he does not specifically state his grouting needs in the specification. The designer may be held liable for his errors in the selection of the type of NONSHRINK grout.

It is important for the designer to consult the grout manufacturer on the selection of the type and performance that he will require.

The specification writer should work closely with the project designer on each project to ensure that the drawings as well as the specifications clearly state where and what type of NONSHRINK grout is to be used.

In selecting the grout, the specifier should carefully evaluate the performance stated in published literature and should require a quality laboratory's test results verifying the NONSHRINK performance and other desired properties.

The cost of grouting is a small portion of the total expense of a construction project, and the material cost of the grout is minor when compared to the labor cost for installation. The specifier should be aware that certain grouts, as with other construction products, may be the most cost effective but not necessarily the least expensive. Therefore, the specifier should be governed primarily by performance and history and not by material cost considerations. The grouting industry is well known for having low cost materials with low cost effectiveness and low performance properties.

It is essential that all grouts specified be manufactured by a company supported by a fully staffed technical service organization and research group. It is also important when selecting a grout for the specifier to give preference to the leading manufacturers who have manufacturing facilities throughout the country to ensure that the grout is readily available.

If the specifier needs assistance in selecting the grout, FIVE STAR PRODUCTS, INC. has a fully equipped Engineering and Technical Center, as well as a research organization, to assist in design or field problems.

The specifier has four primary types of specifications to use in specifying grout. They are as follows, in order of preference:

1. *Proprietary Specification*

    Name the specific grout to be used for each specific application, such as "FIVE STAR SPECIAL GROUT 100 for machinery". Also give the company name and address, such as "Manufactured by U. S. GROUT CORPORATION, Fairfield, CT."

2. *Or Approved Equal with Identical Properties*

    Name of a proprietary product with the clause "or approved equal with identical properties" after the name of the product.

3. *Performance Specification*

    Specific data and performance requirements are listed.

4. *Open Listing*

    Naming three or more grouts.

PROPRIETARY SPECIFICATION

In a proprietary specification there is no question in the mind of the owner, designer, or contractor as to the type and level of performance of the grout required. The specifier can usually obtain a guarantee of performance from the manufacturer when such a specification is written. In addition, no time is lost in the search for, submittal of, or approval of other materials. This also limits the designer's and specifier's liability. This is by far the most desirable specification.

OR APPROVED EQUAL WITH IDENTICAL PROPERTIES

When required by the owner or when the specifier thinks there may be a possibility of additional products meeting his required standards, he should consider the use of a specification that reads, for example, "FIVE STAR GROUT or approved equal with identical properties". This has some of the advantages of the above, but it involves the designer, specifier, and contractor in determining if another grout matches the specified grout's performance. It forces the specifier to spend considerable time evaluating other grouts and rejecting those products that do not achieve the desired performance.

If the phrase "or equal" is used instead of "or approved equal", the owner and specifier have removed from their jurisdiction most of their authority to determine the grout they need for the project. The "or approved equal" type of specification should be used if the proprietary specification listed above cannot be accepted by the owners.

PERFORMANCE SPECIFICATIONS

The specifier, in using a performance type specification, faces many problems. He must clearly delineate the performance requirements and test standards, such as ASTM C 827 for NONSHRINK, strength tests, time of setting, and other desirable properties. The specifier should be aware that this means he will receive many submissions from various manufacturers, all of which may be slightly exaggerated relative to their properties, performance, and claims, and must select from those, products that he believes will meet the criteria he has established. This opens the specifier and designer to liability unless they are experts in the grouting field. The time consumed by the specifier, designer and owner can be quite extensive and nonproductive.

OPEN LISTING

Naming three or more products should never be done unless corporate, government, or client policy dictates that this type of specification be employed. It is often thought that this procedure will lower the bidding price. This seldom happens and the usual result is that the grout that is finally used does not perform.

Unless the specifier has taken the time to carefully research the listed grouts to determine if their performance is satisfactory, the grout used will be selected on the basis of cost rather than performance. This opens up the possibility of the specifier being held liable if the grout does not perform satisfactorily. Further, the possibility is increased that still other low-performing grouts not listed will be submitted for approval on the basis of low cost. This further increases the time and effort of the specifier in determining if these other products are suitable.

COMBINATION SPECIFICATION

Sometimes a specifier is required to use a specification which is a combination of two or more of the above. If this happens, the specifier can limit his liability by specifying a single grout such as FIVE STAR GROUT, and then using a performance specification which will eliminate the so-called "shrinking NONSHRINK grouts".

On the following pages are samples of various types of specifications for various types of grouts.

There are two forms of specifications: a short form and a long form. In most cases, the short form is adequate. For unusual circumstances requiring special conditions, the long form may be desirable.

NONSHRINK CEMENT-BASED
GROUT SPECIFICATIONS
Examples of Short Form Specifications

1. *PROPRIETARY SPECIFICATIONS*

    All grouting as called for on the drawings and/or in specifications shall be performed with FIVE STAR GROUT* as manufactured by U. S. GROUT COR-PORATION, a subsidiary of FIVE STAR PRODUCTS, INC. of Fairfield, Connecticut. No substitutions will be approved.

2. *OR APPROVED EQUAL WITH IDENTICAL PROPERTIES SPECIFICATION*

    All grouting called for on the drawings and/or in the specifications shall be performed with FIVE STAR GROUT* as manufactured by U. S. GROUT COR-PORATION, a subsidiary of FIVE STAR PRODUCTS, INC. of Fairfield, Connecticut, or approved equal with identical properties. The grout must show no shrinkage according to ASTM C 827, must show no shrinkage according to CRD-C-621, and must contain no expansive cements or metallic powders such as aluminum or iron filings.

    (*The specifier should select the particular grout required from the literature at the back of Section I of this Handbook.)

3. *PERFORMANCE SPECIFICATION*

    See the following pages for performance specifications.

4. *OPEN LISTING - Naming Three or More Grouts in a Specification*

    The short form cannot be used in this type of specification because standards have to be established to determine whether the grout can meet the requirements. Only the long form specification should be used in this case.

SHORT FORM PERFORMANCE SPECIFICATION FOR NONSHRINK CEMENT GROUT

All grouting as called for on the drawings and/or in the specifications shall be performed with a material meeting the performance requirements that follow.

Cement-based grouts must have a minimum 15 year history of use, contain DEVOIDER, and meet the following performance requirements at maximum water. They must not contain expansive cement or metallic particles such as aluminum powder or iron filings

(A) Plastic Volume Change

   The grout shall show no shrinkage (0.0%) and a maximum 4.0% expansion from time of placement until final set when tested according to ASTM C 827.

(B) Hardened Volume Change

   The grout shall show no shrinkage (0.0%) and a maximum 0.2% expansion in the hardened state when tested according to CRD C-621.

(C) Compressive Strength

   The grout shall show a minimum 28-day compressive strength of 5,000 psi when tested according to ASTM C 109, restrained.

(D) Creep

   The grout shall show creep equal to or less than the high strength concrete on which it is bearing.

(E) Working Time

   The grout shall show a consistency greater than 125% for a minimum 45 minutes when tested according to applicable consistency sections of ASTM C 827 at 15 minute intervals.

(F) Tests

   The Cylinder Plate Test shall be run on all field shipments.

SECTION 03600
PERFORMANCE SPECIFICATION
FOR
NONSHRINK CEMENT GROUT

PART I - GENERAL

All cement-based grouting as indicated in designer's specification, equipment manufacturer's specification and on drawings shall apply to this section. Generally, these products are supplied by the contractor installing the grout. They are used for grouting of equipment and column baseplates, setting precast concrete and anchor bolts.

1.01 **REFERENCES**

ASTM C 109   Standard Test Method for Compressive Strength of Hydraulic Cement Mortars

ASTM C 191   Standard Test Method for Time of Set of Hydraulic Cement by Vicat Needle

ASTM C 827   Standard Test Method for Change in Height at Early Ages of Cylindrical Specimens from Cementitious Mixtures

CRD C 621   Corps of Engineers Specification for Nonshrink Grout

1.02 **SUBMITTALS**

The contractor must submit, prior to installation, for designer's approval, manufacturer's literature and certified test data that material complies with requirements in Articles 1.06 and 2.02. Designer should, at contractor's expense, buy any submitted material in the open marketplace, without the contractor's or manufacturer's knowledge, and test material at an independent laboratory to verify compliance with this specification.

1.03 **QUALITY ASSURANCE**

All material suppliers should be approved suppliers under NRC regulation 10 CFR 50, Appendix B Quality Assurance Criteria for Nuclear Power Plants and Fuel Reprocessing Plants.

1.04 DELIVERY, STORAGE AND HANDLING

All cement-based grouts shall be preblended, prepackaged materials requiring only the addition of water. They must be delivered to the jobsite in original, unopened packages, clearly labeled with the manufacturer's identification and printed instructions. All cement-based materials shall be stored and handled in accordance with the recommendations of the manufacturer and the American Concrete Institute.

1.05 ENVIRONMENTAL CONDITIONS

Refer to the manufacturer's literature for any physical or environmental limitations or contact the manufacturer directly.

1.06 WARRANTY

The material manufacturer shall warranty that the nonshrink grout shall never go below its initial placement volume when tested in accordance with ASTM C 827.

PART II - PRODUCT

2.01 MANUFACTURER

The following manufacturer supplies materials which meet this specification and offers field service.

Manufacturer   *Products*

U. S. GROUT CORPORATION FIVE STAR GROUT
A Subsidiary of **FIVE STAR PRODUCTS, INC.**
Fairfield, Connecticut
800-243-2206 or 203-336-7900

Other materials which meet this specification must be submitted to the designer for approval with the prime contractor's original bid documents by following the procedures outlined in Article 1.02.

2.02 MATERIALS

Cement-based grouts must have a minimum 15 year history of use and meet the following performance requirements at maximum water. They must not contain expansive cement or metallic particles such as aluminum powder or iron filings.

(A) Plastic Volume Change

The grout shall show no shrinkage (0.0%) and a maximum 4.0% expansion from time of placement until final set when tested according to ASTM C 827.

(B) Hardened Volume Change

The grout shall show no shrinkage (0.0%) and a maximum 0.2% expansion in the hardened state when tested according to CRD C-621.

(C) Compressive Strength

The grout shall show a minimum 28-day compressive strength of 5,000 psi when tested according to ASTM C 109, restrained.

(D) Creep

The grout shall show creep equal to or less than .6 in./in. $\times$ 10^{-3} at 70°F *for a minimum of one year* when tested according to CPR Creep Test (extrapolated data is not acceptable).

(E) Working Time

The grout shall show a consistency greater than 125% for a minimum 45 minutes when tested according to applicable consistency sections of ASTM C 827 at 15 minute intervals.

(F) Tests

The Cylinder Plate Test shall be run on all field shipments.

PART III - EXECUTION

3.01 INSPECTION

(A) Inspect concrete surfaces to receive grout and verify that they are free of ice, frost, dirt, grease, oil, curing compounds, paints, impregnations and all loose material or foreign matter likely to affect the bond or performance of the grout.

(B) Newly placed concrete shall have been placed and cured sufficiently to attain its design strength.

(C) Inspect baseplates for rust, oil, and other deleterious substances.

3.02 PREPARATION

(A) In order to ensure proper bond to the baseplate and the concrete, all grease, oil, dirt, curing compounds, laitance and other deleterious materials must be completely removed from the concrete and bottom of baseplate.

(B) Roughen the surfaces by chipping, sandblasting or other mechanical means to assure bond of the grout to the existing concrete. Loose or broken concrete shall be removed.

(C) After concrete surfaces have been washed clean, they shall then be saturated with water for 24 hours prior to placement of cement-based grout.

(D) Upon completion of saturation period excess water shall be removed with clean compressed air prior to grouting.

(E) Forms to be built as needed.

3.03 INSTALLATION

(A) Carefully read and understand the manufacturer's instructions as printed on the unit.

(B) Mixing - A mortar mixer is recommended. Prewet the mixer, empty excess water. Add premeasured amount of potable water to mixer, then add grout. Mix for at least 3, but not more than 5 minutes, then place.

(C) Placing - Grout may be drypacked, flowed, vibrated or pumped into place. All grouting shall take place from one side of a plate to the other to avoid trapping air.

(D) Cutback - Just before the grout has reached its final set, the grout must be cut back to the lower edge of the plate. A 45 degree angle or vertical cutback is recommended.

(E) Curing - The grout shall be kept moist for a minimum of three days. The method needed to protect the grout will depend on temperature, humidity and wind. Wet burlap, a soaker hose, sun shading, ponding and in extreme conditions a combination of methods shall be employed.

(F) Clean-Up - Upon completion of placement, equipment and tools shall be cleaned in such a manner as recommended by manufacturer.

CHAPTER 10
TECHNICAL DATA ON FIVE STAR
CEMENTITIOUS GROUTS

FIVE STAR

GROUTS

This chapter contains product literature, magazine re-prints and technical bulletins on **FIVE STAR** cementitious grouts. **FIVE STAR** products are designed to provide a higher level of performance.

FIVE STAR® GROUT

DESCRIPTION Five Star Grout is the world's leading cement-based, nonmetallic, nonshrink grout. It is the highest performing, most versatile, reliable, general purpose precision grout. The advanced technology of this patented product combines the following advantages that no other manufacturer can offer.

UNIQUE ADVANTAGES
- Precision Nonshrink
- Highest Effective Bearing Area[1]
- Contains Devoider[2]

SPECIAL ADVANTAGES
- High Early Strength
- Long Working Time
- Most Versatile

TYPICAL PHYSICAL PROPERTIES   In-Place Properties

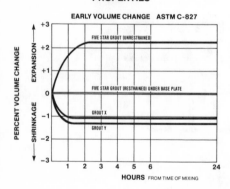

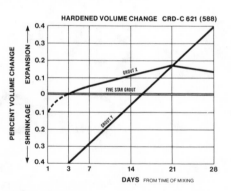

Early Volume Change: ASTM C-827: 0.00% shrinkage
Hardened Volume Change: CRD-C 621 (588): 0.00% shrinkage; 0.00% expansion after set
Effective Bearing Area[1]: 95% minimum
Compressive Strength, ASTM C-109: 5000 psi/7 Days
Meets Corps of Engineers Specification for Nonshrink Grout, CRD-C 621 (588)
Approved by New York City Board of Standards and Appeals under Cal No 1030-66SM
Approved for use on Federal, State, Municipal, Nuclear and Military Projects

[1]EBA: Effective Bearing Area - percent final surface area of grout in direct contact with bearing plate.

[2]All Five Star Grouts contain Devoider™, which offers the unique advantage of preventing cavities; overcoming plastic shrinkage, keeping the grout tightly against the plate for permanent support; producing the highest Effective Bearing Area.

I.2

Placement Properties

Five Star Grout may be mixed to a non-sag, plastic, or flowable consistency. Five Star Grout also provides a very long working time, allowing ample placement time to ensure the highest Effective Bearing Area is achieved. In addition, Five Star Grout has the unique and versatile ability to be placed using mechanical devices such as pumps, plungers, rods, or vibrators to further facilitate placement without compromising the in-place properties.

APPLICATIONS

- Large, Heavy Operating Equipment
- Structural Columns
- Anchors
- Precast and Prestressed Panels
- Patching

PLACEMENT GUIDELINES

1. **Surface Preparation:** All surfaces to be in contact with Five Star Grout shall be entirely free of oil, grease, laitance, or other foreign substances. Roughen surface to ensure a good bond to existing concrete. Clean thoroughly with liberal quantites of water, leaving concrete saturated but free of standing water.
2. **Mixing:** Five Star Grout shall be thoroughly mixed to any desired consistency by varying the amount of water used. Do not exceed maximum recommended amount of mixing water. Follow printed instructions on each package.
3. **Methods of Placing:** Five Star Grout may be dry packed, troweled, flowed, pumped, or vibrated into place.
4. **Post-Placement Procedures:** Five Star Grout should be cured for a minimum of three days with wet burlap or approved curing compound. In-service operation may begin immediately after minimum required grout strengths have been reached.

ENGINEERING & TECHNICAL CENTER

U.S. Grout Corporation maintains the industry's foremost Engineering and Technical Center staffed with engineers, available for consultation and on-site technical service worldwide. Call (203) 336-7900.

SPECIFICATION GUIDELINES

All cement-based nonshrink grouting shall be performed with Five Star Grout as manufactured by U.S. Grout Corporation, Fairfield, Connecticut. The grout shall be mixed and installed according to manufacturer's recommendations. No substitutions will be permitted. Technical service shall be made available by the manufacturer upon request.

For a more detailed specification guideline, call or write Engineering and Technical Center, U.S. Grout Corporation for assistance.

PACKAGING, YIELD, ORDERING AND AVAILABILITY

Five Star Grout is packaged in heavy-duty, polyethylene-lined bags producing one cubic foot of hardened grout. For ordering, determine the total number of cubic feet required, add 5% wastage, and contact U.S. Grout Corporation or one of your local Five Star® dealers throughout the United States. Five Star Grouts are manufactured in plants throughout the United States and are also manufactured and available worldwide.

STORAGE AND HANDLING

Five Star Grout should be stored in a cool, dry place in accordance with the recommendations of the American Concrete Institute.

Guarantee: Five Star Grout is guaranteed never to shrink below its original placement volume when tested in accordance with ASTM C-827. U.S. Grout Corporation stands behind all its products when used by competent workmen in accordance with manufacturer's directions. No responsibility for product use is assumed or implied where inferior workmanship is encountered or difficulty caused by other materials is evident. U.S. Grout's liability is limited to replacement of material found to be defective.

ENGINEERING & TECHNICAL CENTER, U.S. GROUT CORPORATION, 401 STILLSON ROAD, FAIRFIELD, CONN. 06430 • (203) 336-7900
CABLE: FIVE STAR • TELECOPIER (203) 336-7939 • TELEX: 643857 • COPYRIGHT 1984

FIVE STAR® INSTANT GROUT

DESCRIPTION   Five Star Instant Grout is the world's leading very rapid strength gaining special cement-based, nonmetalic, nonshrink grout. It is also the highest performing, selective chemical resistant, cement-based precision grout. The advanced technology of this patented product combines the following advantages that no other manufacturer can offer.

UNIQUE ADVANTAGES
- Precision Nonshrink
- Highest Effective Bearing Area[1]
- Contains Devoider[2]

SPECIAL ADVANTAGES
- Very Rapid Strength Gain
- Selective Chemical Resistance
- Fluid Consistency

TYPICAL PHYSICAL PROPERTIES

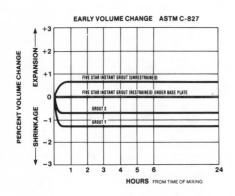

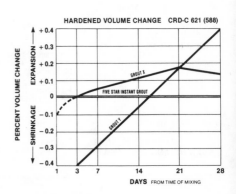

Early Volume Change: ASTM C-827: 0.00% shrinkage
Hardened Volume Change: CRD-C621 (588): 0.00% shrinkage; 0.00% expansion after set
Effective Bearing Area[1]: 95% minimum
Compressive Strength, ASTM C-109: 3000 psi/4 Days; 6000 psi/1 day
Meets Corps of Engineers Specification for Nonshrink Grout, CRD-C 621 (588)

[1]EBA: Effective Bearing Area—percent final surface area of grout in direct contact with bearing plate.
[2]All Five Star Grouts contain Devoider™, which offers the unique advantage of preventing cavities; overcoming plastic shrinkage, keeping the grout tightly against the plate for permanent support; producing the highest Effective Bearing Area.

Placement Properties

Five Star Instant Grout may be mixed to a dry pack, plastic, flowable, or fluid consistency. Five Star Instant Grout is formulated for rapid placement. To delay the set, Summerset®, as manufactured by U.S. Grout Corporation may be added in accordance with printed instructions. In addition, Five Star Instant Grout has the unique and versatile ability to be placed using mechanical devises such as plungers, rods, or vibrators to further facilitate placement without compromising the in-place properties.

APPLICATIONS
- Large, Heavy Operating Equipment—Start Up in 4 Hours
- Precision Grouting in Selective Chemical Attack Areas
- Rapid Anchoring
- Fast Patching

PLACEMENT GUIDELINES

1. **Surface Preparation:** All surfaces to be in contact with Five Star Instant Grout shall be entirely free of oil, grease, laitance, or other foreign substances. Roughen surface to ensure a good bond to existing concrete. Clean thoroughly with liberal quantities of water, leaving concrete saturated but free of standing water.
2. **Mixing:** Five Star Instant Grout shall be thoroughly mixed to any desired consistency by varying the amount of water used. Do not exceed maximum recommended amount of mixing water. Follow printed instruction on each package.
3. **Methods of Placing:** Five Star Instant Grout may be dry packed, troweled, flowed, or vibrated into place. For placements deeper than 3 inches contact U.S. Grout Corporation.
4. **Post-Placement Procedures:** Five Star Instant Grout should be protected from fast drying by keeping it wet or applying an approved curing compound.

ENGINEERING & TECHNICAL CENTER

U.S. Grout Corporation maintains the industry's foremost Engineering and Technical Center staffed with engineers, available for consultation and on-site technical service worldwide.

SPECIFICATION GUIDELINES

All very rapid strength gaining and/or selective chemical resistant special cement-based nonshrink grouting shall be performed with Five Star Instant Grout as manufactured by U.S. Grout Corporation, Fairfield, Connecticut. The grout shall be mixed and installed according to manufacturers recommendations. No substitutions will be permitted. Technical service shall be made available by manufacturer upon request.

For a more detailed specification guideline, call or write Engineering and Technical Center, U.S. Grout Corporation for assistance.

PACKAGING, YIELD, ORDERING AND AVAILABILITY

Five Star Instant Grout is packaged in heavy duty waterproof plastic pails producing one half cubic foot of hardened grout. For ordering, determine the total number of cubic feet required, add 5% wastage, and contact U.S. Grout Corporation or one of your local Five Star® dealers throughout the United States. Five Star products are manufactured in plants throughout the United States and are also manufactured and available worldwide.

STORAGE AND HANDLING

Five Star® Instant Grout should be stored in a cool, dry place in accordance with the recommendations of the American Concrete Institute.

Warranty: Five Star Cement Grouts are warranteed never to shrink below their original placement volume when tested in accordance with ASTM C-827. U.S Grout Corporation stands behind its products when used by competent workmen in accordance with manufacturer's directions. No responsibility for product use is assumed or implied where inferior workmanship is encountered, or difficulty caused by other materials is evident. U.S. Grout Corporation's liability is limited to replacement of materials found to be defective. These recommended procedures are for normal field practice. They may be modified by the designer, specifier, purchaser or their authorized agent since only they are responsible for the design, installation and supervision of specific conditions and installations.

ENGINEERING & TECHNICAL CENTER, U.S. GROUT CORPORATION, SUBSIDIARY OF FIVE STAR PRODUCTS, INC.

401 STILLSON ROAD, FAIRFIELD, CONN. 06430 • (203) 336-7900 • CABLE FIVE STAR • FACSIMILE: (203) 336-7939 • TELEX:643857 • COPYRIGHT 1987 • 8875K

FIVE STAR® SPECIAL GROUT 100

DESCRIPTION Five Star Special Grout 100 is the first cement-based, nonmetallic, nonshrink grout that maintains a fluid consistency for a very long time. It is the highest performing, most reliable, versatile, general purpose fluid precision grout. The advanced technology of this patented product combines the following advantages that no other manufacturer can offer.

UNIQUE ADVANTAGES
- Precision Nonshrink
- Highest Effective Bearing Area[1]
- Contains Devoider[2]

SPECIAL ADVANTAGES
- Fluid Consistency
- Long Working Time
- High Early Strength

TYPICAL PHYSICAL PROPERTIES   In-Place Properties

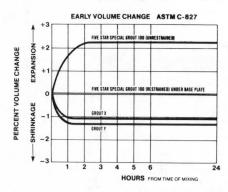

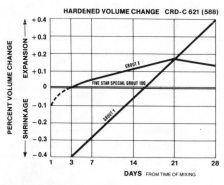

Early Volume Change: ASTM C-827: 0.00% shrinkage
Hardened Volume Change: CRD-C 621 (588): 0.00% shrinkage; 0.00% expansion after set
Effective Bearing Area[1]: 95% minimum
Compressive Strength, ASTM C-109: 5000 psi/7 Days
Meets Corps of Engineers Specification for Nonshrink Grout, CRD-C 621 (588)

---

[1]EBA: Effective Bearing Area - precent final surface area of grout in direct contact with bearing plate.

[2]All Five Star Grouts contain Devoider™, which offers the unique advantage of preventing cavities; overcoming plastic shrinkage, keeping the grout tightly against the plate for permanent support; producing the highest Effective Bearing Area.

I.6

Placement Properties

Five Star Special Grout 100 may be mixed to a non-sag, plastic, flowable, or fluid consistency. Five Star Special Grout 100 also maintains these consistencies for a very long time allowing ample placement time to ensure the highest Effetive Bearing Area is achieved. In addition, Five Star Special Grout 100 has the unique ability to be placed using mechanical devices to further facilitate placement without compromising the in-place properties.

APPLICATIONS

- Large, Heavy Operating Equipment with very tight clearances
- Structural Columns with very tight clearances
- Anchors with very tight clearances
- Precast and Prestressed Panels with very tight clearances
- Patching

PLACEMENT GUIDELINES

1. **Surface Preparation:** All surfaces to be in contact with Five Star Special Grout 100 shall be entirely free of oil, grease, laitance, or other foreign substances. Roughen surface to ensure a good bond to existing concrete. Clean thoroughly with liberal quantities of water, leaving concrete saturated but free of standing water.
2. **Mixing:** Five Star Special Grout 100 shall be thoroughly mixed to any desired consistency by varying the amount of water used. Do not exceed maximum recommended amount of mixing water. Follow printed instructions on each package.
3. **Methods of Placing:** Five Star Special Grout 100 is designed to be poured into place. However, it may be flowed, pumped, troweled or dry packed into place.
4. **Post-Placement Procedures:** Five Star Special Grout 100 should be cured for a minimum of three days with wet burlap or approved curing compound. In-service operation may begin immediately after minimum required grout strengths have been reached.

ENGINEERING & TECHNICAL CENTER

U.S. Grout Corporation maintains the industry's foremost Engineering and Technical Center staffed with engineers, available for consultation and on-site technical service worldwide.

SPECIFICATION GUIDELINES

All cement-based nonshrink grout to be placed at fluid consistency shall be Five Star Special Grout 100 as manufactured by U.S. Grout Corporation, Fairfield, Connecticut. The grout shall be mixed and installed according to manufacturer's recommendations. No substitutions will be permitted. Technical service shall be made available by the manufacturer upon request.

For a more detailed specification guideline, call or write Engineering and Technical Center, U.S. Grout Corporation for assistance.

PACKAGING, YIELD, ORDERING AND AVAILABILITY

Five Star Special Grout 100 is packaged in heavy-duty, polyethylene-lined bags producing one cubic foot of hardened grout. For ordering, determine the total number of cubic feet required, add 5% wastage, and contact U.S. Grout Corporation or one of your local Five Star® dealers throughout the United States. Five Star Grouts are manufactured in plants throughout the United States and are also manufactured and available worldwide.

STORAGE AND HANDLING

Five Star Special Grout 100 should be stored in a cool, dry place in accordance with the recommendations of the American Concrete Institute.

Warranty: Five Star Cement Grouts are warranteed never to shrink below its original placement volume when tested in accordance with ASTM C-827. U.S. Grout Corporation stands behind its products when used by competent workmen in accordance with manufacturer's directions. No responsibility for product use is assumed or implied where inferior workmanship is encountered, or difficulty caused by other materials is evident. U.S. Grout Corporation's liability is limited to replacement of materials found to be defective. These recommended procedures are for normal field practice. They may be modified by the designer, specifier, purchaser or their authorized agent since only they are responsible for the design, installation and supervision of specific conditions and installations.

ENGINEERING & TECHNICAL CENTER, U.S. GROUT CORPORATION, 401 STILLSON ROAD, FAIRFIELD, CONN. 06430 • (203) 336-7900

CABLE FIVE STAR • FACSIMILE (203) 336-7939 • TELEX: 643857 • COPYRIGHT 1986 • 10865K

FIVE STAR® SPECIAL GROUT 110

DESCRIPTION

Five Star Special Grout 110 is the first cement-based, nonmetallic, nonshrink grout specifically formulated for superior pumping performance. It is the highest performing, versatile, reliable, pump grade, precision grout. The advanced technology of this patented product combines the following advantages that no other manufacturer can offer.

UNIQUE ADVANTAGES

- Precision Nonshrink
- Highest Effective Bearing Area[1]
- Contains Devoider[2]

SPECIAL ADVANTAGES

- Superior Pumping Performance
- Very Long Working Time
- Versatile

TYPICAL PHYSICAL PROPERTIES   **In-Place Properties**

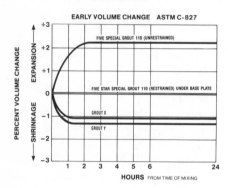

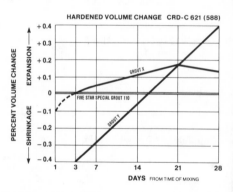

Early Volume Change, ASTM C-827: 0.00% shrinkage
Hardened Volume Change: CRD-C 621 (588): 0.00% shrinkage; 0.00% expansion after set
Effective Bearing Area[1]: 95% minimum
Compressive Strength, ASTM C-109: 5000 psi/7 Days
Meets Corps of Engineers Specification for Nonshrink Grout, CRD-C 621 (588)

[1]EBA: Effective Bearing Area - precent final surface area of grout in direct contact with bearing plate.

[2]All Five Star Grouts contain Devoider™, which offers the unique advantage of preventing cavities; overcoming plastic shrinkage, keeping the grout tightly against the plate for permanent support; producing the highest Effective Bearing Area.

Placement Properties

Five Star Special Grout 110 may be mixed to a pumpable consistency. Five Star Special Grout 110 also provides a very long working time, allowing ample placement time to ensure the highest Effective Bearing Area is achieved. Five Star Special Grout 110 has the unique and versatile ability to be placed using mechanical devices such as pumps, plungers, rods, or vibrators to further facilitate placement without compromising the in-place properties.

APPLICATIONS

- Large Volume Placements
- Extremely Large, Heavy Operating Equipment
- Extremely Large Structural Column Plates
- Difficult and Limited Access Areas

PLACEMENT GUIDELINES

1. **Surface Preparation:** All surfaces to be in contact with Five Star Special Grout 110 shall be entirely free of oil, grease, laitance, or other foreign substances. Roughen surface to ensure a good bond to existing concrete. Clean thoroughly with liberal quantities of water, leaving concrete saturated but free of standing water.

2. **Mixing:** Five Star Special Grout 110 shall be thoroughly mixed to any desired consistency by varying the amount of water used. Do not exceed maximum recommended amount of mixing water. Follow printed instructions on each package.

3. **Methods of Placing:** Five Star Special Grout 110 is designed for pumping. However, it may be dry packed, troweled, flowed, pumped, or vibrated into place.

4. **Post-Placement Procedures:** Five Star Special Grout 110 should be cured for a minimum of three days with wet burlap or approved curing compound. In-service operation may begin immediately after minimum required grout strengths have been reached.

ENGINEERING & TECHNICAL CENTER

U.S. Grout Corporation maintains the industry's foremost Engineering and Technical Center staffed with engineers, available for consultation and on-site technical service worldwide.

SPECIFICATION GUIDELINES

All cement-based non-shrink grout to be pumped shall be Five Star Special Grout 110-PG as manufactured by U.S. Grout Corporation, Fairfield, Connecticut. The grout shall be mixed and installed according to manufacturer's recommendations. No substitutions will be permitted. Technical service shall be made available by the manufacturer upon request.

For a more detailed specification guideline, call or write Engineering and Technical Center, U.S. Grout Corporation for assistance.

PACKAGING, YIELD, ORDERING AND AVAILABILITY

Five Star Special Grout 110 is packaged in heavy-duty, polyethylene-lined bags producing one cubic foot of hardened grout. For ordering, determine the total number of cubic feet required, add 5% wastage, and contact U.S. Grout Corporation or one of your local Five Star® dealers throughout the United States. Five Star Grouts are manufactured in plants throughout the United States and are also manufactured and available worldwide.

STORAGE AND HANDLING

Five Star Special Grout 110 should be stored in a cool, dry place in accordance with the recommendations of the American Concrete Institute.

Warranty: Five Star Cement Grouts are warranteed never to shrink below its original placement volume when tested in accordance with ASTM C-827. U.S. Grout Corporation stands behind its products when used by competent workmen in accordance with manufacturer's directions. No responsibility for product use is assumed or implied where inferior workmanship is encountered, or difficulty caused by other materials is evident. U.S. Grout Corporation's liability is limited to replacement of materials found to be defective. These recommended procedures are for normal field practice. They may be modified by the designer, specifier, purchaser or their authorized agent since only they are responsible for the design, installation and supervision of specific conditions and installations.

ENGINEERING & TECHNICAL CENTER, U.S. GROUT CORPORATION, 401 STILLSON ROAD, FAIRFIELD, CONN. 06430 • (203) 336-7900

CABLE FIVE STAR • FACSIMILE (203) 336-7939 • TELEX: 643857 • COPYRIGHT 1986 • 10865K

FIVE STAR® SPECIAL GROUT 120

DESCRIPTION   Five Star Special Grout 120 is the world's leading high salt water resistant, cement-based, nonmetallic, nonshrink grout. This high performing, reliable, precision grout features very long working time with high salt water resistance. The advanced technology of this patented product combines the following advantages that no other manufacturer can offer.

UNIQUE ADVANTAGES
- Precision Nonshrink
- Highest Effective Bearing Area[1]
- Contains Devoider[2]

SPECIAL ADVANTAGES
- High Salt Water Resistance
- Very Long Working Time
- Versatile

TYPICAL PHYSICAL PROPERTIES   **In-Place Properties**

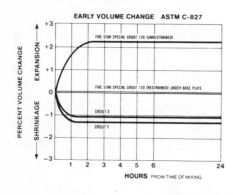

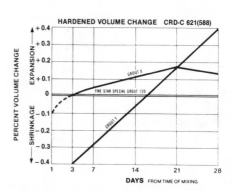

Early Volume Change: ASTM C-827: 0.00% shrinkage
Hardened Volume Change: CRD-C621 (588): 0.00% shrinkage; 0.00% expansion after set
Effective Bearing Area[1]: 95% minimum
Compressive Strength, ASTM C-109: 5000 psi/7 Days
Meets Corps of Engineers Specifications for Nonshrink Grout, CRD-C 621 (588)

[1]EBA: Effective Bearing Area—percent final surface area of grout in direct contact with bearing plate.
[2]All Five Star Grouts contain Devoider™, which offers the unique advantage of preventing cavities; overcoming plastic shrinkage, keeping the grout tightly against the plate for permanent support; producing the highest Effective Bearing Area.

Placement Properties

Five Star Special Grout 120 may be mixed to a non-sag, plastic, or flowable consistency. Five Star Special Special Grout 120 also provides a very long working time, allowing maximum placement time to ensure the highest Effective Bearing Area is achieved. In addition, Five Star Special Grout 120 has the unique and versatile ability to be placed using mechanical devices such as pumps, plungers, rods, or vibrators without compromising the in-place properties.

APPLICATIONS

- Large, Heavy Operating Equipment in Salt Water Attack Areas
- Structural Columns in Salt Water Attack Areas
- Anchors in Salt Water Attack Areas
- Patching in Salt Water Attack Areas

PLACEMENT GUIDELINES

1. **Surface Preparation:** All surfaces to be in contact with Five Star Special Grout 120 shall be entirely free of oil, grease, laitance, or other foreign substances. Roughen surface to ensure a good bond to existing concrete. Clean thoroughly with liberal quantities of water, leaving concrete saturated but free of standing water.

2. **Mixing:** Five Star Special Grout 120 shall be thoroughly mixed to any desired consistency by varying the amount of water used. Do not exceed maximum recommended amount of mixing water. Follow printed instructions on each package.

3. **Methods of Placing:** Five Star Special Grout 120 may be dry packed, troweled, flowed, pumped or vibrated into place.

4. **Post-Placement Procedures:** Five Star Special Grout 120 should be cured for a minimum of three days with wet burlap followed by an approved curing compound. In-service operation may begin immediately after minimum required grout strengths have been reached.

ENGINEERING & TECHNICAL CENTER

U.S. Grout Corporation maintains the industry's foremost Engineering and Technical Center staffed with engineers, available for consultation and on-site technical service worldwide.

SPECIFICATION GUIDELINES

All high salt water resistant cement-based, nonshrink grouting shall be performed with Five Star Special Grout 120 as manufactured by U.S. Grout Corporation, Fairfield, Connecticut. The grout shall be mixed and installed according to manufacturer's recommendations. No substitutions will be permitted. Technical service shall be made available by the manufacturer upon request.

For a more detailed specification guideline, call or write Engineering and Technical Center, U.S. Grout Corporation for assistance.

PACKAGING, YIELD, ORDERING AND AVAILABILITY

Five Star Special Grout 120 is packaged in heavy-duty, polyethylene-lined bags producing one cubic foot of hardened grout. For ordering, determine the total number of cubic feet required, add 5% wastage, and contact U.S. Grout Corporation or one of your local Five Star dealers throughout the United States. Five Star Grouts are manufactured in plants throughout the United States and are also manufactured and available worldwide.

STORAGE AND HANDLING

Five Star Special Grout 120 should be stored in a cool, dry place in accordance with the recommendation of the American Concrete Institute.

Warranty: Five Star Cement Grouts are warranteed never to shrink below their original placement volume when tested in accordance with ASTM C-827. U.S. Grout Corporation stands behind its products when used by competent workmen in accordance with manufacturer's directions. No responsibility for product use is assumed or implied where inferior workmanship is encountered, or difficulty caused by other materials is evident. U.S. Grout Corporation's liability is limited to replacement of materials found to be defective. These recommended procedures are for normal field practice. They may be modified by the designer, specifier, purchaser or their authorized agent since only they are responsible for the design, installation and supervision of specific conditions and installations.

ENGINEERING & TECHNICAL CENTER, U.S. GROUT CORPORATION, SUBSIDIARY OF FIVE STAR PRODUCTS, INC.

401 STILLSON ROAD, FAIRFIELD, CONN. 06430 • (203) 336-7900 • CABLE FIVE STAR • FACSIMILE (203) 336-7939 • TELEX 643857 • COPYRIGHT 1987 • 3875K

FIVE STAR® SPECIAL GROUT 130

DESCRIPTION Five Star Special Grout 130 is the only architectural cement-based, nonmetallic, non-shrink grout available in white and may be pigmented to any color. It is the highest performing, most versatile, reliable, nonstaining, architectural precision grout. The advanced technology of this patented product combines the following advantages that no other manufacturer can offer.

UNIQUE ADVANTAGES
- Precision Nonshrink
- Highest Effective Bearing Area[1]
- Contains Devoider[2]

SPECIAL ADVANTAGES
- White—Nonstaining
- High Early Strength
- Long Working Time

TYPICAL PHYSICAL PROPERTIES   **In-Place Properties**

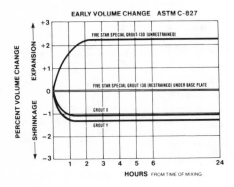

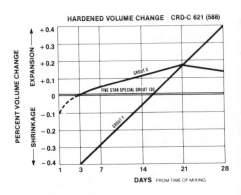

Early Volume Change, ASTM C-827: 0.00% shrinkage
Hardened Volume Change, CRD-C 621 (588): 0.00% shrinkage; 0.00% expansion after set
Effective Bearing Area[1]: 95% minimum
Compressive Strength, ASTM C-109: 5000 psi/7 Days
Meets Corps of Engineers Specification for Nonshrink Grout, CRD-C 621 (588)

[1]EBA: Effective Bearing Area - precent final surface area of grout in direct contact with bearing plate.

[2]All Five Star Grouts contain Devoider™, which offers the unique advantage of preventing cavities; overcoming plastic shrinkage, keeping the grout tightly against the plate for permanent support; producing the highest Effective Bearing Area.

Placement Properties

Five Star Special Grout 130 may be mixed to a non-sag, plastic, or flowable consistency. Five Star Special Grout 130 also provides a very long working time, allowing ample placement time to ensure the highest Effective Bearing Area is achieved. In addition, Five Star Special Grout 130 has the unique ability to be placed using mechanical devices such as pumps, plungers, rods, or vibrators to further facilitate placement without compromising the in-place properties.

APPLICATIONS

- Precast and Prestressed Panels
- Limestone, Marble and Granite Panels
- Special Architectural Patching
- Exposed Architectural-Structural Grouting

PLACEMENT GUIDELINES

1. **Surface Preparation:** All surfaces to be in contact with Five Star Special Grout 130 shall be entirely free of oil, grease, laitance, or other foreign substances. Roughen surface to ensure a good bond to existing concrete. Clean thoroughly with liberal quantities of water, leaving concrete saturated but free of standing water.
2. **Mixing:** Five Star Special Grout 130 shall be thoroughly mixed to any desired consistency by varying the amount of water used. Do not exceed maximum recommended amount of mixing water. Follow printed instructions on each package.
3. **Methods of Placing:** Five Star Special Grout 130 may be dry packed, troweled, flowed, pumped, or vibrated into place.
4. **Post-Placement Procedures:** Five Star Special Grout 130 should be wet cured for a minimum of three days or an approved nonstaining curing compound may be used. In-service operation may begin immediately after minimum required grout strengths have been reached.

ENGINEERING & TECHNICAL CENTER

U.S. Grout Corporation maintains the industry's foremost Engineering and Technical Center staffed with engineers, available for consultation and on-site technical service worldwide.

SPECIFICATION GUIDELINES

All architectural cement-based nonshrink grouting shall be performed with Five Star Special Grout 130 as manufactured by U.S. Grout Corporation, Fairfield, Connecticut. The grout shall be mixed and installed according to manufacturer's recommendations. No substitutions will be permitted. Technical service shall be made available by the manufacturer upon request.

For a more detailed specification guideline, call or write Engineering and Technical Center, U.S. Grout Corporation for assistance.

PACKAGING, YIELD, ORDERING AND AVAILABILITY

Five Star Special Grout 130 is packaged in heavy-duty, polyethylene-lined bags producing one cubic foot of hardened grout. For ordering, determine the total number of cubic feet required, add 5% wastage, and contact U.S. Grout Corporation or one of your local Five Star® dealers throughout the United States. Five Star Grouts are manufactured in plants throughout the United States and are also manufactured and available worldwide.

STORAGE AND HANDLING

Five Star Special Grout 130 should be stored in a cool, dry place in accordance with the recommendations of the American Concrete Institute.

Warranty: Five Star Cement Grouts are warranteed never to shrink below its original placement volume when tested in accordance with ASTM C-827. U.S. Grout Corporation stands behind its products when used by competent workmen in accordance with manufacturer's directions. No responsibility for product use is assumed or implied where inferior workmanship is encountered, or difficulty caused by other materials is evident. U.S. Grout Corporation's liability is limited to replacement of materials found to be defective. These recommended procedures are for normal field practice. They may be modified by the designer, specifier, purchaser or their authorized agent since only they are responsible for the design, installation and supervision of specific conditions and installations.

ENGINEERING & TECHNICAL CENTER, U.S. GROUT CORPORATION, 401 STILLSON ROAD, FAIRFIELD, CONN. 06430 • (203) 336-7900

CABLE FIVE STAR • FACSIMILE: (203) 336-7939 • TELEX: 643857 • COPYRIGHT 1986 • 10865K

FIVE STAR® SPECIAL GROUT 150

DESCRIPTION   Five Star Special Grout 150 is the world's leading high sulfate resistant, cement-based, nonmetallic, nonshrink grout. This high performing, reliable, precision grout features low heat of hydration and high sulfate resistance. The advanced technology of this patented product combines the following advantages that no other manufacturer can offer.

UNIQUE ADVANTAGES
- Precision Nonshrink
- Highest Effective Bearing Area[1]
- Contains Devoider[2]

SPECIAL ADVANTAGES
- High Sulfate Resistance
- Low Heat of Hydration
- Very Long Working Time

TYPICAL PHYSICAL PROPERTIES   In-Place Properties

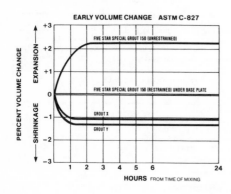

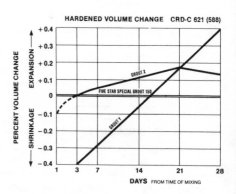

Early Volume Change, ASTM C-827: 0.00% shrinkage
Hardened Volume Change, CRD-C 621 (588): 0.00% shrinkage; 0.00% expansion after set
Effective Bearing Area[1]: 95% minimum
Compressive Strength, ASTM C-109: 5000 psi/28 Days
Meets Corps of Engineers Specification for Nonshrink Grout, CRD-C 621 (588)

[1]EBA: Effective Bearing Area - precent final surface area of grout in direct contact with bearing plate.

[2]All Five Star Grouts contain Devoider™, which offers the unique advantage of preventing cavities; overcoming plastic shrinkage, keeping the grout tightly against the plate for permanent support; producing the highest Effective Bearing Area.

Placement Properties

Five Star Special Grout 150 may be mixed to a non-sag, plastic, or flowable consistency. Five Star Special Grout 150 also provides a very long working time, allowing maximum placement time to ensure the highest Effective Bearing Area is achieved. In addition, Five Star Special Grout 150 has the unique and versatile ability to be placed using mechanical devices such as pumps, plungers, rods, or vibrators to further facilitate placement without compromising the in-place properties.

APPLICATIONS

- Large, Heavy Operating Equipment in Sulfate Attack Areas
- Structural Columns in Sulface Attack Areas
- Deep Placements
- Anchors in Sulfate Attack Areas
- Patching in Sulfate Attack Areas

PLACEMENT GUIDELINES

1. **Surface Preparation:** All surfaces to be in contact with Five Star Special Grout 150 shall be entirely free of oil, grease, laitance, or other foreign substances. Roughen surface to ensure a good bond to existing concrete. Clean thoroughly with liberal quantities of water, leaving concrete saturated but free of standing water.

2. **Mixing:** Five Star Special Grout 150 shall be thoroughly mixed to any desired consistency by varying the amount of water used. Do not exceed maximum recommended amount of mixing water. Follow printed instructions on each package.

3. **Methods of Placing:** Five Star Special Grout 150 may be dry packed, troweled, flowed, pumped, or vibrated into place.

4. **Post-Placement Procedures:** Five Star Special Grout 150 should be cured for a minimum of three days with wet burlap followed by an approved curing compound. In-service operation may begin immediately after minimum required grout strengths have been reached.

ENGINEERING & TECHNICAL CENTER

U.S. Grout Corporation maintains the industry's foremost Engineering and Technical Center staffed with engineers, available for consultation and on-site technical service worldwide.

SPECIFICATION GUIDELINES

All high sulfate resistant and/or low heat of hydration cement-based nonshrink grouting shall be performed with Five Star Special Grout 150 as manufactured by U.S. Grout Corporation, Fairfield, Connecticut. The grout shall be mixed and installed according to manufacturer's recommendations. No substitutions will be permitted. Technical service shall be made available by the manufacturer upon request.

For a more detailed specification guideline, call or write Engineering and Technical Center, U.S. Grout Corporation for assistance.

PACKAGING, YIELD, ORDERING AND AVAILABILITY

Five Star Special Grout 150 is packaged in heavy-duty, polyethylene-lined bags producing one cubic foot of hardened grout. For ordering, determine the total number of cubic feet required, add 5% wastage, and contact U.S. Grout Corporation or one of your local Five Star® dealers throughout the United States. Five Star Grouts are manufactured in plants throughout the United States and are also manufactured and available worldwide.

STORAGE AND HANDLING

Five Star Special Grout 150 should be stored in a cool, dry place in accordance with the recommendations of the American Concrete Institute.

Warranty: Five Star Cement Grouts are warranted never to shrink below its original placement volume when tested in accordance with ASTM C-827. U.S. Grout Corporation stands behind its products when used by competent workmen in accordance with manufacturer's directions. No responsibility for product use is assumed or implied where inferior workmanship is encountered, or difficulty caused by other materials is evident. U.S. Grout Corporation's liability is limited to replacement of materials found to be defective. These recommended procedures are for normal field practice. They may be modified by the designer, specifier, purchaser or their authorized agent since only they are responsible for the design, installation and supervision of specific conditions and installations.

ENGINEERING & TECHNICAL CENTER, U.S. GROUT CORPORATION, 401 STILLSON ROAD, FAIRFIELD, CONN. 06430 • (203) 336-7900

CABLE FIVE STAR • FACSIMILE: (203) 336-7939 • TELEX: 643857 • COPYRIGHT 1986 • 10865K

FIVE STAR® SPECIAL GROUT 160
For Radiation Shielding

DESCRIPTION   Five Star Special Grout 160 is the first cement-based, high density, noncorrosive, non-shrink grout formulated for radiation shielding. It is the most reliable, versatile, cement-based shielding grout for penetration closures at nuclear facilities. The advanced technology of this patented product combines the following advantages that no other manufacturer can offer.

UNIQUE ADVANTAGES
- Precision Nonshrink
- Highest Effective Bearing Area[1]
- Contains Devoider[2]

SPECIAL ADVANTAGES
- High Density
- Long Working Time
- Versatile

TYPICAL PHYSICAL PROPERTIES   **In-Place Properties**

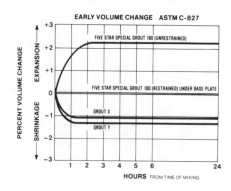

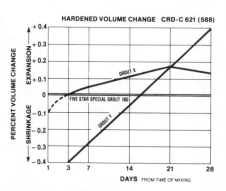

Early Volume Change: ASTM C-827: 0.00% shrinkage
Hardened Volume Change: CRD-C621 (588): 0.00% shrinkage; 0.00% expansion after set
Effective Bearing Area[1]: 95% minimum
Compressive Strength, ASTM C-109: 5000 psi/7 Days
Meets Corps of Engineers Specifications for Nonshrink Grout, CRD-C 621 (588)
Density: 155 lbs/cubic foot (minimum)

[1]EBA: Effective Bearing Area—percent final surface area of grout in direct contact with bearing plate.
[2]All Five Star Grouts contain Devoider™, which offers the unique advantage of preventing cavities; overcoming plastic shrinkage, keeping the grout tightly against the plate for permanent support; producing the highest Effective Bearing Area.

Placement Properties
Five Star Special Grout 160 may be mixed to a non-sag, plastic, or flowable consistency. Five Star Special Special Grout 160 also maintains these consistencies for a very long time allowing ample placement time to ensure the highest Effective Bearing Area is achieved.

APPLICATIONS
- Radiation Shielding
- Nuclear Reactor Foundations
- Penetration Closures

PLACEMENT GUIDELINES

1. **Surface Preparation:** All surfaces to be in contact with Five Star Special Grout 160 shall be entirely free of oil, grease, laitance, or other foreign substances. Roughen surface to ensure a good bond to existing concrete. Clean thoroughly with liberal quantities of water, leaving concrete saturated, but free of standing water.
2. **Mixing:** Five Star Special Grout 160 shall be thoroughly mixed to any desired consistency by varying the amount of water used. Do not exceed maximum recommended amount of mixing water. Follow printed instructions on each package.
3. **Methods of Placing:** Five Star Special Grout 160 may be dry packed, troweled, or flowed into place.
4. **Post-Placement Procedures:** Five Star Special Grout 160 should be cured for a minimum of three days with wet burlap followed by an approved curing compound. In-service operation may begin immediately after minimum required grout strengths have been reached.

ENGINEERING & TECHNICAL CENTER
U.S. Grout Corporation maintains the industry's foremost Engineering and Technical Center staffed with engineers, available for consultation and on-site technical service worldwide.

SPECIFICATION GUIDELINES
All radiation shielding cement-based, non-shrink grout shall be Five Star Special Grout 160 as manufactured by U.S. Grout Corporation, Fairfield, Connecticut. The grout shall be mixed and installed according to manufacturer's recommendations. No substitutions will be permitted. Technical service shall be made available by the manufacturer upon request.

For a more detailed specification guideline, call or write Engineering and Technical Center, U.S. Grout Corporation for assistance.

PACKAGING, YIELD, ORDERING AND AVAILABILITY
Five Star Special Grout 160 is packaged in a heavy duty waterproof plastic pail producing one half cubic foot of hardened grout. For ordering, determine the total number of cubic feet required, add 5% wastage, and contact U.S. Grout Corporation or one of your local Five Star dealers throughout the United States. Five Star Grouts are manufactured in plants throughout the United States, and are also manufactured and available worldwide.

STORAGE AND HANDLING
Five Star® Special Grout 160 should be stored in a cool, dry place in accordance with the recommendation of the American Concrete Institute.

Warranty: Five Star Cement Grouts are warranteed never to shrink below their original placement volume when tested in accordance with ASTM C-827. U.S. Grout Corporation stands behind its products when used by competent workmen in accordance with manufacturer's directions. No responsibility for product use is assumed or implied where inferior workmanship is encountered, or difficulty caused by other materials is evident. U.S. Grout Corporation's liability is limited to replacement of materials found to be defective. These recommended procedures are for normal field practice. They may be modified by the designer, specifier, purchaser or their authorized agent since only they are responsible for the design, installation and supervision of specific conditions and installations.

ENGINEERING & TECHNICAL CENTER, U.S. GROUT CORPORATION, SUBSIDIARY OF FIVE STAR PRODUCTS, INC.

401 STILLSON ROAD, FAIRFIELD, CONN. 06430 • (203) 336-7930 • CABLE FIVE STAR • FACSIMILE: (203) 336-7939 • TELEX:643857 • COPYRIGHT 1987 • 3875K

FIVE STAR® SPECIAL GROUT 200

DESCRIPTION   Five Star Special Grout 200 is the world's leading cement-based, nonmetallic, nonshrink grout for applications with operating temperatures up to 2400°F. This high performing, reliable, precision grout features high strength at elevated temperatures. The advanced technology of this patented product combines the following advantages that no other manufacturer can offer.

UNIQUE ADVANTAGES
- Precision Nonshrink
- Highest Effective Bearing Area[1]
- Contains Devoider[2]

SPECIAL ADVANTAGES
- High Temperature Resistance—Up to 2400°F

TYPICAL PHYSICAL PROPERTIES   **In-Place Properties**

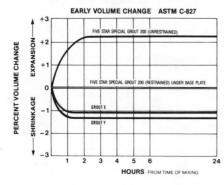

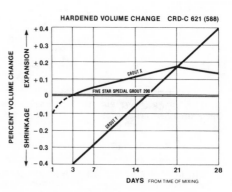

Early Volume Change: ASTM C-827: 0.00% shrinkage
Hardened Volume Change: CRD-C621 (588): 0.00% shrinkage; 0.00% expansion after set
Effective Bearing Area[1]: 95% minimum
Compressive Strength, ASTM C-109: 4000 psi/7 Days @ 72°F,
3000 psi @ 220°F, 2500 psi @ 1000°F, 1000 psi @ 1500°F
Meets Corps of Engineers Specifications for Nonshrink Grout, CRD-C 621 (588)

[1]EBA: Effective Bearing Area—percent final surface area of grout in direct contact with bearing plate.
[2]All Five Star Grouts contain Devoider™, which offers the unique advantage of preventing cavities; overcoming plastic shrinkage, keeping the grout tightly against the plate for permanent support; producing the highest Effective Bearing Area.

Placement Properties

Five Star Special Grout 200 may be mixed to a non-sag, plastic, or flowable consistency. Five Star Special Special Grout 200 also provides a long working time, allowing maximum placement time to ensure the highest Effective Bearing Area is achieved. In addition, Five Star Special Grout 200 has the unique and versatile ability to be placed using mechanical devices such as pumps, plungers, rods, or vibrators without compromising the in-place properties.

APPLICATIONS

- Large, Heavy Equipment at Temperatures up to 2400°F
- Structural Columns at Temperatures up to 2400°F
- Anchors at Temperatures up to 2400°F
- Patching in Sulfate Attack Areas at Temperatures up to 2400°F

PLACEMENT GUIDELINES

1. **Surface Preparation:** All surfaces to be in contact with Five Star Special Grout 200 shall be entirely free of oil, grease, laitance, or other foreign substances. Roughen surface to ensure a good bond to existing concrete. Clean thoroughly with liberal quantities of water, leaving concrete saturated, but free of standing water.

2. **Mixing:** Five Star Special Grout 200 shall be thoroughly mixed to any desired consistency by varying the amount of water used. Do not exceed maximum recommended amount of mixing water. Under rare circumstances, a false set may occur which may be corrected by merely remixing (without the addition of more water). Follow printed instructions on each package.

3. **Methods of Placing:** Five Star Special Grout 200 may be dry packed, troweled, flowed, pumped, or vibrated into place.

4. **Post-Placement Procedures:** Five Star Special Grout 200 requires a special curing procedure based on the specific application and environmental conditions. Please call U.S. Grout Corporation for the exact curing procedure required for your installation.

ENGINEERING & TECHNICAL CENTER

U.S. Grout Corporation maintains the industry's foremost Engineering and Technical Center staffed with engineers, available for consultation and on-site technical service worldwide.

SPECIFICATION GUIDELINES

All high temperature resistant cement-based nonshrink grouting shall be performed with Five Star Special Grout 200 as manufactured by U.S. Grout Corporation, Fairfield, Connecticut. The grout shall be mixed and installed according to manufacturer's recommendations. No substitutions will be permitted. Technical service shall be made available by the manufacturer upon request.

For a more detailed specification guideline, call or write Engineering and Technical Center, U.S. Grout Corporation for assistance.

PACKAGING, YIELD, ORDERING AND AVAILABILITY

Five Star Special Grout 200 is packaged in heavy-duty polyethylene-lined bags producing 0.9 cubic foot of hardened grout. For ordering, determine the total number of cubic feet required, add 5% wastage, and contact U.S. Grout Corporation or one of your local Five Star® dealers throughout the United States. Five Star Grouts are manufactured in plants throughout the United States, and are also manufactured and available worldwide.

STORAGE AND HANDLING

Five Star® Special Grout 200 should be stored in a cool, dry place in accordance with the recommendation of the American Concrete Institute.

Warranty: Five Star Cement Grouts are warranteed never to shrink below their original placement volume when tested in accordance with ASTM C-827. U.S. Grout Corporation stands behind its products when used by competent workmen in accordance with manufacturer's directions. No responsibility for product use is assumed or implied where inferior workmanship is encountered, or difficulty caused by other materials is evident. U.S. Grout Corporation's liability is limited to replacement of materials found to be defective. These recommended procedures are for normal field practice. They may be modified by the designer, specifier, purchaser or their authorized agent since only they are responsible for the design, installation and supervision of specific conditions and installations.

ENGINEERING & TECHNICAL CENTER, U.S. GROUT CORPORATION, 401 STILLSON ROAD, FAIRFIELD, CONN. 06430 • (203) 336-7900

CABLE FIVE STAR • FACSIMILE: (203) 336-7939 • TELEX:643857 • COPYRIGHT 1987 • 8875K

FIVE STAR® SPECIAL GROUT 400

DESCRIPTION Five Star Special Grout 400 is a cement-based, nonshrink, nonmetallic, fluid grout specifically formulated for grouting and providing corrosion protection for cables and rods in small, annular spaces. Five Star Special Grout 400 does not contain chlorides, aluminum powder, or other chemicals which contribute to hydrogen embrittlement and other forms of corrosion. The advanced technology of this patented product combines the following advantages that no other manufacturer can offer.

UNIQUE ADVANTAGES
- Precision Nonshrink
- Contains Devoider[1]

SPECIAL ADVANTAGES
- Fluid Consistency
- Non-Bleeding
- High Early Strength
- Long Pumping Time
- Greater Penetration

TYPICAL PHYSICAL PROPERTIES   **In-Place Properties**

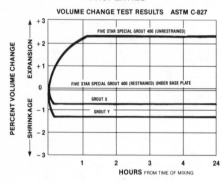

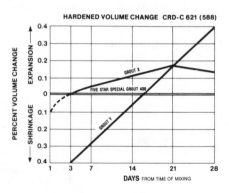

Early Volume Change, ASTM C-827: 0.00% shrinkage
Meets Corps of Engineers' Specification, CRD-C 621 (588)
Compressive Strength, ASTM C-109: 3500 psi/1 Day; 6000 psi/7 Days
Rate of flow, CRD-C 611: Less than 30 seconds
Flexural Strength, ASTM C-78: 400 psi/1 Day; 700 psi/7 Days
Modulus of Elasticity, ASTM C-469: 1.0×10^6 psi/1 Day; 1.7×10^6 psi/7 Days
Split Tensile Strength, ASTM C-496: 200 psi/1 Day; 400 psi/7 Days

[1]All Five Star Grouts contain Devoider™, which offers the unique advantage of preventing cavities and overcoming plastic shrinkage.

Placement Properties

Five Star Special Grout 400 is mixed to a fluid consistency and can easily be pumped long distances through small, annular spaces.

APPLICATIONS

- Tendon Grouting
- Cable Grouting
- Grouting Small Annular Spaces

PLACEMENT GUIDELINES

1. **Surface Preparation:** Cables, rods, and ducts should be entirely free of oil, grease, laitance, or other foreign substances. Concrete holes and ducts should be thoroughly saturated with water but free of standing water prior to grouting.

2. **Temperature:** Temperature affects the fluidity and pumping time of the grout. The best temperature for pumping is between 45°F and 70°F. For conditions outside of this range, contact U.S. Grout's Engineering and Technical Center for assistance.

3. **Mixing:** Five Star Special Grout 400 shall be thoroughly mixed in accordance with the Prestressed Concrete Institute's standards. Mix the grout with clean, potable water only. Use the minimum amount of water necessary to achieve required fluidity. Do not exceed the maximum recommended amount of mixing water. Follow printed instructions of each package. A paddle-type mortar mixer or low-speed (under 300 rpm), vertical-shaft vane mixer is best. Mix to produce a uniform, thoroughly-blended grout without inducing excessive air entrapment or temperature increase.

4. **Pumping:** The pump hopper should be equipped with a screen to reject lumps and other foreign material. All valves and fittings should be watertight to prevent loss of water. If any delay occurs, the discharge hose should be placed into the hopper to recirculate the grout and maintain slow agitation. Duct closure valves or plugs must remain in place until grout has reached initial set, or if residual pressures are specified, until minimum required grout strengths have been achieved.

ENGINEERING & TECHNICAL CENTER

U.S. Grout Corporation maintains the industry's foremost Engineering and Technical Center staffed with engineers, available for consultation and on-site technical service worldwide.

SPECIFICATION GUIDELINES

All tendon and cable grouting shall be done with Five Star Special Grout 400 as manufactured by U.S. Grout Corporation, Fairfield, Connecticut. The grout shall be mixed and installed according to manufacturer's recommendations. No substitutions will be permitted. Technical service shall be made available by the manufacturer upon request.

For a more detailed specification guideline, call or write Engineering and Technical Center, U.S. Grout Corporation for assistance.

PACKAGING, YIELD, ORDERING AND AVAILABILITY

Five Star Special Grout 400 is packaged in heavy-duty, polyethylene-lined bags producing one cubic foot of hardened grout. For ordering, determine the total number of cubic feet required, add 5% wastage, and contact U.S. Grout Corporation or one of your local Five Star® dealers throughout the United States. Five Star Grouts are manufactured in plants throughout the United States and are also manufactured and available worldwide.

STORAGE AND HANDLING

Five Star Special Grout 400 should be stored in a cool, dry place in accordance with the recommendations of the American Concrete Institute.

Warranty: Five Star Cement Grouts are warranteed never to shrink below its original placement volume when tested in accordance with ASTM C-827. U.S. Grout Corporation stands behind its products when used by competent workmen in accordance with manufacturer's directions. No responsibility for product use is assumed or implied where inferior workmanship is encountered, or difficulty caused by other materials is evident. U.S. Grout Corporation's liability is limited to replacement of materials found to be defective. These recommended procedures are for normal field practice. They may be modified by the designer, specifier, purchaser or their authorized agent since only they are responsible for the design, installation and supervision of specific conditions and installations.

ENGINEERING & TECHNICAL CENTER, U.S. GROUT CORPORATION, 401 STILLSON ROAD, FAIRFIELD, CONN. 06430 • (203) 336-7900

CABLE FIVE STAR • FACSIMILE: (203) 336-7939 • TELEX: 643857 • COPYRIGHT 1986 • 10865K

FIVE STAR® SPECIAL GROUT 550

DESCRIPTION   Five Star Special Grout 550 is the first cement-based, non-shrink grout formulated for grouting at temperatures up to 115°F with no ice or cold water. It is a high performing, versatile, reliable, hot weather, high sulfate resistant, precision grout. The advanced technology of this patented product combines the following advantages that no other manufacturer can offer.

UNIQUE ADVANTAGES
- Precision Nonshrink
- Highest Effective Bearing Area[1]
- Contains Devoider[2]

SPECIAL ADVANTAGES
- Excellent Placeability up to 115°F
- No Ice or Cold Water Required
- Long Working Time
- High Sulfate Resistance
- High Salt Water Resistance

TYPICAL PHYSICAL PROPERTIES   **In-Place Properties at 110°F (43°C) Mix Temperature**

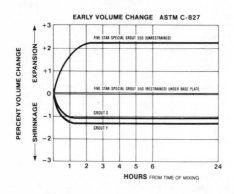

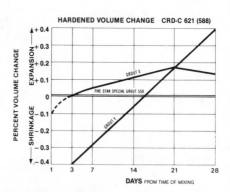

Early Volume Change: ASTM C-827: 0.00% shrinkage
Hardened Volume Change: CRD-C621 (588): 0.00% shrinkage; 0.00% expansion after set
Effective Bearing Area[1]: 95% minimum
Compressive Strength, ASTM C-109: 5000 psi/7 Days
Meets Corps of Engineers Specifications for Nonshrink Grout, CRD-C 621 (588)

[1]EBA: Effective Bearing Area—percent final surface area of grout in direct contact with bearing plate.
[2]All Five Star Grouts contain Devoider™, which offers the unique advantage of preventing cavities; overcoming plastic shrinkage, keeping the grout tightly against the plate for permanent support; producing the highest Effective Bearing Area.

Placement Properties

Five Star® Special Grout 550 may be mixed to a trowelable or flowable consistency, even at mix temperatures up to 115°F (46°C) with no ice or cold water. Five Star Special Grout 550 also provides a long working time without early stiffening, allowing ample placement time to ensure that the highest Effective Bearing Area is achieved. Five Star Special Grout 550 has the unique and versatile ability to be placed using mechanical devices such as pumps, plungers, rods or vibrators without compromising the in-place properties.

APPLICATIONS

- Grouting Large, Heavy Operating Equipment in Extreme Hot Weather
- Grouting Structural Columns in Extreme Hot Weather
- Grouting Anchors in Extreme Hot Weather
- Grouting Precast and Prestressed Panels in Extreme Hot Weather

PLACEMENT GUIDELINES

1. **Surface Preparation:** All surfaces to be in contact with Five Star Special Grout 550 shall be entirely free of oil, grease, laitance, or other foreign substances. Roughen surface to ensure a good bond to existing concrete. Clean thoroughly with liberal quantities of water, leaving concrete saturated, but free of standing water.

2. **Mixing:** Five Star Special Grout 550 shall be thoroughly mixed to the desired consistency by varying the amount of water used. Do not exceed maximum recommended amount of mixing water. Follow printed instructions on each package.

3. **Methods of Placing:** Five Star Special Grout 550 is designed to be troweled, flowed, pumped, or vibrated into place. During hot weather it is desirable to place the grout in the late afternoon or early evening when the tempurature is dropping. This allows heat development to take place during the coolest hours.

4. **Post-Placement Procedures:** Five Star Special Grout 550 should be cured for a minimum of three days with wet burlap followed by an approved curing compound. In-service operation may begin immediately after minimum required grout strengths have been reached.

ENGINEERING & TECHNICAL CENTER

U.S. Grout Corporation maintains the industry's foremost Engineering and Technical Center staffed with engineers, available for consultation and on-site technical service worldwide.

SPECIFICATION GUIDELINES

All hot weather cement-based, non-shrink grouting shall be performed with Five Star Special Grout 550 as manufactured by U.S. Grout Corporation, Fairfield, Connecticut. The grout shall be mixed and installed according to manufacturer's recommendations. No substitutions will be permitted. Technical service shall be made available by the manufacturer upon request.

For a more detailed specification guideline, call or write Engineering and Technical Center, U.S. Grout Corporation for assistance.

PACKAGING, YIELD, ORDERING AND AVAILABILITY

Five Star Special Grout 550 is packaged in heavy duty Polyethylene-lined bags producing one cubic foot of hardened grout. For ordering, determine the total number of cubic feet required, add 5% wastage, and contact U.S. Grout Corporation or one of your local Five Star dealers throughout the United States. Five Star Grouts are manufactured in plants throughout the United States, and are also manufactured and available worldwide.

STORAGE AND HANDLING

Five Star Special Grout 550 should be stored in a cool, dry place in accordance with the recommendation of the American Concrete Institute.

Warranty: Five Star Cement Grouts are warranteed never to shrink below their original placement volume when tested in accordance with ASTM C-827. U.S. Grout Corporation stands behind its products when used by competent workmen in accordance with manufacturer's directions. No responsibility for product use is assumed or implied where inferior workmanship is encountered, or difficulty caused by other materials is evident. U.S. Grout Corporation's liability is limited to replacement of materials found to be defective. These recommended procedures are for normal field practice. They may be modified by the designer, specifier, purchaser or their authorized agent since only they are responsible for the design, installation and supervision of specific conditions and installations.

ENGINEERING & TECHNICAL CENTER, U.S. GROUT CORPORATION, SUBSIDIARY OF FIVE STAR PRODUCTS, INC.

401 STILLSON ROAD, FAIRFIELD, CONN. 06430 • (203) 336-7900 • CABLE FIVE STAR • FACSIMILE: (203) 336-7939 • TELEX:643857 • COPYRIGHT 1987 • 8875K

PLANT
FACILITIES
Construction-Modernization-Maintenance-Operations
Two keys to
good roofs:
Insulation and
maintenance

Key grout characteristics:
A checklist for users

Complex system of pipes, pumps and turbines in this generating plant requires a high performance grout that provides the highest EBA.

by H. Nash Babcock

Successful operation of $1 million worth of industrial equipment may well depend upon an inch or two of grout.

The job of an industrial grout is critical, requiring it to stand up under heavy machinery, impact and vibration over long periods of time and continuous use. If the grout is not wisely selected, serious cracking and breakouts will eventually weaken the foundation, causing machine misalignment and vibration damage. In the long run, maintenance costs will go up, and the plant manager must order costly shutdowns for repairs.

What should the user look for in purchasing a grout and what pitfalls should he avoid? Grouts vary according to manufacturer, but every grout should possess certain characteristics which are essential if it is to perform satisfactorily. The two basic types of grouts discussed here —cementitious and resinous—both have a distinct set of critical properties which should be seriously considered in the selection process.

Cementitious grouts

Cementitious grouts, generally considered the "all-purpose" grouts, are specially formulated to contain a mixture of cement and properly proportioned aggregates. Some grouts also contain chemical additives which act as accelerators to speed the set, pumping aids, or water reducing agents to reduce the amount of water needed. Unfortunately, these chemicals often have a counter reaction which adversely affects the grout's performance.

Although the manufacturer is not required to specify which chemicals have been used, the purchaser should ask the vendor to certify that these additives do not compromise the quality of the end product. It is preferable, however, to avoid altogether grouts which contain any chemical additives.

• **Shelf life:** Because grout is usually kept in inventory as part of the plant's maintenance program, shelf life becomes highly important. If properly packaged and stored under the manufacturer's recommendations (in a cool, dry area), the shelf life should be *indefinite,* but certainly no less than one year. The user should realize that shelf life can be lessened by the addition of chemicals in some grouts which tend to disintegrate over a period of time. A grout which is over-aged can lose some degree of workability and compressive strength as well as exhibit shrinkage.

• **Working time:** In order to allow a reasonable amount of time for installation the grout must not stiffen too quickly. It should have a minimum working time of 45 minutes, preferably one hour after the addition of water. To maintain grout in a workable state, it is advisable to place at ambient temperatures between 40 and 90F, bringing it to room temperature before use. A good rule of thumb is the colder the temperature, the longer the working time.

The buyer, however, should be cautioned that the use of chemical additives can either speed up or inhibit the working time, and in some cases, virtually destroy the set time. In situations where production lines are shut down due to equipment failures, there are non-shrink instant grouts which allow equipment startup in only 3 or 4 hours and still provide adequate working time.

• **Workability:** Some manufacturers recommend the use of a fluid grout on the basis that it is more workable and therefore easier to install.

Determining grout shrinkage

The EBA glass plate demonstration is illustrated above. Large voids due to shrinkage are shown on left; no shrinkage has occurred on right.

Cement experts, however, have warned for years against using excessive amounts of water which are needed to attain this fluid consistency. Although chemicals are frequently added to reduce the water, they tend to increase shrinkage.

In the final analysis, fluid grouts are more costly because they require construction of expensive forms, because the overall grouting time is greater, and because they cause increased shrinkage in the end product. Since grout in most cases can be installed in a trowelable state, it is best to forego fluidity and to use as stiff a consistency as possible. This will ensure maximum economy, high strength and a non-shrink performance.

- **Non-shrink/EBA:** The most important requirement of any grout is that it completely fills the cavity in which it is placed in order to effectively support the machinery baseplate. Some grouts, however, undergo volume loss or shrinkage which lessens the grout's ability for support, thereby reducing the critical effective bearing area (EBA).

To select a non-shrink grout, the purchaser should request test data which shows no shrinkage when tested according to ASTM C-827. This is the national standard set by The American Society for Testing and Materials (ASTM) for measuring plastic shrinkage of cementitious mixtures. It is important because it begins measuring only a few minutes after mixing the grout and covers the entire plastic phase when over 90% of the shrinkage occurs. Test data should also be obtained for The Corps of Army Engineers test CRD-588-76 which measures for shrinkage in the hardened stage.

The combination of these two testing procedures provide a complet series of non-shrink tests and correlates with practical results ob-

The user can conduct a simple experiment which visually demonstrates a grout's ability to maintain EBA (effective bearing area). Fill a small cylinder with the plastic mix, level it off, and set a clean steel plate, free of oils, on the top. After 72 hours, if there has been no shrinkage, the steel plate will have completely bonded to the surface of the hardened grout, which provides maximum EBA.

This method may be used to test epoxy as well, this time using a glass plate, the surface of which has been treated for easy removal. After 24 hours, removal of the glass plate should show the surface of a non-shrink epoxy grout free of bubbles and voids. If these have developed, the material is *not* non-shrink, and does not provide maximum EBA.

To obtain a non-shrink product, the purchaser should make sure that the epoxy has been tested for shrinkage according to ASTM C-827 (see article below).

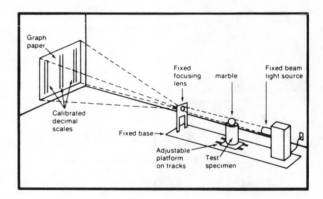

ASTM C-827—The most recent test method for measuring early volume shrinkage in cementitious mixtures. Fill a container with the plastic mixture, a marble or indicator ball halfway into the grout. Place the container in front of a light projector in order to project the image of the ball through a lense and onto a wall graph. Vertical volume change is measured by the up or downward movement of the marble's image on the chart.

This test differs from the above tests in that it measures vertical volume change as opposed to linear, and covers the entire plastic stage, when over 90% of shrinkage occurs.

How to Specify

Harold J. Rosen, PE, FCSI

GROUTS

Defining Non-Shrink

Specifiers as the communications segment of the construction industry are very conscious of the choice of words, their definitions, meanings and connotations. Quite often, literally thousands of dollars can hang in the balance because the parties to a contract will take issue with the intent of a specification because of the language used and how it is to be interpreted. By and large most competent specifiers recognize this and are quite careful and judicious in the selection of terminology.

Unfortunately, there are some areas which are often beyond their control. One has to do with material standards, recommended practices and association standards which are drafted and promulgated by others and which can sometimes be vague and undefined. Another source of potential specification inaccuracy occurs when specifiers utilize recommendations proposed by materials manufacturers who cite certain test standards in their literature that

do not necessarily correlate with actual in-place field conditions.

Often a manufacturer will choose standard test methods to measure certain physical characteristics of his product, which were not necessarily designed for his product, but which the manufacturer believes to be appropriate. This is especially true when there is no industry standard or agreement on standards. So while the products offered have a commonality or purported identical use, there is no consensus on the test methods or procedures by the manufacturing community or by specifiers.

A case in point is grout, often used for setting columns, supporting equipment, grouting post tensioned cables and grouting joints, where no trade association exists and where no recommended industry standards are suggested for those specifying grout.

For a number of years, some manufacturers of grout listed ASTM C157 "Length Change of Hardened Cement Mortar and Concrete" as a standard to measure an increase or decrease in a

linear dimension of a test specimen of mortar. They would then report, on the basis of an increase in length by means of the test method that their product was a non-shrink grout. This test method suited them ideally since non-shrink is an attribute highly desired by engineers and specifiers for the intended function of a grout material. However, a review of two of the earlier test procedures is in order since it is questionable whether these test methods correlate with a field condition of grouting.

Early Test Methods

Under ASTM C157, a bar of mortar approximately 1 inch square by 11¼ inches long is cast using the grout mix. The specimens are then cured in a mold for approximately 24 hours at a relative humidity of 90% at 73.4°F. The specimens are then removed from the mold, placed in water for 15 minutes and then measured for length. After the initial length measurement (which occurs approximately 24 hours after casting), the specimens are cured in lime saturated water at 73.4°F. for 28 days. At the end of this curing period the specimens are measured for length again.

The test method was used for years to report length change of grouts. The question to be asked is how does this test procedure correlate with grout curing in the field. Are grouts cured in the field under similar conditions? The test results were generally favorable since shrinkage is virtually impossible under the test procedure. The grout manufacturer, on the basis of this test method and the results which showed length increases, indicated in his literature that he had a non-shrink grout.

Apropos this claim to non-shrink, one recalls the Federal Trade Commission order back in 1973 when plastics manufacturers were called to task for labelling some plastic building products as "non-burning". What the manufacturer neglected to state in their literature was that their product was "non-burning" in accordance with ASTM D1692, which is a laboratory screening method for plastic evaluation and has nothing to do with a real fire situation.

The Corps of Engineers has a test method for expansive grouts—CRD-C589-70 entitled "Methods of Sampling and Testing Expansive Grouts." Many grout manufacturers make reference to this test method and as a result of the test procedure, label their grouts non-shrink since the test results invariably show an increase in volume.

Under CRD-C589, two cylinders, 6 inches high by 3 inches in diameter are filled with grout mixture. The cylinders are then covered with a 4″ x 4″ glass plate and initial height readings are taken to the top of the glass plate from a bridge above the cylinders. Four hours after final set (which is determined by a test on another sample of the same grout mix), the glass plate is removed and the top of the specimen is covered to prevent evaporation of moisture except when measurements are made. At 3, 7, and 28 days, measurements are made to the top of the grout. After making a correction for the thickness of the glass plate, the vertical expansion is given as a percent

for the 6 inch high cylinder.

Note that the mixing water in the grout is contained by the steel cylinder since it is covered with either a glass plate or other means to prevent evaporation except when measurements are taken. Again the test procedure is likely to show non-shrink behavior since moisture is prevented from leaving the test cylinders. Many grout manufacturers are reporting their grouts as non-shrink since the test results by CRD-C589 show expansion of their grout product.

Analysis of Early Test Methods

Let us now review the two test methods ASTM C157 and CRD-C589. Under ASTM C157, the specimens are cured under water for approximately 28 days with the first measurement taken 24 hours after casting and the next measurement at 28 days. Under method CRD-C589, water is not permitted to evaporate, and the initial reading to the top of the glass plate is taken with subsequent readings at 3, 7 and 28 days. In both CRD-C589 and ASTM C157, wet curing of the sample is specified. Under these conditions, most Portland cement materials would be expected to expand and show no shrinkage during the hardened state. However, under both test procedures there are no measurements taken during the plastic state (before hardening). The shrinkage that takes place in the plastic state is many times larger than the drying shrinkage.

Non-shrink by the above two test methods means therefore that the grout must be kept moist and the measurements taken only after hardening has occurred. Obviously, if a grout manufacturer uses either of these two test procedures and finds that an expansion occurs with his product as a result of the measurement, he is able to advertise his product as non-shrink. But what happens in field placement of grout? Does one keep grout moist for 28 days?

Early Volume Change Test Method

In December 1975, ASTM published a new test standard-ASTM C827-entitled

"Early Volume Change of Cementitious Mixtures". Of special interst to those who are concerned with definitions, there is a statement in the test method which reads: "This method affords a means of comparing the relative shrinkage or expansion of cementitious mixtures. It is particularly applicable to grouting, patching and form filling where the objective is to completely fill a cavity or other defined space with a plastic mixture that will continue to fill the same space after hardening."

Under the ASTM C827, a watertight cylinder with an internal height twice the internal diameter is used. The cylinder for testing grout is 4 inches high. The cylinder is filled with the grout mixture using the amount of water recommended by the grout manufacturer to provide a stiff, plastic or flowable mixture. The testing begins within 5 minutes after the cylinder is filled. Since a mechanical measurement would be quite difficult with a plastic mixture, a light source is used to measure the expansion or contraction that takes place vertically in the cylinder (Figure 1).

The test can be conducted so that the specimen is free to evaporate or if moist cure condition is specified, a few drops of motor oil may be placed on the exposed surface to prevent evaporation. The test is so designed that volume changes that occur during the plastic state including shrinkage, or expansion due to subsidence, hydration, evaporation and other physical and chemical effects can be measured within 5 minutes after placing the grout mixture in the cylinder. Testing can continue long after final set has occurred so that longterm shrinkage or expansion of the hardened sample can be measured under moist-cured or air-dried conditions.

In effect the value of ASTM C827 is that it allows the engineer or specifier to observe the behavior of a grout under different conditions of curing from the plastic state through the hardened state. He can then recognize what happens in the field with respect to expansion or contraction and how to specify his curing conditions and for how long, since there is better correlation as between the

Figure 1

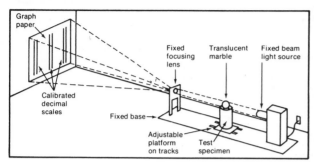

Projection test uses simple principles to magnify volume changes.

Figure 2

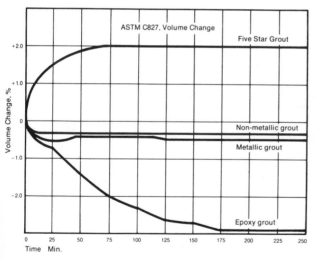

field condition and the test method.

Evaluation of Grouts with ASTM C827

As a result of the new test method, ASTM C827, that became available in December 1975, a number of grouts were tested by several independent testing laboratories around the country that selected leading locally available grouts in their areas. In all instances except one (the exception being Five Star Grout manufactured by U.S. Grout Corp.), the grouts selected and tested under ASTM C827 exhibited shrinkage during the plastic state even when moist cured. Five Star Grout expanded slightly during the same period.

A compilation of some test results obtained from this independent survey is shown in Figure 2.

One way to verify whether a grout expands in the field, since test methods ASTM C157 and CRD-C589 indicate expansion for most grouts, is to fill a cylinder with the grout mix at the job site and then place a steel plate with 2 bolt holes over it. If a grout is truly non-shrink, it should never go below its placing volume and should upon expansion permanently bond to the steel plate. During the plastic state, only Five Star Grout expands and bonds to the steel plate. But the expansive forces are small so that no displacement occurs.

Workability

Besides the critical non-shrink behavior, the specifier should consider another important grouting criteria, workability. A measure of workability is the grout's flow characteristics at the actual time of placement and the initial time of set.

Flows are defined in ASTM C827 as "stiff", "plastic" and "flowable or pourable". As a general guide for the degree of flow, the following is suggested:

Application	Flow Characteristics
Inaccessible areas	Flowable or Pourable
Accessible areas	Plastic or Trowelable
Unusual conditions	Stiff or Dry Mix
Major installations	Pumpable

The amount of water required to achieve these flow characteristics will vary with each manufacturer recommending different amounts. The flow characteristics at time of placement can be ascertained by means of a flow cone as described in Corp. of Engineers Method CRD-C79. Flow can be checked in the field with this device at time of actual grouting.

The time of initial set, prior to which the grout mixture can be placed, moved and vibrated is of significance as to workability. Time of set may be determined by ASTM C191. This is a measure of the "pot life" or working time available from mixing to placing in its final position. Some grouts which may exhibit flowable or pourable flow characteristics may have a very short pot life and require almost instantaneous placement.

Specifying Grouts

To assure that field placing of grout which includes volume change, curing, workability and set have some relevance to test procedures, it is suggested that the following test methods be specified:

The engineer and specifier can now evaluate the grouts currently available to ascertain which grouts are non-shrink, what the "pot lifes" and flow characteristics are, the compressive strengths required and how much curing must be done to achieve the non-shrink characteristics.

For public work, where some agencies may not permit the use of trade names, a performance specification can be written incorporating the test procedures outlined above for acceptance of non-shrink grouting materials.

In summary, there has been a good deal of confusion in specifying grouting since various grout manufacturers promote their products by using a wide variety of claims based on many different testing procedures. As a result great care must be exercised by engineers and specifiers in selecting products and writing specifications in order to minimize product failures and resulting liability.

Until a nationally established standards organization such as ASTM develops a specific specification on non-shrink grouts (on which it is now working), it is recommended that design firms

and specifiers use the test methods outlined above, along with the specific qualifications designed to make them applicable to job conditions. The procedures should not only be used in the actual grouting specifications, but should be used for evaluation and selection of grout materials.

Do not rely solely on manufacturers literature. Tests from independent laboratories should be requested when possible.

Harold J. Rosen, FCSI, PE, has been engaged in writing specifications and in materials research for over 30 years. He is a former chief of Specifications and Materials Research at Skidmore, Owings & Merrill, and at the office of Gruzen & Partners—both in New York City. Currently he is a Construction Specifications Consultant with an office in Merrick, New York.

Since 1956 Mr. Rosen has been a Contributing Editor and author of "Specifications Clinic", a monthly column which appears in *Progressive Architecture*. In addition he is the author of two books: *Principles of Specification Writing*, Reinhold Publishing Co.; and *Construction Specifications Writing—Principles and Procedures*, John Wiley & Sons.

Requirement	Test Method	Remarks
Volume Change	ASTM C827	To verify whether grout does not shrink below placement volume. Also establishes type and length of cure.
Workability Initial Set	ASTM C191	To verify that grout can be placed within
Flow	CRD-C79	45 minutes of mixing and initial set.
Comprehensive Strength	ASTM C109	To verify specified strength characteristics.
Non-Shrink	Field Test*	To test field mixes for non-shrink.

*Fill standard 6" x 12" test cylinder with grout mix. Place ½" steel plate with two ½" holes over freshly screeded concrete in cylinder. After 3 days plate should be bonded to grout.

Reprinted Courtesy of: The Construction Specifier
The Construction Specifications Institute

New Cement Formulation Reduces Early Shrinkage in Concrete

An

Engineering News-Record

Reprint

March 7, 1968

New Cement Formulation Reduces

Producers of a chemically inert aggregate that can be included in portland cement grouts, concrete patching products and bulk cement claim that now, for the first time, without the use of aluminum, iron or chemicals the construction industry can produce cement products that will expand from the first wetting, stop expanding before final set, and never shrink below their initial mixing volume.

The material is trade-named Five Star when sold in premixed packages for grouting and patching and Seacon Cement when sold alone for inclusion in bulk cement. It was developed by H. Nash Babcock, a Connecticut consulting engineer, and is being manufactured by the U.S. Grout Corp., of Old Greenwich, Conn.

Among other claims for the material are that it provides a fast sound bond with old concrete, has a greater strength than other comparable materials, can

provide highway patches that can carry traffic an hour after placement and require no special handling, storing or curing methods. With all this, the manufacturer says that the use of Five Star and Seacon products can reduce the average current surcharge for nonshrinkage cement products by as much as 50%.

The maker says that many major industries, several eastern highway departments and some federal agencies have tested their product and like it. (A Corps of Engineers' source told ENR last week that a sample had, in fact, been sent to the Waterways Experiment Station, in Vicksburg, Miss., "just to see what made it tick." The key component is activated carbon. He would not comment one way or the other on the company's claims, saying only "We know what's in it and how it works." Until now the manufacturer had not revealed the components.

Babcock says that most tests for shrinkage of concrete are performed 24 hours after mixing. This, he says, neglects the period during which the major portion of shrinkage occurs. For this reason, Construction Products Research, Inc., an Old Greenwich firm headed by Mr. Babcock, has devised an unusual light projection test that permits an accurate visual check on expansion and contraction of cement products almost from the instant of mixing.

The equipment needed for the test is simple: a slide projector, a ball or translucent marble, a test container, a lens and a piece of graph paper.

In a recent test made before highway engineers of several state highway departments, ENR photographed the test procedure and the material tested.

In one hour the shadow of a marble on a cylinder of ordinary sand-cement grout moved 3 in. on the scale, indi-

How tests were run

A technician mixes a sample of the material, places it immediately in a small container and screeds the material flush with the top. He then places a marble on top of the material and seats it firmly, allowing the top of the marble to extend well above the container. The container is then placed between a light projector and a lens so that the image of the marble is cast on a graduated scale on the wall. The scale starts at the center at zero and is marked both above and below in inches. By watching the shadow of the marble, observers are able to detect to thousandths of an inch any change in concrete volume.

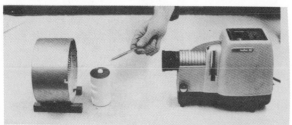

TEST EQUIPMENT includes projector, sample with ball on top and lens.

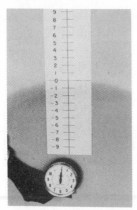

STARTING POINT is zero. Each mark equals 0.4% change in volume . . .

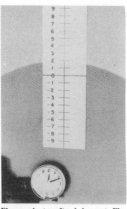

Eleven minutes after being wet, Five Star grout expands 0.008 in./in. . . . .

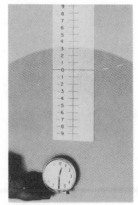

In 30 minutes shadow tops 3 in. on scale, a 1.2% expansion . . .

Early Shrinkage in Concrete

ating a shrinkage of 0.012 in. per in. of material. The marbles on two other samples said by Babcock to contain competitive shrinkage compensating materials moved about 1½ in. indicating a shrinkage of 0.006 in. per in. In the same time, the shadow of a marble on a sample of Five Star grout moved 3½ in. in the other direction indicating an expansion of 0.014 in. per in. From this point on, there was no further expansion, nor was there any visible reduction in size.

(Since the image of the marble is projected through a single lens the reflected movement is inverted. For the sake of clarity the photographs below have also been inverted to reflect the proper direction of movement.)

Perhaps the most surprising claim made by U.S. Grout is that its product is completely inert chemically. It has no chemical reaction with cement and effects no chemical changes in cement

Theoretically the magnification potential of the setup is infinite: for the most part though, CPR works with a 64 to 120 magnification. The company's engineers determine the accuracy of the test in a simple way. For example: By holding a ⅛-in. high speed drill between the projector and the lens they adjust the entire setup until the shadow of the drill projects to exactly 8 in. on the scale. This guarantees a magnification of 64. Then, since the containers used are 4 in. high, a change of 1 in. in the marble's shadow indicates a shrinkage factor of 0.004 inches per inch of material or 0.4%.

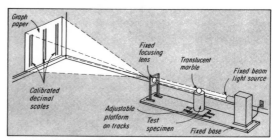

PROJECTION TEST uses simple principles to magnify volume changes.

mixtures. Its effect is purely physical. Furthermore, the material does not change the color of the finished product.

A 100-lb bag of the grout comprises 42.5 lb of high-early-strength cement, 50 lb of silica sand, 7.5 lb of aggregate. The yield for a 100-lb bag is said to be /.½ cu ft, and the lightness of the aggregate reduces the weight of 150-lb-per-cu-ft concrete to 145 lb. The aggregate was originally developed and premixed as a grout for use in underpinning and for filling in under machine bases, but after a major food processor successfully used the grout as a patch material, U.S. Grout modified its premix for that purpose. The major difference between the grout and the patch is that the latter has finer materials to facilitate feather edging. The aggregate has reportedly been approved by the New York City Board of Standards and Appeals for use in bulk concrete.

Claims for the strength of grouts using the aggregate are impressive. The company reports that a year-old cube of grout had developed a compressive strength of 14,000 psi. The state of New York, after what it describes as a "very limited series of tests on Five Star grout" reports strengths of 7,775 psi in one day, 8,883 psi in four days and 9,275 psi in seven days, with a final expansion of 0.111%. The state also reports that when five cubes were subjected to 55 freeze-thaw cycles in a 10% solution of sodium chloride the average weight loss was approximately 2%.

In a pull-out test made by the State of Connecticut a 0.907-in.-dia smooth steel bar was set in a 2½-in.-dia hole filled with Five Star grout to a depth of 10¾ in. It took a pull of 27,820 lb to remove the dowel, indicating a bond strength of about 900 psi of dowel surface area.

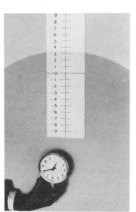

Expansion of grout begins to slow 40 minutes after it is mixed . . .

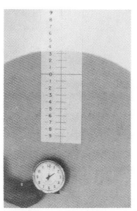

Final reading indicates a total expansion of 0.014 in./in. or 1.4%.

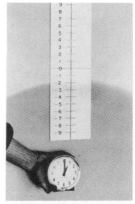

Another "non-shrink" material tested lost 0.6% of its volume in one hour.

3ER 16, 1969

Engineering
lews-Record

W-HILL'S CONSTRUCTION WEEKLY

Seventy-five Cents

Contents on page 21

Piggyback Building

20 Stories of precast concrete rise atop cast-in-place garage

Precast Bearing Walls Rise

The walls and floors of a 20-story office building nearing completion in Philadelphia were erected by only one trade instead of the four or five that generally might be required for such work. The reduction in the number of skills, which helped speed construction, was accomplished by use of a precast concrete bearing wall system. This building is probably the tallest of its type in the U.S.

The $10-million tower for Mutual Benefit Life Insurance Co., erected atop a five-story garage without interrupting its services, contains no interior columns, and has exterior walls that serve both architectural and structural functions. They were erected at the rate of one floor a week by the structural ironworkers, with much of the work performed last winter. Started only last fall, tenants already occupy the lower floors, while the upper floors are substantially completed except for tenant changes.

The job was also simplified and speeded by the use of different modules, 5 ft for walls and 40 in. for floor panels, which automatically provided the space for installation of vertical mechanical components.

Although the Mutual Benefit tower is not entirely precast—it has a cast-in-place elevator-stairway core—the success of the project has encouraged a New York City consulting firm to design a fully precast 30-story building. According to Paul Gleason, president of Formigli Corp., of Philadelphia, which cast and erected the wall panels

and floor planks, the precast system has no height limits.

The tower, 200 ft long by 85 ft 9 in. wide, is centered above a 225 x 150-ft cast-in-place concrete garage owned by the Philadelphia Parking Authority.

The present garage was originally four stories high. Because the columns needed to support the tower cut into available parking areas within the garage, part of the owner's air-rights agreement called for casting a fifth floor above the original structure. This was done by Keystone Concrete Co., of Philadelphia. Dick Concrete Corp., also of Philadelphia, handled the cast-in-place core of the tower.

The new columns were cast adjacent to existing columns within the garage, making them rectangular rather than square. They were topped by an 11-ft-high peripheral transfer beam that supports the full weight of the tower walls.

To put the old garage in architectural harmony with the new tower, Formigli bolted precast panels to the face of its five floors.

The precast panels of the Mutual tower are 20 ft wide by 11 ft high. They consist of three full mullions between four windows and two half mullions on the outside edges, all connected to spandrel beams, top and bottom. The mullions are designed for column action. Originally, the spandrels were to be exposed, but at the request of the owner they were covered with a black glass to accent the vertical lines of the mullions.

These panels were cast in two For-

migli plants, and delivered to the job, two at a time, on low-boy trailers. They were supported on the trailer on opposite sides of a narrow A-frame in an almost vertical position.

The near-vertical delivery simplified and speeded erection, reduced the amount of mild steel reinforcing needed (the units are not prestressed) and virtually eliminated handling damage to the architecturally finished wall faces.

The panels, averaging 12 tons, were erected by a pair of tower cranes.

There are no horizontal connections between adjacent panels. The vertical joints are simply caulked, inside and out. The stability of the panels is achieved mainly through vertical dowels cast in the top of each section, including the transfer beam. Each dowel-receiving hole in the base of the wall panels is linked to the interior face by a pair of pressure grout holes, the lowest of which is for the grout pipe, the upper for bleeding of air and grout.

Before each succeeding section was placed, the contractor shimmed and over-grouted the top edge of each mullion with a non-shrink grout. This grout was encompassed by an oval of plastic rope that served as a dam.

An opening in the oval allowed excess grout to escape into the building, thus eliminating the possibility of staining the exterior of the building.

The floor panels are hollow-cored, 40 in. wide 10 in. thick and about 33 ft long. The floor planks are placed on the lip of the wall panels and the core, with a 20-in. space between them. This space

WALL PANELS were trucked almost vertically on low boys.

KNEE BRACES steady panels before floor planks are placed.

0 Stories

is filled with a permanent corregated steel floor form that is simply dropped onto a lip cast in the panels, 2 in. below the top surface. When Dick Concrete cast the 2-in.-thick floor topping, the space separating each plank was also filled to the same elevation as the topping.

The space between the floor panels provided adequate space for cast-in-place concrete in which to run utility crossovers and to anchor reinforcing rods bent over from the top of the wall panels. The cast-in-place concrete helped stabilize the structure, and made it possible for the mechanical contractors to install vertical components through holes cut in the floor form with tin snips.

The cranes were erected in wells prepared at the quarter-points on the longitudinal axis of the building. Because of the setback resulting from the width of the parking garage, the location of the tower cranes put them beyond the reach of a street-based truck crane. The contractor therefore used a 60-ton crane to raise a 25-ton truck crane to the roof of the garage. This machine then picked up and erected one of the tower cranes. The truck crane was then removed and the first tower crane erected the second.

Speed of erection was partly the result of cooperation between Dick Concrete and Formigli in the use of the tower cranes which had been rented and erected by Formigli. Dick used one of the cranes to form and erect one or two floors of the cast-in-place core on one-half the building. Dick then moved to

PRECAST WALLS are both structural and architectural in function.

the second tower crane for the other half, while Formigli took over the first crane to do its work. In this manner, the contractors were able to coordinate their work without interfering with each other.

The building's architects are Nowicki & Polillo, of Philadelphia, and Eggers & Higgins, of New York. The engineers are David Bloom Associates, of Philadelphia, and Robert Rosenwasser, of New York.

The structure is owned by E. J. Frankel Enterprises, of Philadelphia.

DECK PLANK connects cast-in-place core and precast wall.

SPACE between deck planks simplifies anchoring of wall panels.

Electrical World

September 1, 1970

GENERATION

Non-shrink grout maintains turbojet engine-generator alignment

Required shaft-coupling alignment between 12 turbojet engines and their driven generators is being maintained at Consolidated Edison Co's Astoria plant through the use of support bases constructed with a newly developed nonshrink grout.

In each of three independent units, four pairs of Pratt & Whitney Aircraft industrial turbojets are set up so that each pair drive an Electric Machinery Co generator. The twelve generators being installed will add 480,000 kw to the system.

The required shaft coupling alignment tolerance of 0.002 in. is maintained by using Five Star grout. The nonshrink quality of the grout is attained by use of an inert aggregate. This aggregate eliminates the early shrinkage that occurs in conventional concrete and results in a grout that never goes below its initial placement volume which is unique in the grouting industry. The grout bonds firmly under the machinery being set and closes tightly around reinforcing or anchor rods. It will not lift machinery or distort forming as it contains no corrosive metals. The material can develop a strength of 12,000 psi in 28 days.

Each of the three generating units is installed in separate buildings 112 x 117 ft. Under the engines a base concrete slab is 26 in. thick and at the generators it is 30 in. At each machine a separate block of concrete about 30 in. high has anchor bolts for positiong the equipment. On this, the concrete is roughly bus-hammered where grout is placed under the main frames, leveling blocks are set to rough elevation, and equipment lowered on them. Screw jacks are used to attain exact position, vertically and horizontally.

Extreme accuracy in setting the equipment is attained by a carefully established routine. Measurement is made with a Brown & Sharpe electronic gaging system. This reads to a millionth of an inch, but for this application was used to 0.00008 in. with the expectation of attaining an actual variation of less than 0.002 inches at the flexible coupling connecting the turbojet engine shaft with the generator.

A rough reading and adjustment is first made and then two more successively finer readings are made on vertical and horizontal alignment to achieve the required alignment tolerance. The grout manufacturer claims that machinery can be permanently held to tolerance of 0.0001 in.

Placing of the grout is also closely controlled. About 4 in. of space is left between the concrete base and the machinery bed. This space and the anchor bolt holes are filled at one time. The space to be grouted is formed with plywood held tightly against the foundation block. The area is saturated with water, but all free water is removed including any in the anchor bolt sleeves. Grout to be placed around the anchor bolts is made to a "pumpable" consistency with 10½ quarts of water to 100-lb of premixed grout. Material for the more open spaces is made "firm" with 8½ quarts of water to 100-lb of grout. The firm mix is placed from one side and rodded under the base plates with narrow boards, thus preventing formation of voids from entrapped air.

The new grout, developed by a Civil Engineer, H. Nash Babcock to meet special needs for firm machinery support, is marketed by US Grout Corp, Old Greenwich, Conn. It contains only a Type III high-early-strength cement, a graded silica sand and the inert shrinkage elimination aggregate.

Reportedly, because it is noncorrosive and contains no iron or aluminum filings, plastics or chemicals, it can be used indoors and out, in high and low temperatures and humidity areas without breaking out or deteriorating. It has the appearance of regular concrete. ∎

Before grouting, turbine set on leveling blocks is jacked into final position for precise shaft-alignment with turbojet

After precise alignment of drive/driven units non-shrink grout is installed to hold alignment within a tolerance of 0.0001 in.

Fast-setting grout facilitated installation of 4 main power generators in pump stations on trans-Alaska pipeline

"Instant-setting" grout expedites construction of trans-Alaska pipeline

New Solutions to Plant Problems

Problem: Alaska's abnormal climatic conditions prevented the use of conventional grouting materials to secure the mounting plates for the huge gate and check valves on the trans-Alaska pipeline. A different type of grout was required that would remain workable and still set up at very low temperatures, provide a high compressive strength in a very short time, and be able to withstand freeze-thaw conditions.

Solution: In February 1974, while the project was still in the preliminary stages, Alyeska engineers evaluated a newly developed hydraulic cement containing a fine aggregate than can be used at temperatures as low as −20°F and has a trowelable working time of 15 minutes, or flowable working time of 20 minutes depending on the water/solids ratio. The "instant-setting" material has a compressive strength of 4000 psi after only four hours and up to 8000 psi in 4 hours under special conditions, when tested by the ASTM C-109 method. Other tests proved that the original placement volume is maintained since there is no shrinkage during curing period. The grout contains no corrosive salts or metals and is resistant to moisture, most oils and chemicals, and freeze-thaw conditions.

The grout was initially used under the base plates for the 72 buried 48″ pipeline

check, manual and remotely controlled gate valves.

The contractor responsible for installing the equipment in the 12 pumping stations also used the regular grout offered by the same company, in addition to the special fast-setting grout. This product can be placed without difficulty at 40°F and reaches a compressive strength of 3000-4000 psi within 24 hours which is about twice the rate of conventional grout. The non-metallic mixture also contains a chemically inert aggregate to maintain the original placement volume. Non-shrinkage is essential to provide the highest effective bearing area for the rotating equipment bases.

Results: Installation of valve base plates and rotating equipment, 800 hp and under, for the trans-Alaska pipeline was facilitated by using a non-shrink grout that remains workable at extremely low temperatures and rapidly attains a high compressive strength. Machines can be put into operation within 4 hours, so the fast-setting feature offers a substantial reduction in equipment downtime even under more normal temperature conditions. ∎

Five Star Instant and regular Five-Star grout for setting machinery, waterproofing and patching concrete are products of U.S. Grout Corp.

CURING COMPOUNDS

U. S. GROUT CORPORATION recommends a period of a minimum of three days moist curing as outlined in "A Professional's Handbook on Grouting, Concrete Repair and Waterproofing". When this is not possible, cementitious grouts should be coated with two (2) coats of an approved curing compound.

An "approved" curing compound will have the following characteristics and properties:

1. It will be "resin-based".

2. It will be white pigmented.

3. It will have the capability of being applied by spray, brush or roller to a uniform coating.

4. It will have a moisture loss of not more than 0.031g per sq. cm. after 7 days when tested in accordance with CRD-C 302 or ASTM C 156.

In general, any curing compound meeting the requirements listed above and CRD-C 300 is acceptable. Compounds meeting the moisture loss requirements above and otherwise meeting ASTM C 309 are also acceptable.

Technical Bulletin #25
1800P/10
Rev. 1/7/88
Copyright 1988 by U. S. GROUT CORPORATION

U. S. GROUT CORPORATION, 401 STILLSON ROAD, FAIRFIELD, CONNECTICUT 06430 ● (203) 336-7900

TECHNICAL BULLETIN

FIVE STAR

ANCHOR GROUTING WITH FIVE STAR GROUT

TOTAL LOAD
Pounds at Pullout or Bar Failures

(Designers should allow a factor of safety.)

MODERATE STRENGTH STEEL   –   YIELD STRENGTH   –   80,000 psi

Bar Diameter	Plain Bar	Reinforcing Bar (Deformed)	Threaded Bar
One Foot Embedment			
1/4"	3,930*	3,930*	3,930*
1/2"	15,700*	15,700*	15,700*
3/4"	28,200	35,400*	35,400*
1"	37,700	56,500	62,900*
Five Foot Embedment			
1"	62,900*	62,900*	62,900*
1-1/2"	141,500*	141,500*	141,500*
2"	252,000*	252,000*	252,000*
3"	565,000*	565,000*	565,000*
Ten Foot Embedment			
1"	62,900*	62,900*	62,900*
2"	252,000*	252,000*	252,000*
3"	565,000*	565,000*	565,000*
4"	1,005,000*	1,005,000*	1,005,000*

HIGH STRENGTH STEEL   –   YIELD STRENGTH   –   135,000 psi

Ten Foot Embedment			
2"	424,000*	424,000*	424,000*
3"	955,000*	955,000*	955,000*
4"	1,505,000	1,700,000*	1,700,000*
5"	1,880,000	2,650,000*	2,650,000*

*Denotes bar failure rather than pullout.
Calculations based on independent laboratory tests.
(c) 1986 by U. S. GROUT CORPORATION   1028P

–I.39–

U. S. GROUT CORPORATION, 401 STILLSON ROAD, FAIRFIELD, CONNECTICUT 06430 ● (203) 336-7900

I.41

FIVE STAR GROUT

FIVE STAR INSTANT GROUT

ANCHOR BOLT GROUTING

SURFACE PREPARATION

Bolts: Free of oil, grease and rust. Preferably sandblasted to "bright metal" condition.

Holes: A. Dry drilled holes shall be cleaned of dust and debris.
           B. Wet drilled holes shall be cleaned of drilling slurry.
           C. Formed holes shall be scarified to remove laitance.
           D. Concrete shall be saturated with water for 24 hours prior to grouting.
           E. Standing water shall be removed immediately prior to grouting.

DIMENSIONS

The dimensions called for in this technical bulletin are designed to eliminate the possibility of a grout failure. A concrete or steel failure is still possible. Therefore, if the concrete is designed to withstand maximum steel tension, the bolt yield strength will be the governing design factor.

L	=	Length of Embedment
D	=	Diameter of Hole
d	=	Diameter of Bolt/Bar
fy	=	Yield Strength of Bolt/Bar
C	=	Bolt/Bar Shape Factor
C	=	1.0 for Smooth Bolt/Bar
C	=	1.5 for Deformed Bolt/Bar
C	=	2.0 for Threaded Bolt/Bar

-I.40-

U. S. GROUT CORPORATION, 401 STILLSON ROAD, FAIRFIELD, CONNECTICUT 06430 ● (203) 336-7900

Length of Embedment

The lengths called for in this bulletin are minimum lengths. Additional embedment shall provide a higher factor of safety.

Minimum L = fy d / 4,000 C

Therefore: With fy = 80,000 psi (moderate strength steel)

Min. L = 20 D for Smooth Bolt/Bar
Min. L = 15 D for Deformed Bolt/Bar
Min. L = 10 D for Threaded Bolt/Bar

With fy = 135,000 psi (high strength steel)

Min. L = 34 D for Smooth Bolt/Bar
Min. L = 23 D for Deformed Bolt/Bar
Min. L = 16 D for Threaded Bolt/Bar

Hole Diameter

The diameters called for in this bulletin are minimum diameters. The requirements will ensure an adequate size bonding surface between grout and concrete. Larger dimensions may ease placement procedures on deep or awkward pours.

When bolt diameter (d) is one inch or less, hole diameter shall be a minimum two inches.

When bolt diameter (d) is greater than one inch, hole diameter shall be a minimum 2d.

SECTION II
NONSHRINK EPOXY GROUTS
INTRODUCTION

The definition of a NONSHRINK epoxy grout is: once the grout is in place, there is no plastic or hardened vertical shrinkage at any time.

Since their inception, epoxy grouts have been promoted as "NONSHRINK" or as evidencing "negligible" shrinkage. Test methods supposedly verifying NONSHRINK performance date back to the early 1960's, but it is now apparent that these methods are inadequate for epoxy grouts, since they do not measure vertical volume change. A modification of the current ASTM C 827-87 (Standard Test Method for Change in Height at Early Ages of Cylindrical Specimens from Cementitious Mixtures) which has proven so successful in NONSHRINK cementitious grouts, is now being used for epoxy grouts. It shows that *most epoxy grouts exhibit even greater vertical shrinkage* than the shrinking cement-based grouts. Loss of EBA (Effective Bearing Area) and failures of epoxy grout can be directly correlated to plastic shrinkage (*vertical volume change*).

At the time of the printing of this Handbook, there are no ASTM standards for measuring the vertical shrinkage of epoxy grouts. Since no other standards are available for measuring the vertical shrinkage of epoxy grout, it is recommended that the specifier use ASTM C 827 modified (indicator ball changed to specific gravity of 1.0) in evaluating the NONSHRINK properties of any epoxy grout.

Epoxy grouts must be prepackaged, premeasured systems in order to avoid costly failures. Each epoxy system has a unique viscosity requiring tailoring of a blended aggregate to that system.

The use of an aggregate that has not been carefully matched with the particular system invites segregation, foaming or frothing, which leads to poor EBA. Field purchasing of aggregates should be avoided since it is impossible to properly match aggregates to the epoxy system. In a field-proportioned system attempts at measuring may result in improper ratios of all the epoxy components. This results in a resinous system that will be spongy and unable to support the design load.

The advantages of epoxy grouts over cement-based materials are the following:

1. High Impact and Vibration Resistance
2. Chemical Resistance
3. High Compressive Strength
4. High Flexural Strength
5. High Tensile Strength
6. High Bond Strength

An epoxy grout should be chosen where one or more of the above characteristics is required or desired.

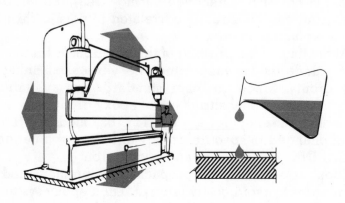

RECENT DEVELOPMENTS

A successful development which has proven very attractive is the use of a very fast strength-gain NONSHRINK cementitious grout for the early phases of a deep pour, then topping that grout off with a rapid strength-gain NON-SHRINK epoxy grout. This procedure saves a good deal of time and money for both the contractor and the client.It enables the user to get the equipment into operation sooner, while obtaining the maximum benefits of cementitious products and epoxies with the superb ability of the epoxy to withstand vibration. This is particularly useful under compressors and other vibrating machinery.

In recent years, there have been several combination developments in epoxy which are appearing in the market. One is the modification of cementitious products by the addition of epoxy admixtures. This modification may result in a lower price, but generally it reduces the desirable properties of each.

Regardless of the type of NONSHRINK epoxy grout chosen, it should be NONSHRINK when tested by appropriate ASTM standards. *Effective Bearing Area should be the ultimate criteria for acceptance.*

CHAPTER 1
SELECTING AN EPOXY GROUT

Discussion

Assuming that any one of the following conditions will exist, an epoxy grout should be used.

1. Impact
2. Vibration
3. Chemical Attack

However, additional factors should be considered in choosing *which* epoxy grout to use. No single epoxy grout will meet all of the various requirements which will exist for a given application. A few of the major considerations include:

1. Volume Change
2. Operating Temperatures
3. Creep
4. Strengths:
    a. Compressive Strength
    b. Bond Strength
    c. Flexural Strength
    d. Tensile Strength
5. Thermal Coefficient of Expansion
6. Dimensions of Grout Placement (in particular, thickness)
7. Possible Segregation
8. Working Time

Regardless of the above considerations, any epoxy grout selected should be NONSHRINK with a minimum EBA (Effective Bearing Area) of 95%.

To assist the Engineer, Specifier and Contractor, an Epoxy Grout Selection Chart follows:

EPOXY GROUT SELECTION CHART

CONDITION:

| • Impact and/or Vibration
• Chemical Attack
• High Strength
• Bond Strength | No | See Section I
Nonshrink Cementitious
Grouts |

 Yes

Use Epoxy Grout

CONDITION:

| • Operating temperature
over 140° F to 200° F
• Highest Chemical Resistance
• Overnight Start-up
• Highest Creep Resistance | No | FIVE STAR
EPOXY GROUT |

 Yes

Use FIVE STAR ET
EPOXY GROUT

CONDITION:

| • Small Annular Spaces
• 2-4 hour start-up | No | FIVE STAR
EPOXY GROUT |

 Yes

FIVE STAR RAPID EPOXY GROUT —
Annular Space less than 3"

FIVE STAR SPEED EPOXY GROUT —
Annular Space less than 1"

CONDITIONS:

| • Other |

 Yes

Contact **FIVE STAR PRODUCTS, INC.**
Engineering & Technical Center
for recommendations.

CHAPTER 2
PERFORMANCE PROPERTIES AND TESTS

A. VERTICAL VOLUME CHANGE/EBA*

Vertical volume change/EBA is one of the most important considerations in evaluating an epoxy grout. It will determine whether the grout is in contact with the equipment it is intended to support.

Although a test for vertical volume change exists, it has in the past been confined to cementitious materials. No standard test has been issued for epoxy grouts. Fortunately, it has been found that the ASTM C 827 test needs only a slight modification to make it acceptable for epoxy grouts. It is the only method currently available to determine this most important property. ASTM C 827 requires only that the specific gravity of the indicator ball be changed to approximately 1.0.

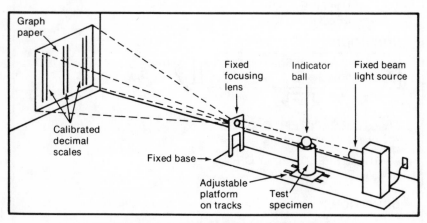

"ASTM Shrinkage Test for Grouts"

*Effective Bearing Area

While this method results in numerical values, it should be run with a companion test, the EBA Test. The EBA Test is described under "Quality Assurance Programs", Chapter 11.

Any epoxy grout selected should be NONSHRINK when tested according to ASTM C 827 (Modified) and should result in a minimum 95% EBA, when tested according to the "EBA Test."

B. COMPRESSIVE STRENGTH

This property is well understood and should be determined in accordance with ASTM C 579 (Test Method for Compressive Strength of Chemical-Resistant Mortars and Monolithic Surfacings), Method A or B.

The generally accepted minimum compressive strength for epoxy grouts is 10,000 psi in 7 days.

C. CREEP

The phenomenon of creep occurs in all materials. Creep is defined as deformation under the action of a constant load. Epoxies will deform without failing.

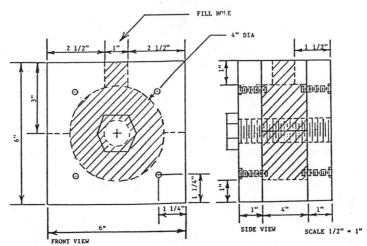

"Specimen Mold for CPR Creep Test"

Organic materials, such as epoxy grouts, generally exhibit higher creep characteristics than inorganic (cementitious) materials. Because of this creep tendency, it is very important that engineers, specifiers and contractors know in advance what the creep tendencies of a particular epoxy grout are.

Creep can result in loss of torque in anchor bolts and misalignment of equipment. Sufficient creep can result in excessive wear in shafts and bearings.

When selecting an epoxy grout, the creep tendencies should be known. Short term (24-48 hour) tests from which data has been extrapolated should be ignored. A creep test should be of at least one year's duration with all data actual, not extrapolated. An acceptable test for creep is printed at the back of this Section, and is about to be approved by the ASTM. A photograph of the creep assembly follows.

"CPR Creep Test Method"

To ensure that creep will remain within an acceptable range, two main rules should be followed:

1.   Select an epoxy grout for which long term data are available at the temperature at which the grout must operate.

2.   Design such that the total of dead load (weight of equipment) plus live load (bolt torque load) does not exceed 500 psi.

Long term creep data are available, at various operating temperatures, for **FIVE STAR EPOXY GROUTS.**

D. PLACEABILITY

Epoxy grouts are formulated for a given consistency which should not be altered at the job site. Altering the consistency of an epoxy grout has caused foaming, segregation, excessive heat generation and other problems which affect its ability to perform as intended. In order to facilitate placement under all types of baseplates, epoxy grouts should be formulated for a flowable consistency. Although the flowable condition is not always necessary, it is the single most versatile method of placement, particularly for epoxy grouts, when consistency cannot be varied.

Epoxy grouts which give off noxious fumes and are highly volatile should not be used. FIVE STAR EPOXY GROUT has been formulated to alleviate these problems. Due to the serious nature of this problem, the specifier and the supervisors in the field should prohibit the use of any epoxy grout which gives off noxious fumes or volatiles.

Fluid-tight forms must be built for all types of epoxy grouting, except in confined spaces. The epoxy grout is usually poured into a hydraulic headbox located on one side of the plate. Using a plunger to exert pressure in the headbox aids the grout to flow into place. In addition, it eliminates voids and entrapped air created by the insertion of straps or chains under the baseplate.

E. WORKING TIME

The working time (time of placeability) of an epoxy grout is directly related to rate of strength gain. The "standard" epoxy grouts (FIVE STAR EPOXY GROUT for example), will have a working time of a minimum of 45 minutes at 75°F. Working time will decrease as material and ambient temperatures increase and vice versa.

For rapid strength gaining materials (FIVE STAR RAPID EPOXY GROUT and FIVE STAR SPEED EPOXY GROUT), the working time will be 15-20 minutes.

Placement should be planned so as to take these times into consideration.

F. SEGREGATION

In order to increase placeability, some manufacturers have resorted to the use of large aggregate (3/16"–1/4") particles in their epoxy grout. This tends to increase flowability - and also segregation.

The potential for deleterious segregation should be checked by using the specimen cast for the ASTM C 827 test. The specimen should be stripped from its mold and split along its long axis. Any evidence of unusual accumulation of large aggregate in the bottom portion of the specimen should be cause for rejection of the epoxy grout.

G. THERMAL COEFFICIENT OF EXPANSION

All materials change dimension as temperature changes. Most materials expand (lengthen) as their temperatures increase, and contract (shorten) as their temperatures decrease (water is an exception). The amount that they change is known as "Coefficient of Expansion" and is expressed in decimal fractions of an inch per inch of dimension per degree Fahrenheit (centimeters per centimeter per degree centigrade in the metric system). Unfortunately, concrete and epoxy grouts have vastly different "coefficients".

When using epoxy grouts, the shoulders *should be kept to a minimum*. Wide shoulders present the problem of trying to contract when temperature drops, but the concrete doesn't want to contract as fast or as much. This "tug-of-war" is always won by the epoxy, due to the superior strength and bonding properties of epoxy. In poorly planned large shoulders, the epoxy tries to curl upward and tears the concrete apart - the result being a crack at some point in the concrete below the bond line.

The sketch below gives a picture view of what's been described!

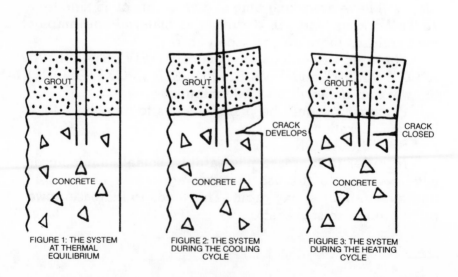

FIGURE 1: THE SYSTEM AT THERMAL EQUILIBRIUM

FIGURE 2: THE SYSTEM DURING THE COOLING CYCLE

FIGURE 3: THE SYSTEM DURING THE HEATING CYCLE

Where wide shoulders are required, there are a number of ways to counter the above tendencies. See SHOULDERS (page 126) for suggested special remedies and/or consult U. S. GROUT CORPORATION, a subsidiary of FIVE STAR PRODUCTS, INC.

H.   RELIABILITY & DURABILITY

The reliability of a material to behave in a predictable manner during placement is critical. To achieve this, epoxy grouts *must* be prepackaged in premeasured units.

The reliability of a grout is dependent on the manufacturer controlling the quality of the materials used in the grout, the manufacturing and blending procedures, the packaging, storage, handling and shipping, as well as the assurance of an approved Quality Control Program.

With epoxy-based materials, durability may be compromised due to an unusually high coefficient of thermal expansion. The coefficient of thermal expansion for unfilled epoxy is approximately ten times that of concrete (60×10^{-6}). This can be reduced significantly with proper use of aggregate to make an epoxy grout that is more compatible with concrete.

Peak exotherm (maximum temperature rise) should also be kept as low as possible in order to minimize cracking. Due to stresses set up during cooling, as well as to prevent possible warping. Procedures for handling high temperature situations are covered under Grout Placement Procedures.

CHAPTER 3
QUALITY ASSURANCE PROGRAMS
FOR MANUFACTURER & FIELD

Quality Assurance programs should be required for all grout manufacturers, and are required for many critical installations. There are two categories of Quality Assurance programs: manufacturer and field.

QUALITY ASSURANCE PROGRAM
- MANUFACTURER

The grout manufacturer must maintain records of all the sands, aggregates, resin and hardener used. All containers of raw materials and finished product should have a code marking so that the source of all materials can be traced and verified as meeting the manufacturer's standards. The manufacturer should regularly take samples from the plant and verify them in his own test laboratory as meeting his requirements, including NONSHRINK properties.

The manufacturer must maintain test records on production runs and should retain them for at least one year. Shipping tickets should be maintained at the plant and at the main office for all shipments.

Epoxy products stored beyond twelve months should not be shipped without the manufacturer's certification that the products meet the manufacturer's standards. The manufacturer should furnish written certification when required, stating that the material is in accordance with the project and manufacturer's specifications.

Resin subjected to temperatures below 60°F may crystallize. The tendency to do so and the temperature at which it may occur varies with the batch of base resin used. All epoxy grout resins exhibit this tendency to some extent. When it occurs the resin looks like and has the consistency of lard. No permanent damage results, but the resin should be returned to its original liquid form by heating it at approximately 100°F while stirring as shown below.

The manufacturer should have instructions for normal placement conditions printed on the outside of the package.

The manufacturer should have posted instructions for manufacturing the material at the plant. The accuracy of the weighing scales at the plant must be checked every six months, as required in a good Quality Assurance program.

The manufacturer should provide access to his production facilities by the engineer upon receipt of adequate notice for the auditing of the Quality Assurance Program. If a manufacturer cannot comply with this Quality Assurance Program verification, his product should not be approved.

QUALITY ASSURANCE PROGRAM - FIELD

To verify that the epoxy grout will exhibit a high Effective Bearing Area (EBA), fill a 2″ x 4″ cylinder or can with the freshly mixed epoxy grout until it is slightly overfilled. Carefully place a glass plate (sprayed with silicone release) on top of the cylinder so as to avoid air entrapment, and place a weight on top of the plate as shown below.

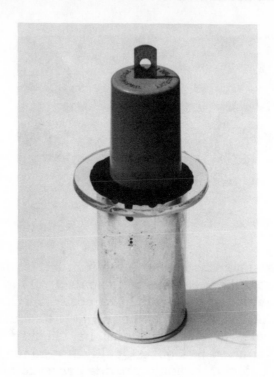

If air is entrapped, mark the location of the voids on the glass plate.

Twenty-four hours after placement, remove the plate and inspect the sample for voids by probing with a sharp instrument. If, after eliminating the effect of the trapped voids, the EBA is less than 95 percent, the epoxy grout should be rejected.

Following these simple, practical procedures protects the owner, architect, engineer and contractor from the use of products that are not NONSHRINK and that do not meet the specification. Field testing of epoxy-based grouts should be a part of all construction documents.

(FSEG)

A NONSHRINK epoxy grout will exhibit none of the voids, bubbles, or froth that reduces the effective bearing area. FIVE STAR EPOXY GROUTS (top right) provide a minimum 95% effective bearing area.

CHAPTER 4
ESTIMATING & PURCHASING EPOXY GROUT

Estimating the quantity of NONSHRINK epoxy grout is done by calculating the volume of the area to be grouted in cubic feet and adding 3-5 percent for waste.

Unfortunately, not all epoxy grouts are sold in cubic foot units. Epoxy grouts are sold in units of varying weight and volume. To ensure that all prices are directly comparable, all quotation requests should be made in cubic foot units.

EPOXY GROUT PRODUCTS

EPOXY GROUT PRODUCTS
PRECISION NONSHRINK * HIGH CREEP RESISTANCE * HIGHEST EFFECTIVE BEARING AREA * VERY FLOWABLE * HIGH IMPACT RESISTANCE * HIGH CHEMICAL RESISTANCE * HIGH EARLY STRENGTH * NO SEGREGATION * HIGH TEMPERATURE RESISTANCE * RAPID STRENGTH GAIN

CHAPTER 5
EPOXY GROUT DELIVERY & STORAGE PROCEDURES

A. DELIVERY AND STORAGE CONDITIONS

Hardener and resin should be delivered in sealed, premeasured containers. They should be stored at a temperature preferably between 70°F and 80°F, but not below 60°F and not above 90°F. As mentioned under "Quality Assurance," resin may crystallize at temperatures below 60°F.

Two or three days before installation is to take place, it is well advised to inspect each pail of resin Component "A" that is to be used, to determine its condition. Resin and hardener cans should be checked for crystallization. (See Chapter 3.) If any of the resin or hardener cans are leaking, they should be immediately removed from the site.

Where epoxy grout aggregate is provided as a separate component, it should be premeasured, palletized, shrink-wrapped, and delivered in sound, dry bags.

B. STORAGE DAMAGE

Any material which becomes damp or otherwise defective should be immediately removed from the site.

C. STORAGE TIME

Job storage time of epoxy grout should be limited to the manufacturer's recommended storage limit.

NONSHRINK EPOXY GROUT
ESTIMATING SHEET

From Premeasured Units

		FIVE STAR	PRODUCT "X"
A.	Cost per Unit	_____	_____
B.	Yield per Unit (Cubic feet/unit)	_____	_____
C.	Cost per Cubic Foot (A divided by B)	_____	_____
D.	Total Cubic Feet Required (From field estimates)	_____	_____
E.	Total Material Cost (C x D)	_____	_____

CHAPTER 6
EPOXY GROUT PLACEMENT PROCEDURES

INSTALLATION
A. GENERAL
    1. The general application procedures outlined below
        are for use under normal conditions. Temperatures
        below 70°F tend to slow the set and stiffen the consis-
        tency of epoxy grout, and temperatures above 70°F
        tend to accelerate the set and loosen the consis-
        tency of epoxy grout. If grouting is to be done when
        ambient temperatures are not between 60°F and 90°F,
        follow additional recommendations outlined in
        Chapter 6, sections H and I, Hot Weather Grouting
        and Cold Weather Grouting for Epoxy Grouts. If
        other unusual or difficult conditions exist, (low
        clearances, shear keys, etc.), the contractor should
        contact the owner's engineer and the grout manu-
        facturer's Technical Service Department.
    2. All necessary tools and materials should be as close
        as possible to the area being grouted. Mortar box,
        mortar mixer (with moving blades), wheelbarrow,
        hoe, shovels, trowels and grout components should
        be within easy reach. (See Technical Bulletin, Mate-
        rial and Equipment Check List in this section.)
    3. If it is desirable that the set times and strength gains
        are to be maintained at the 70°F rate, the applicable
        hot weather or cold weather instructions contained
        in this section should be reviewed for guidance.

B. SURFACE PREPARATION
   1. *CONCRETE*
      a. The concrete on which the grout will bear should be dry and have attained its design strength before grouting.
      b. *Do not wet concrete*. All surfaces to be in contact with grout should be dry and entirely free of oil, grease, laitance, curing compounds, frost, and other potential bond-preventing substances.
      c. Roughen the surfaces by chipping, sand-blasting or other mechanical means to remove any laitance or weak surface layer.
   2. *BASEPLATES*
      a. All metal surfaces of equipment bases which are to be in contact with the grout should be thoroughly cleaned to "bare metal" if bond is required.
      b. Leveling and alignment of baseplates should be performed according to the recommendation of the equipment manufacturer and/or project specifications. The leveled baseplates should provide a minimum of 1/2 inch clearance throughout when very flowable grouts such as FIVE STAR SPEED EPOXY GROUT are used. For conventional epoxy grouts such as FIVE STAR EPOXY GROUT, a minimum 1-1/2 inch clearance should be provided. For baseplates wider than three feet, provide an additional one inch of clearance for each three feet of width. Grout pours deeper than four inches present the potential for cracking due to excessive internal heat development and subsequent cooling. Deeper pours can be accomplished by pouring in lifts and/or by using reinforcing bars in the epoxy. Embedded rebars act as heat sinks for curing epoxy. Both methods reduce temperature rise. For placements deeper than four inches, the grout manufacturer should be contacted for detailed procedures.

      c.   Shims, wedges and blocks which are to be removed should be covered with putty, grease or similar non-bonding material to prevent the grout from adhering.

3. *ANCHOR BOLTS*

      a.   Equipment manufacturers or design engineers often require anchor bolts to be grouted. All surfaces should be thoroughly cleaned of oil, grease and other deleterious substances, and must be dry. Holes must be dried by evaporation, compressed air, or wicking with absorbent rags. Any compressor used to blow out water or other substances from surfaces in contact with the grout should be equipped with an oil trap in the air line to prevent oil from being blown onto the contact surface and affecting the bond of the grout.

      b.   If the equipment manufacturers or design engineers require anchor bolts to remain isolated, sleeves should be used and filled with a pliable material such as duct seal, putty, silicone rubber molding compound or other materials specified by the equipment manufacturer. Wrapping bolts in duct tape or foam insulation also works well.

4. *SURFACE DRYNESS*

      All surfaces must be kept completely dry before grouting.

5. *GROUT REMOVAL*

      Surfaces from which grout is to be removed after placing should be treated with a paste wax or release agent before placement.

C. FORMING

1. *GENERAL*

      Forming or other leakproof containment is always required with epoxy grout. The forms require careful attention to prevent any leakage. If forms are not liquid tight, the grout will leak out and leave voids.

Forms must be designed to provide a hydraulic head. If additional hydraulic head is required at the point of placement, head boxes may be used as shown below.

All chamfer edges required in the grouts should be incorporated into the forms because epoxy grout cannot be cut or trimmed after hardening unless a grinder is used.

2. *FORM STRENGTH*

All forms should be built of materials of adequate strength, securely anchored and shored to withstand liquid head and the forces developed by plunging the grout into place.

3. *SEALING AND WAXING FORMS*

Caulking, such as glazier's putty, butyl rubber caulking or duct seal should be used to make all joints liquid tight. This particularly applies to the joint between the form and the concrete. All forms may be lined with polyethylene for easy grout release. Carefully waxing forms with two coats of heavy floor or paste wax, preferably colored, to ensure 100% waxed area is also acceptable.

4. CONTROL JOINTS AND REINFORCEMENT

Control joints should be placed on 3 to 4 foot centers. Control joints should extend full depth and full length from form to form.

Joint material can be closed cell styrofoam, thick rubber, thick sheet metal covered with polyethylene, 1/4" thick steel or wood strips covered with polyethylene tape, all of which will make removal of the joints relatively easy by preventing the epoxy grout from bonding to them or similar performing materials.

For deep or long pours and under extreme temperature conditions, reinforcing bars should be placed in the grout. To distribute the stresses under these conditions, #6 reinforcing bars should be placed parallel to the equipment frame between the control joints. See photograph below. Bars may be placed into the previously placed and leveled grout and should be approximately one inch below the surface and within two inches of anchor bolts. If wide shoulders or extreme depths are required, consult the grout manufacturer for number and spacing of reinforcing bars.

"Joint and Reinforcing Bar Installation"

5. *AIR RELIEF HOLES*

With some baseplate designs, air relief holes are mandatory. Baseplates with a skirt around the perimeter should have relief holes (minimum 1/8" diameter) in each dead corner. If the plate is bisected with stiffening members, then relief holes should be provided at the intersections with the skirt. (See Figure G for minimum required air relief holes.)

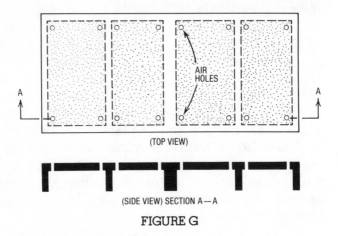

(TOP VIEW)

(SIDE VIEW) SECTION A—A

FIGURE G

6. *SHOULDERS*

The difference in coefficient of thermal expansion between epoxy grout and concrete induces stresses in shoulders. It is recommended that shoulders not exceed a maximum of 2 to 3 inches. If wide shoulders are mandatory, special anchoring must be provided as shown below and the manufacturer must be contacted for specific instructions.

PROBLEMS

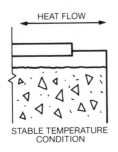

STABLE TEMPERATURE
CONDITION

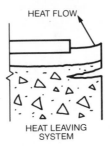

HEAT LEAVING
SYSTEM

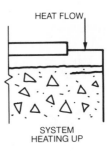

SYSTEM
HEATING UP

SOLUTIONS

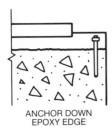

ANCHOR DOWN
EPOXY EDGE

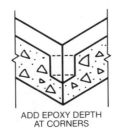

ADD EPOXY DEPTH
AT CORNERS

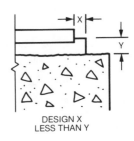

DESIGN X
LESS THAN Y

D. MIXING

1. FOLLOW DIRECTIONS

Grout should be mixed according to the procedures recommended by the manufacturer. Carefully
read all mixing information on the packages and the
latest literature. If in doubt about the mixing procedures, call the manufacturer.

2. MIXER TYPE

If a mechanical mixer is used, it should be a
mortar mixer (with moving blades) (as shown below)
inside the drum as opposed to a concrete mixer with
fins on a rotating drum. For smaller quantities, use a
concrete wheelbarrow and a mortar hoe. Mixing
equipment should be clean and dry.

For materials prepackaged in one container,
the epoxy grout may be mixed in the container using a low speed (500 rpm max.) drill and a "Jiffy"
type paddle.

"Typical Mortar Mixer"

3. *CONSISTENCY*

Many years of experience have shown that epoxy grouts and aggregates must be supplied in premeasured quantities to ensure a precision product. Do not vary the ratio of components or *add solvent to change the consistency*. High temperatures will increase flowability and reduce pot life, while cold weather will decrease flowability and extend pot life. An ideal balance is developed at 75°F.

The only exception to this rule is for initial coating of mortar mixer (with moving blades) or wheelbarrow, when used, on the first unit mixed.

Some of the liquids will wet the mixer; therefore, about ten pounds of aggregate per unit should be discarded on the first batch. All following batches should be mixed in accordance with manufacturer's recommendations with no modifications.

4. *MIXING TIME*

The epoxy hardener (B Component) should first be added to the pail of resin (A Component) and thoroughly mixed for two to three minutes, without whipping air into the mix and until no unmixed streaks exist. Hand stirring or a low speed mixer should be used. Pour all mixed resin and hardener into a clean, dry mortar mixer (with moving blades) or wheelbarrow. Add the entire bag of aggregate at once and mix only until the aggregate is wetted and free of lumps. Overmixing results in excess entrapped air. To maintain proper proportions of resin, hardener and aggregate, always mix full units only. Under no circumstances should partial units be used.

For materials prepackaged in one container, such as FIVE STAR SPEED EPOXY GROUT or FIVE STAR RAPID EPOXY GROUT, follow instructions on manufacturer's label.

5. *CLEANING EQUIPMENT*

After grouting is completed, or if delays occur, clean mixer, tub, wheelbarrows, tools, etc. with solvent. Solvesso, Xylol, lacquer thinner, ketones, or similar solvents have been used. Adding gravel or regular sand to the solvent will assist in cleaning a mortar mixer. USE CAUTION IN CLEANING POWERED EQUIPMENT WHEN HIGHLY VOLATILE SOLVENTS SUCH AS LACQUER THINNER OR KETONES ARE USED.

E. PLACING
   1. *GENERAL*
      a. *Check Temperature Conditions*
         Determine if ambient temperature will be between 40°F and 90°F at time of grouting. If not, compensating procedures outlined in Chapter 6, sections H and I, Hot and Cold Weather Epoxy Grouting sections should be used.
      b. *Working Time*
         Temperature affects the consistency of epoxy grout and therefore can affect placement time. Check placement temperature of materials to estimate the time available for placing grout.
      c. *Transporting Grout*
         Use wheelbarrows or buckets to transport grout to point of placement.
      d. *Elimination of Voids*
         Grout placement should proceed in a manner that will assure the filling of all spaces and intimate contact of grouting materials with the surfaces to be grouted. The placement should be rapid and continuous so as to avoid cold joints and voids under the baseplate. All grouting should take place from one side to avoid trapping air.
         When using grout holes or stand pipes, start placing grout in adjacent grout holes or stand pipes only when grout has reached the adjacent hole.
      e. *Check for Leaks*
         Forms must be constantly checked for leaks. All leaks must be sealed immediately or voids will develop.
   2. *USE OF A HEAD BOX*
      When hydraulic head pressure is used to flow grout in place, the level of grout in the head box must never fall below the top of the baseplate, because air will be trapped. The head box should be filled to the maximum height and worked (plunged) down to the top of the baseplate. This procedure is repeated until the grout moves completely under the baseplate, pushing air out in front of it, and rising

above the bottom of the baseplate on the far side. (See following photo.)

F. FINISHING

Epoxy grout cannot be trimmed after set. It must be left at final placement level, with all chamfer strips built into forms. To provide a smooth surface, puddle the grout so all aggregate is covered. Bubbles can be broken by spraying LIGHTLY with solvent. After initial stiffening, finish with trowel moistened with low volatility solvent or diesel oil. All further finishing will require grinding after cure period is complete.

G. CURING

1. *FOLLOW INSTRUCTIONS*

Grout should be cured in accordance with the manufacturer's specifications and recommendations. Read and follow the directions printed on the packages.

2. *FORMS*

All forms should remain in place overnight when fast curing grouts are not used. FIVE STAR RAPID EPOXY GROUT and FIVE STAR EPOXY GROUT may have forms removed as soon as the material "rings" when hit with a hammer.

3. *TEMPERATURE*

The temperature of the baseplate, supporting concrete foundation and grout should be maintained between 50°F and 90°F during grouting and for a minimum of 24 hours thereafter. See grout manufacturer's literature for cure schedules.

4. *MOIST CURING*

Water interferes with proper curing of epoxy grouts. DO NOT MOIST CURE EPOXY GROUT!

H. HOT WEATHER GROUTING
INSTRUCTIONS FOR EPOXY GROUT

1. *PRECONDITIONING TEMPERATURE*

All epoxy grout components should be stored in a dry, weatherproof area until all epoxy grout components reach a temperature between 70°F and 80°F. Since aggregate is the major portion of the mix, its temperature will be the most critical in determining final mix temperature.

2. *COOLING AND SHADING*

Shading or other methods should be used to cool baseplates to below 90°F. Extreme caution should be used because all surfaces in contact with epoxy grout must be completely dry before grouting.

Concrete, steel and forms should be shaded from direct sunlight beginning 24 hours prior to placing grout and kept shaded until at least one day after placement.

3. *MIXING PRECAUTIONS*

    Do not allow mixed resin and hardener to remain without aggregate for more than 5 minutes.

4. *TIME OF PLACEMENT*

    The placement of the grout should take place in the evening or later, when the temperature is dropping. This lets heat development take place during the coolest part of the day.

I. COLD WEATHER GROUTING
INSTRUCTIONS FOR EPOXY GROUT

1. *PRECONDITIONING TEMPERATURE*

    All epoxy grout components should be stored in a dry, weatherproof area until all epoxy grout components reach a temperature between 70°F and 80°F. Since aggregate is the major portion of the mix, its temperature will be the most critical in determining final mix temperature.

    Determine if the resin has crystallized as described under "Quality Assurance". If it has, follow instruction given for returning it to a liquid consistency.

2. *SURFACE CONDITIONS*

    All surfaces in contact with grout must be maintained at a temperature of at least 50°F for at least 24 hours prior to, and at least 48 hours subsequent to grouting. It is important to prevent frost formation on these surfaces.

3. *TEMPERATURE DURING CURE*

    Temperature to be maintained during cure will depend upon cure schedule required. In general, epoxies will not proceed with cure below 40°F. Consult the grout manufacturer for advice on techniques best suited to each application.

4. *METHODS*

    There are many methods of maintaining proper preconditioning, preparation and curing temperatures. Consult the grout manufacturer for advice on techniques best suited to each application.

J. MINIMUM DOWNTIME REGROUTING

As mentioned under "Recent Developments", there is a very successful method being used for regrouting of compressors and other vibrating equipment. Rather than waiting 7 to 10 days for conventional materials to cure and gain strength, this combination of rapid setting NONSHRINK cementitious grout and rapid setting NON-SHRINK epoxy grout permits putting the equipment back in service within 48 hours. A description of a project using this procedure is enclosed in this section as a reprint from "*Chemical Processing*" titled "Compressor Foundation Rebuilt in Just 24 Hours With Fast-Setting Grouts". This procedure can be used to rebuild existing bases or construct new ones whenever time is critical.

"Example of minimum downtime grouting. Bottom pour is FIVE STAR INSTANT GROUT topped with FIVE STAR EPOXY GROUT."

1. *SURFACE PREPARATION*
   a. With chipping hammers remove all loose, unsound or cracked concrete.
   b. Sandblast existing reinforcing bars and chipped out area.

c. If the base or foundation did not contain rein-forcing bars, a "cage" should be assembled and put in place.

d. Wet the existing concrete with saturated rags or sponge foam while forms are being constructed. This will save time.

2. *FORMING*

a. Construct all forms watertight. Wrap forms with polyethylene sheet or treat form with a release agent for easy form removal.

b. Forms must be built and supported to withstand rodding and/or vibration of the rapid setting ce-mentitious material.

3. *MIXING*

a. A mortar mixer (with moving blades) is recom-mended for mixing **FIVE STAR INSTANT GROUT.**

b. The mixer should be thoroughly washed out with potable water and all excess water drained out prior to mixing **FIVE STAR INSTANT GROUT.**

c. Water used to mix the **FIVE STAR INSTANT GROUT** *must* be potable. Always begin with the minimum amount of water printed on the pack-aged. Add the measured amount of water into the mixer. If additional water is required, do not exceed maximum amount on container.

d. Sequence of addition of all ingredients should be as follows:
— Potable water
— SUMMERSET if used
— Clean, washed pea gravel
— FIVE STAR INSTANT GROUT

e. Mix for a minimum of two minutes. Do not ex-ceed five minutes of mixing time.

4. *PLACEMENT*

a. Placements of 2″ depth or less:

Place **FIVE STAR INSTANT GROUT** in a single lift (layer). Rod or puddle to ensure inti-mate contact with base concrete.

Just prior to initial set, rake the surface to provide a mechanical bond for the epoxy grout.

b. Placements of 2" to 4" depth:

Extend the FIVE STAR INSTANT GROUT with 100% by weight of clean, washed pea gravel. Mix as directed under "Mixing". Place in a single lift (layer). Rod or vibrate to ensure proper consolidation and bond with concrete base. Just prior to initial set, rake the surface to provide a mechanical bond for the epoxy grout.

c. Placements over 4" in depth:

Extend the FIVE STAR INSTANT GROUT as described above and place the resulting material in two equal lifts. Rake the surface of all lifts and allow a minimum of one hour between successive lifts.

d. When using FIVE STAR RAPID EPOXY GROUT as the final grout, leave a minimum of 1-1/2" of clearance between the final lift of FIVE STAR INSTANT GROUT and the baseplate.

e. Moist cure each lift of FIVE STAR INSTANT GROUT to prevent rapid drying. Allow final lift of FIVE STAR INSTANT GROUT to dry after moist cure before installing FIVE STAR RAPID EPOXY GROUT.

K. FINAL GROUTING WITH FIVE STAR RAPID EPOXY GROUT

1. *SURFACE PREPARATION*

Last lift of FIVE STAR INSTANT GROUT must be *clean* and *dry* prior to placing FIVE STAR RAPID EPOXY GROUT. If possible, sandblast or rake final lift of FIVE STAR INSTANT GROUT.

2. *FORMING*

If forms for FIVE STAR INSTANT GROUT are not carried high enough to permit the placement of FIVE STAR RAPID EPOXY GROUT, a new form must be erected to contain the FIVE STAR RAPID EPOXY GROUT. It must be liquid tight and have chamfer strips built in.

3. *MIXING*

FIVE STAR RAPID EPOXY GROUT is packaged in a five gallon pail which contains all three components. Remove the containers of liquid and the bag of aggregate.

Pour contents of liquid containers into the now empty five gallon pail. Mix these liquids with a slow speed (maximum 500 rpm) electric drill, fitted with a "Jiffy" mixing paddle, until no streaks of unmixed liquids are obvious. Empty contents of plastic bag of aggregate into mixed liquids and continue mixing until all aggregate is wetted and a smooth, pourable grout results. *Do not overmix.* FIVE STAR RAPID EPOXY GROUT is a rapid setting material and must be mixed and placed within 20 minutes at 75°F.

4. *PLACING*

Immediately after mixing FIVE STAR RAPID EPOXY GROUT, place the grout without delay from one side of the form to the other. Additional batches should be mixed and placed quickly to avoid blockages and cold joints.

5. *CURING*

FIVE STAR RAPID EPOXY GROUT does not require any curing and will reach adequate strength within 6 hours (at 75°F) to put equipment back in operation.

Forms may be stripped as soon as FIVE STAR RAPID EPOXY GROUT has stiffened enough to prevent sagging.

CHAPTER 7
TYPICAL EPOXY GROUT APPLICATIONS

"Compressor Grouting"

"Concrete base for compressor"

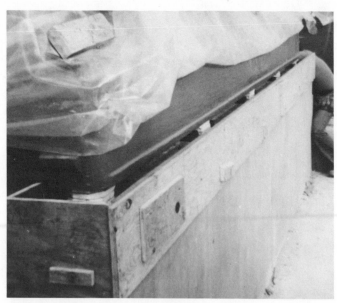

"Compressor in place and forming complete"

TYPICAL
EPOXY GROUT
INSTALLATION

"Placing Five Star
Epoxy Grout"

"Mixing Five Star
Epoxy Grout"

"Compressor grouted in place"

"Crane Rail Grouting"

"Crane Rail Grouting"

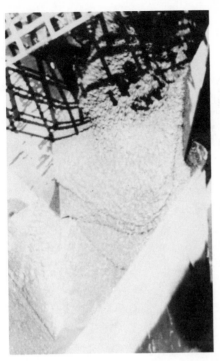

"Precast Bridge Sections"

CHAPTER 8
NONSHRINK EPOXY GROUT SPECIFICATIONS

A general discussion of specifications and types is presented in Chapter 8, Section I. That discussion applies to specifications for epoxy grout.

It should be remembered in specifying an epoxy grout that the purpose of the grout is to fill *completely* and *permanently*, the space to be grouted.

Since their inception, epoxy grouts have been promoted as "NONSHRINK" or as evidencing "negligible" shrinkage. Test methods supposedly verifying NONSHRINK performance date back to the early 1960's, but it is now apparent that these methods are inadequate for epoxy grouts, since they do not measure vertical volume change. A modification of the current ASTM C 827 test method shows that most epoxy grouts exhibit even greater vertical shrinkage than the shrinking cement-based grouts. Loss of EBA and failures of epoxy grout can be directly correlated to plastic shrinkage (vertical volume change).

Loss of effective bearing area will have a dramatic effect on creep of an epoxy grout. It is generally recommended that total load on the epoxy grout (dead plus bolt torque) not exceed 500 psi. This design assumes 100% EBA. At 50% EBA the load increases to 1,000 psi. Tests indicate that creep increases in direct proportion to the increase in load. In the situation mentioned, creep would approximately double! To prevent such an occurrence, a minimum of 95% EBA should be specified.

The most important requirement in an epoxy grout specification is that which requires it to be NONSHRINK. Data verifying this, when tested according to ASTM C 827 (Modified) should be an integral part of the specification.

Following are examples of NONSHRINK epoxy grout specifications.

NONSHRINK EPOXY GROUT
EXAMPLE OF SHORT FORM PROPRIETARY SPECIFICATION

All grouting as called for on the drawings and/or in the specifications shall be performed with FIVE STAR EPOXY GROUT* as manufactured by U. S. GROUT CORPORATION, a subsidiary of FIVE STAR PROD-UCTS, INC. of Fairfield, Connecticut. No substitutions will be approved.

OR APPROVED EQUAL WITH IDENTICAL PROPER-TIES SPECIFICATION

All grouting called for on the drawings and/or in the specifications shall be performed with FIVE STAR EPOXY GROUT* as manufactured by U. S. GROUT CORPORATION, a subsidiary of FIVE STAR PROD-UCTS, INC. of Fairfield, Connecticut, or approved equal with identical properties. The grout must show no shrinkage according to ASTM C 827.

(*The specifier should select the particular grout required from the literature at the back of this section.)

SHORT FORM
PERFORMANCE SPECIFICATION

All grouting as called for on the drawings and/or in the specifications shall be performed with an epoxy grout meeting the performance requirements that follow.

Epoxy grout must have a minimum 5 year history of use and meet the following performance requirements. It must be a 100% solids system and shall not contain any non-reactive diluents.

(A) Volume Change

   The grout shall show no shrinkage (0.0%) and a maximum 4.0% expansion from time of placement when tested according to ASTM C 827, modified to use a ball with a specific gravity between 0.9 and 1.1.

(B) Compressive Strength

   The grout shall show a minimum 7-day compressive strength of 14,000 psi when tested according to ASTM C 579.

(C) Thermal Expansion

   The grout shall show a maximum coefficient of thermal expansion of 30×10^{-6} in/in/°F when tested according to ASTM C 531.

(D) Creep Resistance

   The grout shall show creep equal to or less than 5.0×10^{-3} in./in. at 180°F for one year with a load of 400 psi when tested according to CPR Creep Test. (Extrapolated data is not acceptable.)

SECTION 03600
PERFORMANCE SPECIFICATION
FOR NONSHRINK EPOXY GROUT

PART I - GENERAL

All epoxy-based grouting as indicated in the designer's specification, equipment manufacturer's specification and or drawings shall apply to this section. Generally, these products are supplied by the contractor installing the grout. Epoxy grouts are used for grouting equipment baseplates subject to dynamic and impact loading and in areas subject to chemical attack.

1.01 REFERENCES

ASTM C 531	Test Method for Linear Shrinkage and Coefficient of Thermal Expansion of Chemical Resistant Mortars, Grouts and Monolithic Surfacings
ASTM C 579	Test Method for Compressive Strength of Chemical Resistant Mortars and Monolithic Surfacings
ASTM C 827	Standard Test Method for Change in Height at Early Ages of Cylindrical Specimens from Cementitious Mixtures
CPR CREEP TEST	Test Method for Creep of Epoxy Grouts

1.02 SUBMITTALS

The grout manufacturer must submit, prior to installation, for designer's approval, literature and test data from a laboratory listed in the ASTM Directory of Testing Laboratories that material complies with requirements in Article 1.05 and 2.02. Designer should, at contractor's expense, buy any submitted material in the open marketplace, without the contractor's or manufacturer's knowledge, and test material at an independent laboratory to verify compliance with this specification.

1.03 DELIVERY, STORAGE AND HANDLING

All epoxy-based grouts shall be prepackaged, three-component systems - resin, hardener and specially blended aggregate. They shall be delivered to the jobsite in original, unopened package, clearly labeled with the manufacturer's identification and printed instructions. The grout components shall be stored at 70 ± 5°F in a dry environment.

1.04 ENVIRONMENTAL CONDITIONS

Refer to the manufacturer's literature for any physical or environmental limitations or contact the manufacturer directly.

1.05 WARRANTY

The material manufacturer shall warranty that the nonshrink epoxy grout shall never go below its initial placement volume when tested in accordance with ASTM C 827.

PART II - PRODUCT

2.01 MANUFACTURER

The following manufacturer supplies materials which meet this specification and offers field service.

Manufacturer	*Products*
U. S. GROUT CORPORATION	FIVE STAR
A Subsidiary of	EPOXY GROUT
FIVE STAR PRODUCTS, INC.	
Fairfield, Connecticut	
800-243-2206 or 203-336-7900	

Other materials which meet this specification must be submitted to the designer for approval with the prime contractor's original bid documents by following the procedures outlined in Article 1.02.

2.02 MATERIALS

Epoxy grouts must have a minimum 5 year history of use and meet the following performance requirements. They must be 100% solids system and shall not contain any non-reactive diluents.

(A) Volume Change

The grout shall show no shrinkage (0.0%) and a maximum 4.0% expansion from time of placement when tested according to ASTM C 827, modified to use a ball with a specific gravity between 0.9 and 1.1.

(B) Compressive Strength

The grout shall show a minimum 7-day compressive strength of 14,000 psi when tested according to ASTM C 579.

(C) Thermal Expansion

The grout shall show a maximum coefficient of thermal expansion of 30×10^{-6} in/in/°F when tested according to ASTM C 531.

(D) Creep Resistance

The grout shall show creep equal to or less than 5.0×10^{-3} in./in. at 180°F for one year with a load of 400 psi when tested according to CPR Creep Test. (Extrapolated data is not acceptable.)

PART III - EXECUTION

3.01 INSPECTION

(A) Inspect concrete surfaces to receive grout and verify that they are free of ice, frost, dirt, grease, oil, curing compounds, paints, impregnations, laitance and all loose material or foreign matter likely to affect the bond or performance of the grout.

(B) Newly placed concrete shall have been placed and cured sufficiently to attain its design strength.

(C) Inspect baseplates for rust, oil, and other deleterious substances.

3.02 PREPARATION

(A) If deemed necessary by the designer that adhesion is required, all grease, oil, dirt, curing compounds, laitance and other deleterious materials must be completely removed from the concrete and bottom of baseplate.

(B) Roughen the surfaces by chipping, sandblasting or other mechanical means to assure bond of the grout to the existing concrete. Loose or broken concrete shall be removed.

(C) *Do not wet* concrete substrate.

(D) Forming or other leakproof containment is always required with epoxy grout. Forms must be liquid tight. Caulking such as glazier's putty, butyl rubber caulking or duct seal should be used. All forms may be lined with polyethylene for easy grout release. Forms carefully waxed with two coats of heavy-duty paste wax are also acceptable.

(E) Expansion joints must be placed on two to three foot centers.

3.03 INSTALLATION

(A) Carefully read and understand the manufacturer's instructions as printed on the packaging.

(B) Mixing

Grout shall be mixed according to the procedures recommended by the manufacturer. For large volume placements, a mortar mixer with moving blades is preferred. For smaller quantities, use a concrete wheelbarrow and a mortar hoe. Do not vary the ratio of components or add solvent to change the consistency of the mix.

(C) Placing

Ambient conditions shall be monitored and grout manufacturer contacted for cold weather (50°F) and hot weather (90°F) placement procedures. All grouting should take place from one side to avoid trapping air.

(D) Cutback

Epoxy cannot be trimmed after set. It must be left at final placement level with all chamfer strips built into forms.

(E) Curing

Consult the owners, designer and grout manufacturer for appropriate cure schedule. In no case should any surface in contact with grout be allowed to fall below 50°F for a minimum of 48 hours.

(F) Cleanup

Upon completion of placement, equipment and tools should be cleaned in such a manner as recommended by manufacturer.

CHAPTER 9
TECHNICAL DATA ON
FIVE STAR EPOXY GROUTS

FIVE STAR
EPOXY
GROUTS

This chapter contains product literature, magazine reprints and technical bulletins on **FIVE STAR EPOXY GROUTS**. **FIVE STAR** products are designed to provide a higher level of performance.

FIVE STAR® EPOXY GROUT

DESCRIPTION

Five Star Epoxy Grout is the first nonshrink, high creep resistant, general purpose epoxy grout. It is a 100% solids, three component system carefully formulated to make placement easy. It provides high strength and creep resistance combined with the highest effective bearing area in the industry. The advanced technology of this patented product combines the following advantages that no other manufacturer can offer.

UNIQUE ADVANTAGES
- Precision Nonshrink
- High Creep Resistance
- Highest Effective Bearing Area[1]
- Contains Devoider[2]

SPECIAL ADVANTAGES
- Very Flowable
- High Impact Resistance
- High Chemical Resistance
- High Early Strength
- No Segregation

TYPICAL PHYSICAL PROPERTIES   **In-Place Properties**

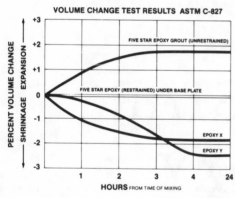

VOLUME CHANGE TEST RESULTS ASTM C-827

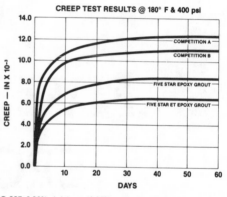

CREEP TEST RESULTS @ 180° F & 400 psi

Volume Change, ASTM C-827: 0.00% shrinkage (0.00% expansion after set)
Effective Bearing Area[1]: 95% minimum

Creep, FSP Creep: 4.4 x 10⁻³ inches/inches at 180°F and 400 psi at 1 year
Compressive Strength, ASTM C-579 Method B: 11,000 psi/24 Hours; 16,000 psi/7 Days
Tensile Strength, ASTM C-307: 1500 psi
Flexural Strength, ASTM C-580: 4000 psi
Flexural Modulus, ASTM C-580 1.67 x 10⁶ psi
Coefficient of Expansion, ASTM C-531: 15x10⁻⁶ in/in/°F
Bond to Concrete: Concrete Failure
Impact Strength: Better than concrete
Peak Exotherm: 83°F, 1000 grams

---

[1]EBA: Effective Bearing Area - percent final surface area of grout in direct contact with bearing plate.
[2]All Five Star Grouts contain Devoider®, which offers the unique advantage of preventing cavities; overcoming plastic shrinkage, keeping the grout tightly against the plate for permanent support; producing the highest Effective Bearing Area.

Placement Properties

Five Star Epoxy Grout is a prepackaged, premeasured unit which provides excellent pourability. Five Star Epoxy Grout also provides a very long working time allowing ample placement time to ensure the highest Effective Bearing Area is achieved.

APPLICATIONS
- High Impact/Heavy Vibrating Equipment
- High Chemical Attack Areas
- Anchors

PLACEMENT GUIDELINES

1. **Surface Preparation:** Concrete shall have reached its designed strength and dimensional stability. All surfaces to be in contact with Five Star Epoxy Grout shall be completely dry and entirely free of oil, grease, laitance, or other foreign substances.

2. **Forms and Control Joints:** Make all forms liquid tight using putty or caulking compound to seal joints. Areas where bond is not desired must be treated with paste wax, polyethylene, or "resin release" agent. Control joints should be placed on 3 to 4 foot centers in both directions. For pours deeper than 4 inch thickness, contact U.S. Grout Corporation.

3. **Mixing:** Pour all of Component B (Hardener) into pail containing Component A (Resin). Mix thoroughly by hand or low speed mixer to avoid air entrapment. Pour all of mixed material into mortar box, mortar mixer or wheelbarrow. Add two bags Five Star Epoxy Aggregate and mix only until all aggregate is wetted and no dry pockets remain. Follow printed instructions on each package.

4. **Methods of Placing:** Five Star Epoxy Grout shoud be placed from one side to avoid air entrapment. Rods and plungers may be used to facilitate placement.

5. **Post-Placement Procedures:** Do not wet cure Five Star Epoxy Grout. It is a chemical curing material. All surfaces, equipment, and tools may be cleaned with lacquer thinner, ketones, or similar solvent before grout hardens. In-service operation may begin immediately after minimum required grout strengths have been achieved. Final finishing of exposed surfaces is aided by applying a very light mist of solvent just before material becomes unworkable.

ENGINEERING & TECHNICAL CENTER

U.S. Grout Corporation maintains the industry's foremost Engineering and Technical Center staffed with engineers, available for consultation and on-site technical service worldwide.

SPECIFICATION GUIDELINES

All general purpose nonshrink, creep resistant epoxy grouting shall be performed with Five Star Epoxy Grout as manufactured by U.S. Grout Corporation, Fairfield, Connecticut. The grout shall be mixed and installed according to manufacturer's recommendations. No substitutions will be permitted. Technical service shall be made available by the manufacturer upon request.

For a more detailed specification guideline, call or write Engineering and Technical Center, U.S. Grout Corporation for assistance.

PACKAGING, YIELD, ORDERING AND AVAILABILITY

Five Star Epoxy Grout is a three-component system consisting of one can of hardener, one pail of resin, and two polyethylene lined bags of aggregate producing one cubic foot of hardened grout. For ordering, determine the total number of cubic feet required, add 5% wastage, and contact U.S. Grout Corporation or one of your local Five Star dealers throughout the United States.

STORAGE AND HANDLING

Five Star® Epoxy Grout should be stored in a cool, dry place in accordance with the manufacturer's recommendations. All components should be conditioned to 70 to 80° F prior to use and checked for crystallization. Protect from freezing for best results.

For Industrial Use Only.

Keep Out of Reach of Children.

Caution: Irritant, toxic, strong sensitizer. Contains epoxy resin and amine. This product may cause skin irritation. Do not inhale vapors. Provide adequate ventilation. Protect against contact with skin and eyes. Wear rubber gloves, long sleeve shirt, goggles with side shields. In case of contact with eyes, flush repeatedly with water and contact a physician. Areas of skin contact should be promptly washed with soap and water. Do not take internally.

Warranty: U.S. Grout Corporation stands behind its products when used by competent workmen in accordance with manufacturer's directions. No responsibility for product use is assumed or implied where inferior workmanship is encountered, or difficulty caused by other materials is evident. U.S. Grout Corporation's liability is limited to replacement of materials found to be defective. These recommended procedures are for normal field practice. They may be modified by the designer, specifier, purchaser or their authorized agent since only they are responsible for the design, installation and supervision of specific conditions and installations.

ENGINEERING & TECHNICAL CENTER, U.S. GROUT CORPORATION, SUBSIDIARY OF FIVE STAR PRODUCTS, INC.

401 STILLSON ROAD, FAIRFIELD, CONN 06430 • (203) 336-7900 • CABLE FIVE STAR • FACSIMILE: (203) 336-7939 • TELEX: 643857 • COPYRIGHT 1988 • 2/88 5K

FIVE STAR® ET EPOXY GROUT

DESCRIPTION

Five Star ET Epoxy Grout is the first nonshrink extremely high temperature creep resistant, epoxy grout. It is a 100 percent solids, three component system consisting of specially formulated resin, hardener, and a carefully blended aggregate. In addition, it is also the highest performing, highest early strength, high impact, and highest chemical resistant precision epoxy grout for operating temperatures up to 250° F. The advanced technology of this patented product combines the following advantages that no other manufacturer can offer.

UNIQUE ADVANTAGES

- Precision Nonshrink
- High Creep Resistance
- Highest Effective Bearing Area[1]
- Contains Devoider[2]

SPECIAL ADVANTAGES

- Very Flowable
- High Impact Resistance
- High Chemical Resistance
- High Early Strength
- No Segregation

TYPICAL PHYSICAL PROPERTIES   **In-Place Properties**

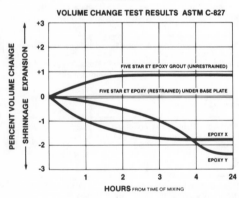

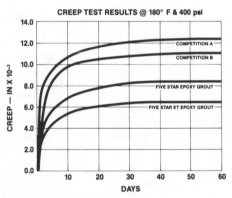

Volume Change, ASTM C-827: 0.00% shrinkage (0.00% expansion after set)

Effective Bearing Area[1]: 95% minimum

Creep, FSP Creep: 3.4×10^{-3} inches/inches at 180°F and 400 psi at 1 year

Compressive Strength, ASTM C-579 Method B: 12,000 psi/24 Hours; 17,000 psi/7 Days

Tensile Strength, ASTM C-307: 1800 psi

Flexural Strength, ASTM C-580: 4000 psi

Flexural Modulus, ASTM C-580 1.67×10^6 psi

Coefficient of Expansion, ASTM C-531: 16×10^{-6} in/in/°F

Bond to Concrete: Concrete Failure

Impact Strength: Better than concrete

Peak Exotherm: 86°F, 1000 grams

---

[1]EBA: Effective Bearing Area - percent final surface area of grout in direct contact with bearing plate.

[2]All Five Star Grouts contain Devoider®, which offers the unique advantage of preventing cavities; overcoming plastic shrinkage, keeping the grout tightly against the plate for permanent support; producing the highest Effective Bearing Area.

II.4

Placement Properties

Five Star ET Epoxy Grout a prepackaged, premeasured unit provides excellent pourability. Five Star ET Epoxy Grout also provides a very long working time allowing ample placement time to ensure the highest Effective Bearing Area is achieved.

APPLICATIONS
- High Impact/Heavy Vibrating Equipment at Operating Temperatures up to 250° F
- High Chemical Attack Areas
- Fast Start Up Epoxy Grouting
- Anchors

PLACEMENT GUIDELINES

1. **Surface Preparation:** Concrete shall have reached its designed strength and dimensional stability. All surfaces to be in contact with Five Star ET Epoxy Grout shall be completely dry and entirely free of oil, grease, laitance, or other foreign substances.

2. **Forms and Control Joints:** Make all forms liquid tight using putty or caulking compound to seal joints. Areas where bond is not desired must be treated with paste wax, polyethylene, or "resin release" agent. Control joints should be placed on 3 to 4 foot centers in both directions. For pours deeper than 4 inch thickness, contact U.S. Grout Corporation.

3. **Mixing:** Pour all of Component B (Hardener) into pail containing Component A (Resin). Mix thoroughly by hand or low speed mixer to avoid air entrapment. Pour all of mixed material into mortar box, mortar mixer or wheelbarrow. Add two bags Five Star ET Epoxy Aggregate and mix only until all aggregate is wetted and no dry pockets remain. Follow printed instructions on each package.

4. **Methods of Placing:** Five Star ET Epoxy Grout shoud be placed from one side to avoid air entrapment. Rods and plungers may be used to facilitate placement.

5. **Post-Placement Procedures:** Do not wet cure Five Star ET Epoxy Grout. It is a chemical curing material. All surfaces, equipment, and tools may be cleaned with lacquer thinner, ketones, or similar solvent before grout hardens. In-service operation may begin immediately after minimum required grout strengths have been achieved. Final finishing of exposed surfaces is aided by applying a very light mist of solvent just before material becomes unworkable.

ENGINEERING & TECHNICAL CENTER

U.S. Grout Corporation maintains the industry's foremost Engineering and Technical Center staffed with engineers, available for consultation and on-site technical service worldwide.

SPECIFICATION GUIDELINES

All general purpose nonshrink, creep resistant epoxy grouting shall be performed with Five Star ET Epoxy Grout as manufactured by U.S. Grout Corporation, Fairfield, Connecticut. The grout shall be mixed and installed according to manufacturer's recommendations. No substitutions will be permitted. Technical service shall be made available by the manufacturer upon request.

For a more detailed specification guideline, call or write Engineering and Technical Center, U.S. Grout Corporation for assistance.

PACKAGING, YIELD, ORDERING AND AVAILABILITY

Five Star ET Epoxy Grout is a three-component system consisting of one can of hardener, one pail of resin, and two polyethylene lined bags of aggregate producing one cubic foot of hardened grout. For ordering, determine the total number of cubic feet required, add 5% wastage, and contact U.S. Grout Corporation or one of your local Five Star dealers throughout the United States.

STORAGE AND HANDLING

Five Star ET Epoxy Grout should be stored in a cool, dry place in accordance with the manufacturer's recommendations. All components should be conditioned to 70 to 80° F prior to use and checked for crystallization. Protect from freezing for best results.

For Industrial Use Only.

Keep Out of Reach of Children.

Caution: Irritant, toxic, strong sensitizer. Contains epoxy resin and amine. This product may cause skin irritation. Do not inhale vapors. Provide adequate ventilation. Protect against contact with skin and eyes. Wear rubber gloves, long sleeve shirt, goggles with side shields. In case of contact with eyes, flush repeatedly with water and contact a physician. Areas of skin contact should be promptly washed with soap and water. Do not take internally.

Warranty: U.S. Grout Corporation stands behind its products when used by competent workmen in accordance with manufacturer's directions. No responsibility for product use is assumed or implied where inferior workmanship is encountered, or difficulty caused by other materials is evident. U.S. Grout Corporation's liability is limited to replacement of materials found to be defective. These recommended procedures are for normal field practice. They may be modified by the designer, specifier, purchaser or their authorized agent since only they are responsible for the design, installation and supervision of specific conditions and installations.

ENGINEERING & TECHNICAL CENTER, U.S. GROUT CORPORATION, SUBSIDIARY OF FIVE STAR PRODUCTS, INC.

401 STILLSON ROAD, FAIRFIELD, CONN 06430 • (203) 336-7900 • CABLE FIVE STAR • FACSIMILE: (203) 336-7939 • TELEX: 643857 • COPYRIGHT 1988 • 2/88 5K

FIVE STAR® RAPID EPOXY GROUT

DESCRIPTION

Five Star Rapid Epoxy Grout is a rapid strength gain epoxy grout. It is a 100% solids, three component system carefully formulated to minimize equipment downtime due to grouting. It provides very high early strengths at a pourable consistency while maintaining full contact with the grouted surfaces. The advanced technology of this patented product combines the following advantages that no other manufacturer can offer.

UNIQUE ADVANTAGES

- Very High Early Strengths

SPECIAL ADVANTAGES

- Very Flowable
- High Impact Resistance
- High Chemical Resistance

TYPICAL PHYSICAL PROPERTIES

In-Place Properties

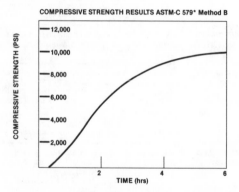

COMPRESSIVE STRENGTH RESULTS ASTM-C 579* Method B

Compressive Strength, ASTM C-579 Method B: 5000 psi/2 Hours;
12,000 psi/1 Day,
16,000 psi/7 Day

Tensile Strength, ASTM C-307: 2200 psi
Flexural Strength, ASTM C-580: 5000 psi
Flexural Modulus, ASTM C-580: 1.5×10^6 psi
Coefficient of Expansion, ASTM C-531: 15×10^6 in/in/°F
Bond to Concrete: Concrete Failure
Impact Strength: Better than concrete

Placement Properties

Five Star Rapid Epoxy Grout is a prepackaged, premeasured unit which provides excellent pourability. Five Star Rapid Epoxy Grout provides 15 minutes working time allowing sufficient placement time to ensure full contact with the grouted surfaces.

*Modified

APPLICATIONS	■ High Impact/Heavy Vibrating Equipment Requiring Fast Turnaround
	■ High´Chemical Attack Areas Requiring Fast Turnaround
	■ Fast Setting of Anchors

PLACEMENT GUIDELINES

1. **Surface Preparation:** Concrete shall have reached its designed strength and dimensional stability. All surfaces to be in contact with Five Star Rapid Epoxy Grout shall be completely dry and entirely free of oil, grease, laitance, or other foreign substances.

2. **Forms and Control Joints:** Make all forms liquid tight using putty or caulking compound to seal joints. Areas where bond is not desired must be treated with paste wax, polyethylene, or "resin release" agent. Control joints should be placed on 2 to 3 foot centers in both directions. For pours deeper than 3 inch thickness, contact U.S. Grout Corporation.

3. **Mixing:** Remove the plastic containers and aggregate from the pail. Pour all of Component A (Resin) and B (Hardener) into pail and mix thoroughly by hand until uniform in color. Add all aggregate and mix only until all aggregate is wetted and no dry pockets remain. Follow printed instructions on each package.

4. **Methods of Placing:** Five Star Rapid Epoxy Grout should be placed from one side to avoid air entrapment. Rods and plungers may be used to facilitate placement. Work rapidly since working time is limited to 15 minutes.

5. **Post-Placement Procedures:** Do not wet cure Five Star Rapid Epoxy Grout. It is a chemical curing material. All surfaces, equipment, and tools may be cleaned with lacquer thinner, ketones, or similar solvent before grout hardens. In-service operation may begin immediately after minimum required grout strengths have been achieved. Final finishing of exposed surfaces is aided by applying a very light mist of solvent just before material becomes unworkable.

ENGINEERING & TECHNICAL CENTER

U.S. Grout Corporation maintains the industry's foremost Engineering and Technical Center staffed with engineers, available for consultation and on-site technical service worldwide.

SPECIFICATION GUIDELINES

All rapid strength gain epoxy grouting shall be performed with Five Star Rapid Epoxy Grout as manufactured by U.S. Grout Corporation, Fairfield, Connecticut. The grout shall be mixed and installed according to manufacturer's recommendations. No substitutions will be permitted. Technical service shall be made available by the manufacturer upon request.

For a more detailed specification guideline, call or write Engineering and Technical Center, U.S. Grout Corporation for assistance.

PACKAGING, YIELD, ORDERING AND AVAILABILITY

Five Star Rapid Epoxy Grout is a three-component system consisting of hardener, resin, and aggregate packaged in a 5 gallon pail which produces one-half cubic foot of hardened grout. For ordering, determine the total number of cubic feet required, add 5% wastage, and contact U.S. Grout Corporation or one of your local Five Star dealers throughout the United States.

STORAGE AND HANDLING

Five Star® Rapid Epoxy Grout should be stored in a cool, dry place in accordance with the manufacturer's recommendations. All components should be conditioned to 70 to 80°F prior to use and checked for crystallization. Protect from freezing for best results.

For Industrial Use Only.

Keep Out of Reach of Children.

Caution: Irritant, toxic, strong sensitizer. Contains epoxy resin and amine. This product may cause skin irritation. Do not inhale vapors. Provide adequate ventilation. Protect against contact with skin and eyes. Wear rubber gloves, long sleeve shirt, goggles with side shields. In case of contact with eyes, flush repeatedly with water and contact a physician. Areas of skin contact should be promptly washed with soap and water. Do not take internally.

Warranty: U.S. Grout Corporation stands behind its products when used by competent workmen in accordance with manufacturer's directions. No responsibility for product use is assumed or implied where inferior workmanship is encountered, or difficulty caused by other materials is evident. U.S. Grout Corporation's liability is limited to replacement of materials found to be defective. These recommended procedures are for normal field practice. They may be modified by the designer, specifier, purchaser or their authorized agent since only they are responsible for the design, installation and supervision of specific conditions and installations.

ENGINEERING & TECHNICAL CENTER, U.S. GROUT CORPORATION, SUBSIDIARY OF FIVE STAR PRODUCTS, INC

401 STILLSON ROAD, FAIRFIELD, CONN 06430 • (203) 336-7900 • CABLE FIVE STAR • FACSIMILE (203) 336-7939 • TELEX 643857 • COPYRIGHT 1987 • 8875K

FIVE STAR® SPEED EPOXY GROUT

DESCRIPTION Five Star Speed Epoxy Grout is a rapid strength gain very flowable epoxy grout. It is a 100% solids, three component system carefully formulated for grouting tight clearances and to minimize equipment downtime due to grouting. It provides extremely high early strength at a very flowable consistency while maintaining full contact with the grouted surfaces. The advanced technology of this patented product combines the following advantages that no other manufacturer can offer.

UNIQUE ADVANTAGES ▪ Extremely High Early Strengths

SPECIAL ADVANTAGES ▪ Extremely Flowable for Tight Clearances
▪ High Impact Resistance
▪ High Chemical Resistance

TYPICAL PHYSICAL PROPERTIES **In-Place Properties**

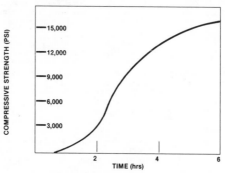

COMPRESSIVE STRENGTH RESULTS ASTM-C 579* Method B

Compressive Strength, ASTM C-579* Method B: 6,000 psi/3 Hours;
16,000 psi/6 Hours,
18,000 psi/1 Day
Tensile Strength, ASTM C-307: 2500 psi
Flexural Strength, ASTM C-580: 5000 psi
Flexural Modulus, ASTM C-580: 1.5×10^6 psi
Coefficient of Expansion, ASTM C-531: 15×10^6 in/in/°F
Bond to Concrete: Concrete Failure
Impact Strength: Better than concrete

Placement Properties

Five Star Speed Epoxy Grout is a prepackaged, premeasured unit which provides excellent pourability. Five Star Speed Epoxy Grout also provides 15 minutes working time allowing sufficient placement time to ensure full contact with the grouted surfaces.

*Modified

APPLICATIONS	▪ High Impact/Heavy Vibrating Equipment With Tight Clearances and Fast Turnaround ▪ High Chemical Attack Areas With Tight Clearances and Fast Turnaround ▪ Fast Setting of Anchors

PLACEMENT GUIDELINES

1. **Material Preparation:** The day prior to installation remove containers of resin, hardener and aggregate from 5 gallon pail. Pour the resin (large container) back into the pail and thoroughly mix with aggregate. Cover pail until installation. Do not add hardener (small container) until immediately prior to placement.

2. **Surface Preparation:** Concrete shall have reached its designed strength and dimensional stability. All surfaces to be in contact with Five Star Speed Epoxy Grout shall be completely dry and entirely free of oil, grease, laitance, or other foreign substances.

3. **Forms and Control Joints:** Make all forms liquid tight using putty or caulking compound to seal joints. Areas where bond is not desired must be treated with paste wax, polyethylene, or "resin release" agent. Control joints should be placed on 2 to 3 foot centers in both directions. For pours deeper than 1-1/2 inch thickness, contact U.S. Grout Corporation.

4. **Mixing:** Add hardener to 5 gallon pail containing premixed resin and aggregate and mechanically mix. If resin and aggregate have not been premixed, then mix resin and hardener in 5 gallon pail until uniform in color. Then add aggregate and mechanically mix until all aggregate is wetted.

5. **Methods of Placing:** Five Star Speed Epoxy Grout should be placed from one side to avoid air entrapment. Rods and plungers may be used to facilitate placement. Work rapidly since working time is limited to 15 minutes.

6. **Post-Placement Procedures:** Do not wet cure Five Star Speed Epoxy Grout. It is a chemical curing material. All surfaces, equipment, and tools may be cleaned with lacquer thinner, ketones, or similar solvent before grout hardens. In-service operation may begin immediately after minimum required grout strengths have been achieved. Final finishing of exposed surfaces is aided by applying a very light mist of solvent just before material becomes unworkable.

**ENGINEERING &
TECHNICAL CENTER**

U.S. Grout Corporation maintains the industry's foremost Engineering and Technical Center staffed with engineers, available for consultation and on-site technical service worldwide.

SPECIFICATION GUIDELINES

All rapid strength gain epoxy grouting with tight clearances shall be performed with Five Star Speed Epoxy Grout as manufactured by U.S. Grout Corporation, Fairfield, Connecticut. The grout shall be mixed and installed according to manufacturer's recommendations. No substitutions will be permitted. Technical service shall be made available by the manufacturer upon request.

For a more detailed specification guideline, call or write Engineering and Technical Center, U.S. Grout Corporation for assistance.

**PACKAGING, YIELD,
ORDERING AND AVAILABILITY**

Five Star Speed Epoxy Grout is a three-component system consisting of hardener, resin, and aggregate packaged in a 5 gallon pail which produces one third cubic foot of hardened grout. For ordering, determine the total number of cubic feet required, add 5% wastage, and contact U.S. Grout Corporation or one of your local Five Star dealers throughout the United States.

STORAGE AND HANDLING

Five Star® Speed Epoxy Grout should be stored in a cool, dry place in accordance with the manufacturer's recommendations. All components should be conditioned to 70 to 80°F prior to use and checked for crystallization. Protect from freezing for best results.

For Industrial Use Only.

Keep Out of Reach of Children.

Caution: Irritant, toxic, strong sensitizer. Contains epoxy resin and amine. This product may cause skin irritation. Do not inhale vapors. Provide adequate ventilation. Protect against contact with skin and eyes. Wear rubber gloves, long sleeve shirt, goggles with side shields. In case of contact with eyes, flush repeatedly with water and contact a physician. Areas of skin contact should be promptly washed with soap and water. Do not take internally.

Warranty: U.S. Grout Corporation stands behind its products when used by competent workmen in accordance with manufacturer's directions. No responsibility for product use is assumed or implied where inferior workmanship is encountered, or difficulty caused by other materials is evident. U.S. Grout Corporation's liability is limited to replacement of materials found to be defective. These recommended procedures are for normal field practice. They may be modified by the designer, specifier, purchaser or their authorized agent since only they are responsible for the design, installation and supervision of specific conditions and installations.

ENGINEERING & TECHNICAL CENTER, U.S. GROUT CORPORATION, SUBSIDIARY OF FIVE STAR PRODUCTS INC

401 STILLSON ROAD. FAIRFIELD. CONN. 06430 • (203) 336-7900 • CABLE FIVE STAR • FACSIMILE (203) 336-7939 • TELEX 643857 • COPYRIGHT 1987 • 8875K

TECHNICAL BULLETIN

FIVE STAR

FIVE STAR EPOXY GROUT
Chemical Resistance Chart

Chemical	Recommendation (See notes for explanation)	Temperature Limit °F (°C)
Acetic Acid 10%	RIW	100 (37.8)
Acetic Acid 50%	NR	--- ---
Acetone	RI	100 (37.8)
Alum	RI	180 (82.2)
Aluminum Sulfate	RI	180 (82.2)
Ammonium Chloride	RI	180 (82.2)
Ammonium Hydroxide	RI	160 (71.1)
Ammonium Nitrate	RI	180 (82.2)
Ammonium Sulfate	RI	180 (82.2)
Barium Hydroxide	RI	180 (82.2)
Benzene	RIW	100 (37.8)
"Black Liquor"	RI	160 (71.1)
Boric Acid	RI	180 (82.2)
Butyl Alcohol	RI	180 (82.2)
Calcium Carbonate	RI	180 (82.2)
Calcium Chloride	R	180 (82.2)
Calcium Hydroxide	RI	180 (82.2)
Carbon Tetrachloride	RI	180 (82.2)
Chlorine (any form)	NR	--- ---
Chloroform	RI	100 (37.8)
Chromic Acid 10%	RIW	100 (37.8)
Citric Acid	RI	160 (71.1)
Corn Oil	RI	100 (37.8)
Dibutyl Phthalate	R	180 (82.2)
Dimethyl Formamide	NR	--- ---
Ethyl Alcohol	R	180 (82.2)
Ethylene Dichloride	NR	--- ---
Ethylene Glycol	RI	160 (71.1)
Ferric Sulfate	RI	180 (82.2)
Fluosilicic Acid	RI	100 (37.8)
Formaldehyde	RI	100 (37.8)
Furfuryl Alcohol	RI	100 (37.8)
Gasoline	R	180 (82.2)

-2-

Chemical	Recommendation (See notes for explanation)	Temperature Limit °F (°C)
Glucose	R	180 (82.2)
Grape Juice	RI	180 (82.2)
Hexane	RI	100 (37.8)
Hydrobromic Acid	NR	--- ---
Hydrochloric Acid 20%	RI	100 (37.8)
Hydrochloric Acid 40%	RIW	100 (37.8)
Hydrofluoric Acid	NR	--- ---
Hydrogen Sulfide	RI	140 (60)
Isopropyl Alcohol	RI	140 (60)
Jet Fuel	RI	140 (60)
Kerosene	RI	140 (60)
Lactic Acid	NR	--- ---
Linseed Oil	RI	100 (37.8)
Maleic Acid	RI	100 (37.8)
Methyl Alcohol	RI	100 (37.8)
Methylene Chloride	NR	--- ---
Methyl Ethyl Ketone	NR	--- ---
Methyl Isobutyl Ketone	NR	--- ---
Milk	RI	180 (82.2)
Naptha	RI	120 (48.9)
Nitric Acid 5%	RIW	100 (37.8)
Nitric Acid (over 5%)	NR	--- ---
Oil, Animal	RI	120 (48.9)
Oil, Crude	RI	180 (82.2)
Oil, Vegetable	RI	120 (48.9)
Oxalic Acid	RI	100 (37.8)
Perchlorethylene	RI	100 (37.8)
Phenol 10% max.	RI	100 (37.8)
Phosphoric Acid (over 20%)	NR	--- ---
Potassium Carbonate	RI	180 (82.2)
Potassium Chloride	RI	180 (82.2)
Potassium Fluoride	RI	180 (82.2)
Potassium Hydroxide	RI	180 (82.2)
Potassium Permanganate	RI	180 (82.2)
Potassium Sulfate	RI	180 (82.2)
Propylene Glycol	R	100 (37.8)
Salt Brine	RI	180 (82.2)
Sodium Bicarbonate	RI	180 (82.2)
Sodium Bisulfite	RI	180 (82.2)
Sodium Carbonate	RI	180 (82.2)

-3-

Chemical	Recommendation (See notes for explanation)	Temperature Limit $^\circ$F ($^\circ$C)
Sodium Chloride	RIW	180 (82.2)
Sodium Fluoride	RI	100 (37.8)
Sodium Hydroxide	RI	180 (82.2)
Sodium Hypochlorite	NR	--- ---
Sodium Sulfate	RI	180 (82.2)
Sodium Sulfite	RI	180 (82.2)
Stearic Acid	RI	100 (37.8)
Sugar	RI	180 (82.2)
Sulfite Liquor	RI	180 (82.2)
Sulfuric Acid 50%	RIW	100 (37.8)
Tetrahydrofuran	NR	--- ---
Toluene	RIW	100 (37.8)
Trichloroethylene	RIW	100 (37.8)
Trisodium Phosphate	RI	180 (82.2)
Turpentine	RI	100 (37.8)
Vinegar	RI	100 (37.8)
Vinyl Acetate	NR	--- ---
Water	R	180 (82.2)
Water, Distilled	RI	180 (82.2)
Xylene	R	100 (37.8)

Notes: Code for "Recommendation"

R - Recommended for immersion.
NR - Not recommended.
RI - Recommended for intermittent exposure or spillage only.
RIW - Recommended for intermittent exposure or spillage only, with fresh water flush.

FOR CHEMICALS AND EXPOSURE CONDITIONS NOT COVERED IN THIS TECHNICAL BULLETIN, PLEASE CONTACT THE TECHNICAL SERVICES GROUP AT U.S. GROUT CORPORATION'S MAIN OFFICE.

8/78 - JH

TECHNICAL ★5★ BULLETIN
FIVE STAR

FIVE STAR EPOXY GROUT
Equipment and Materials Check List

I. PROTECTION: Personnel
   A. Dust masks, goggles with side shields, long–sleeve shirts, hard–hats, rubber gloves, ear protection, as required.
   B. Ventilation, skin cream (Kerodex), etc.
   C. Adequate ventilation for sand–blasting personnel.
   D. All OSHA and EPA requirements for personnel safety and health.

II. PROTECTION: Floors and neighboring equipment.

III. BASIC REQUIREMENTS FOR GROUTING:
   A. Surface Preparation
   B. Forming
   C. Mixing
   D. Placement

   A. Surface Preparation of Concrete
     1. Clean water, rags, pail, brooms, muriatic acid.
     2. Chipping guns and wire brushes or sandblast equipment, as required or specified.
   Surface Preparation of Steel
     1. Power brushes, sandblast equipment and emery paper, as required or specified.
   B. Forming
     1. Lumber, nails, chamfer strips, and carpenter's tools, as required.
     2. Paste wax or sheets of polyethylene to cover forms.
     3. Glazier's putty, spackling compound or caulking to seal forms.
     4. Reinforcing steel, as required or specified.
     5. Expansion joint material.
     6. Split hose and/or fire hose for isolating bolts and/or oil pans.
   C. MIXING
     1. Low speed drill with mixing paddle or hand mixer; spatulas to scrape out pails and cans.
     2. Clean and dry mortar mixer, mortar pan or wheelbarrow, and mortar hoe.
   D. PLACEMENT
     1. Pails – the resin pail (A Component), when scraped out, serves nicely.
     2. Trowels and other mason tools as required.
     3. Grout hoppers – an empty welder's can is easily made into a hopper.
     4. Clean–up solvent.

IV. OTHER MATERIALS AND EQUIPMENT AS REQUIRED OR SPECIFIED:

U. S. GROUT CORPORATION, 401 STILLSON ROAD, FAIRFIELD, CONNECTICUT 06430 ● (203) 336-7900

CREEP — AND HOW TO COPE WITH IT

The phenomenon of Creep occurs in all materials. Creep is defined as that property of a material which enables it to undergo deformation under the action of a constant load, i.e. the material will deform without failing.

Organic materials generally exhibit higher creep characteristics than inorganic materials. Epoxy grout is a good example of an organic material which has higher Creep tendencies than an inorganic material such as our cementitious grout. Although the epoxy grouts attain much higher compressive strengths than cementitious grouts, they are seldom subjected to continuous stresses greater than 500 psi. They shouldn't be! The reason for this is Creep.

The tendency for epoxy grouts to Creep increases with an increase in operating temperature. Since Creep is a function of load (stress) and time, the higher the load (stress), the longer the time -- the greater the Creep.

Most epoxy grout producers recognize this phenomenon and try to educate designers and users to limit load (stress). The following guidelines and the example will help you and your clients to design or calculate loads that will minimize the Creep phenomenon.

1. "Dead load" is defined as the weight of the equipment. "Dead load" divided by the number of bolts gives the "dead load" per bolt. "Bolt load" is defined as the stress exerted on the grout as a result of torquing the bolts. "Maximum load" is defined as the total of "dead load" and bolt load".

2. Maximum total load should not exceed 500 psi. This may seem quite low for material with compressive strengths up to 17,000 psi. However, in some 30 years, I have rarely run into installations where the constant load will exceed 500 psi.

3. The ratio of "bolt load" to "dead load" per bolt should be a minimum of three. Use the table attached to determine the torque that should be used on various size bolts and the corresponding bolt load.

U. S. GROUT CORPORATION, 401 STILLSON ROAD, FAIRFIELD, CONNECTICUT 06430 ● (203) 336-7900

ANCHOR BOLT TORQUE

Dia.	BOLT Threads	TORQUE, FT.-LB. Common	Hi-strength	BOLT LOAD, LB. Common	Hi-strength
(in.)	per inch	Steel	4140	Steel	4140
3/4	10......	60	95	5,940	8,910
1	8......	150	225	10,840	16,260
1-1/4	7......	300	375	17,560	26,340
1-1/2	6......	530	800	25,560	38,340
1-3/4	5......	835	1,250	34,560	51,840
2	4-1/2..	1,250	1,675	45,500	68,250

EXAMPLE:

You have a situation where a piece of equipment weighing 140,000 pounds
is going to be grouted in using epoxy grout. The plate is two feet
by five feet. The equipment will use 25 anchor bolts, 1-1/4 inches in
diameter, 7 threads, ordinary steel. Determine if the plate is large
enough to support the load.

CALCULATE RATIO OF BOLT LOAD TO DEAD LOAD PER BOLT

Equipment Weight ("Dead Load") —— 140,000 Pounds
Number of Anchor Bolts — 25
"Dead Load" Per Bolt — $\frac{140,000 \text{ Pounds}}{25}$ = 5,600 Pounds

Torque from Table — 300 Foot-Pounds
"Bolt Load" — 17,560 Pounds

"Bolt Load" Ratio — $\frac{17,560 \text{ Pounds}}{5,600 \text{ Pounds}}$ = 3.14

This is more than a minimum of three times and, therefore is
acceptable.

CALCULATE TOTAL LOAD PER SQUARE INCH

Total load will be the "dead load" plus all of the load contri-
buted by torquing the bolts.

140,000 Pounds + (25 Bolts x 17,560 Pounds/Bolt) = 579,000 Pounds

Bearing area is length times width.

(2 Feet x 12 Inches) x (5 Feet x 12 Inches) = 1,440 Inches

Total Load Per Square Inch = $\frac{579,000 \text{ Pounds}}{1,440 \text{ Inches}}$ = 402 Psi

This is less than the maximum 500 psi and, therefore, is acceptable.

Design in this fashion will assure that Creep will not be a problem.

© 1987 U.S. Grout Corporation

Method of Test For Compressive Creep of Organic Grouts

1.0 Scope

   1.1   This method is a test for compressive creep of organic grouts under sustained load. Load is applied to cured grout at ambient temperature. Temperatures other than ambient may also be accommodated. Deflections under sustained load are measured and recorded.

2.0 Apparatus

   2.1   Loading device as follows:

   2.1.1   An assembly of two steel plates, with suitable holes, held together with a steel bolt, washers and a nut. (Figure I).

   2.1.2   Torque wrench capable of applying load at least 400 psi on the specimen (64 ft.–lbs.).

   2.1.3   A temperature controlled cabinet capable of maintaining temperatures to 250°F within ± 3°F.

   2.1.4   Mold for casting 2" thick by 4" diameter specimens (Fig. II).

   2.1.5   Depth micrometer with vernier reading to 0.001 inch (Starrett No. 644–441).

3.0 Specimen Preparation

   3.1   Assemble mold as in Fig. II with all contact surfaces treated with release agent. Use "C" clamps to hold mold assembly together.

   3.2   Place grout through hole in top of mold and consolidate (if required) with a 3/8" steel rod rounded at one end. Fill to bottom of hole.

   3.3   Allow specimens to cure in mold at laboratory ambient temperature for 24 hours. Cure an additional 6 days after stripping.

   3.4   Drill a 1–1/8" hole through specimen in exact center of specimen.

4.0 Procedure

4.1 Assemble loading device as shown in Fig. I, centering specimen around bolt so a uniform annular space results.

4.2 Calculate torque required to produce 400 psi load on specimen using the following formula:

$$T = W K D$$

Where T = Torque in foot – lbs.

Where W = Total load required on specimen in lbs.

Where K = A constant of 0.0138

Where D = Diameter of bolt, ins.

4.3 Place assembly in a vise and torque to valve "T" using torque wrench.

4.4 Immediately after torquing, take readings through four corner holes using depth micrometer. Determine average. Record.

4.5 Place specimen(s) in temperature controlled cabinet, set to temperature desired for test.

4.6 At one week intervals, remove assemblies from cabinet and allow to cool to ambient.

4.7 Continue test for 10 weeks (or longer if desired).

5.0 Report

5.1 Name of material.

5.2 Temperature at which tested.

5.3 Subtract each successive reading from initial reading and plot on graph paper, drawing smooth curves through points. Use time in weeks on one scale and cumulative creep on the other.

RAPID EPOXY GROUT
(R.E.G.)

Anchor Bolt Grouting

SURFACE PREPARATION:

Bolts: Degrease, sandblast, pickle, powerbrush or use other
methods to achieve a bright metal surface.

Holes: A. Dry drilled holes shall be cleaned of dust and
debris.
B. Wet drilled holes shall be cleaned of drilled
slurry.
C. Formed holes shall be scarified to remove laitance.
D. Standing water shall be completely removed.

DIMENSIONS:

The dimensions called for in this technical bulletin are designed to
eliminate the possibility of a grout failure. A concrete or steel failure
is still possible. Therefore, if the concrete substrate is designed to
withstand the maximum elastic tensile strength of the steel, the bolt/bar
yield strength will be the governing design factor.

L = Length of embedment (inches)
D = Diameter of hole (inches)
d = Diameter of bolt/bar (inches)
f_y = Yield strength of bolt/bar (psi)
S = Factor of safety
C = Bolt/bar shape factor

C = 1.5 for a smooth bolt/bar
C = 2.0 for a deformed bolt/bar
C = 2.5 for a threaded bolt/bar

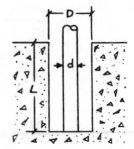

U. S. GROUT CORPORATION, 401 STILLSON ROAD, FAIRFIELD, CONNECTICUT 06430 • (203) 336-7900

II.18

LENGTH OF EMBEDMENT:

The following formula is used to derive the minimum suggested embedment length:

$$L_{min} = S\ f_y\ d/4,000\ C$$

Therefore, with f_y = 80,000 psi (moderate strength steel) and a factor of safety of 1.7

L_{min} = 22.66 d for a smooth bolt/bar.

L_{min} = 17.00 d for a deformed bolt/bar.

L_{min} = 13.60 d for a threaded bolt/bar.

HOLE DIAMETER:

The hole diameters called for in this bulletin are minimum diameters. The requirements will ensure an adequate size bonding surface between the grout and concrete. Larger dimensions may ease the placement of Five Star R.E.G. on deep or awkward pours, but under no circumstance shall the annular space exceed 2 inches.

Minimum Hole Diameter

When d $\leq$ 1-1/2 inches, then D $\geq$ d + 1-1/2 inches

When d > 1-1/2 inches, the D $\geq$ d + 2 inches.

Maximum Hole Diameter

D $\leq$ d + 4 inches

* * * * * * * * * * * * * * * *

WHEN YOU DON'T HAVE TIME TO WASTE

FIVE STAR
RAPID EPOXY GROUT

DEVELOPS THE FASTEST STRENGTH GAIN AVAILABLE

Compressive Strength

(ASTM-C 579)		
	2 hours	5,000 psi
	6 hours	10,000 psi
	24 hours	12,000 psi

* * * * * * * * * * * * * * * *

New Epoxy Grout Eliminates Shrinkage

FIVE STAR EPOXY GROUT exhibits none of the voids, bubbles or froth that reduces the effective bearing surface.

Working closely with RCI's Research and Development staff, U.S. Grout Corporation has produced and marketed a unique epoxy grout system. Specialized epoxy grout systems are used for setting heavy industrial equipment. According to U.S. Grout, FIVE STAR EPOXY GROUT, unlike conventional grouts, does not shrink below its original placement volume when tested under the latest ASTM method (C-827-78) for vertical volume change.

The shrinkage factor is critical in setting equipment. When a grout shrinks, large voids, bubbles and froth form under bearing surfaces reducing the effective bearing area. With less than complete surface contact, the load-carrying capacity, impact and vibration resistance, and prevention of chemical penetration are reduced. This can cause failure of the foundation, misalignment, damage to expensive equipment, and costly downtime.

When the U.S. Grout Corporation started a development program to produce a grout based on a resin system, it came to RCI for assistance. In addition to the non-shrink feature, they wanted to develop a grout that would be highly resistant to chemicals, would have the necessary resilience to withstand impact and dynamic loads, and have excellent pourability and flow characteristics.

Reichhold's Research and Development staff at the Sterling Forest Laboratory worked closely with U.S.Grout's technical personnel to develop a resin system based on epoxy resins and hardeners that would meet these requirements. Special resin and hardener compounds were formulated and tested with special aggregate blends until a product was made that met U.S. Grout's rigid, pre-set performance requirements.

The resin and hardener formulation also provided another benefit, a much lower odor than other epoxy grouts. Workmen find the product less objectionable, resulting in an improved installation.

FIVE STAR EPOXY GROUT has already found wide acceptance for a variety of demanding applications such as setting paper mill machines, metal stamping presses, compressors, chemical pumps, chemical distillation towers, car shakers, coal crushers, turbines, and crane rails.

The U.S. Grout Corporation, with plants strategically located throughout the U.S., is an affiliated company of the Nash Babcock Engineering Company, which has been devoting its efforts toward generating a new technology, eliminating shrinkage in grouting materials. Today, U.S. Grout products are manufactured by licensees all over the world.

The chemical resistance feature of epoxy grout is most important in setting chemical process equipment.

Reprinted for U.S. Grout Corporation — 401 Stillson Road, Fairfield, Connecticut 06430 (203) 336-7900

In quick time, rapid-setting epoxy material developed
for other railway use ties together precast concrete.

'ES grout' speeds bridge installation

These days railroad bridges must endure heavy train loadings such as the 100-ton car unit trains. Typically, older bridges are near the end of their useful life and must be replaced to ensure that the line's capacity is maintained. One way to do this is to use precast concrete bridge components. The new spans could be designed as a full-width structure. However, they would be very difficult to transport, handle and erect.

Logistically, it is advantageous to design and fabricate the bridge spans in smaller parts that can be easily handled, then connect them at the bridge site once they have been erected. Time is of the essence, though, once the bridge span replacement procedure has begun. The same constraints which face track crews when dealing with limited available track time apply equally to bridge replacement crews.

Recently, the Chicago and North Western Transportation Company was able to satisfy these logistical, structural and track time requirements in replacing an old timber pile bridge on mainline trackage north of Council Bluffs, Iowa. This was accomplished by employing precast, prestressed, concrete box girders in the design of the bridge superstructure. A single span is formed by placing two of these box girders side by side singly and "welding" them together with a high-strength, early-setting epoxy.

Three-span replacement

The old, 11-span timber pile bridge was replaced with three 40-ft.-long prestressed concrete spans. Cast-in-place concrete caps on steel H-piling were installed between the timber pile bents of the old bridge. When it was time to place the new concrete spans, the track

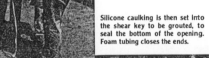

After both box girders are set in place within a span, large steel rods are inserted through the sides of the members, and are torqued to hold them together.

Silicone caulking is then set into the shear key to be grouted, to seal the bottom of the opening. Foam tubing closes the ends.

The two chemical components of the "FIVE STAR R.E.G." (epoxy material) are blended before aggregate is added. On the last span, the mixed material is then poured into the shear opening, filling it to the top surface.

II.21

After final key pouring, the last preassembled track panel is set prior to splicing to previously placed track.

The track was ready for revenue traffic just 12 hours from the start of superstructure work.

was taken out of service and the old timber bridge removed.

As each pair of concrete box girders were placed, they were held together by a large tie rod passing through both units at each end.

Two-part grout

Within each bridge span, the box girders were permanently tied together lengthwise by means of preformed shear keys filled with an early-setting epoxy grout, supplied by U.S. Grout Corp.

According to a company spokesman, the epoxy compound had been developed initially for the rapid placement of railroad track scales. The product's extension to use in precast concrete railroad bridge structures became a natural spinoff of its capabilities.

Premeasured volumes of the double-component material are shipped to and mixed at the site. The components can be hand or mechanically combined, and then poured directly into place from their mixing bucket. Within two hours after mixing, the epoxy attains a 5000-psi compressive and a 2000-psi shear strength. This early cure was sufficient during the course of the C&NW bridge operation to permit ballast cars to move onto the spans and lay ballast in newly installed track panels.

Within six hours from mixing, the material reaches a compressive strength of 10,000 psi. Consequently, the bridge spans were completely installed, and the track and ballast placed so that revenue traffic could be restored just 12 hours from the start of the superstructure operation. ■

II.22

Reprinted from March 1986

Chemical Processing

Special Report

Plant Maintenance

Compressor foundation rebuilt in just 24 hours with fast-setting grouts

EDWARD SAMUELS, Chief Engineer, Cominco American, Inc.
DANIEL RADFORD, Plant Engineer, Cominco American, Inc.
AL GAINES, Senior Associate Editor

Problem

Cominco American, Inc. in Borger, Texas is a major processor of ammonia and urea for fertilizer and animal feed products. During routine inspection early in 1985, large cracks were observed in the concrete foundation for the inlet cylinder of a 1500 hp, 4-stage reciprocating compressor. The resulting settling of the 8000 lb cantilevered cylinder head eventually sheared five of the eight bolts that fasten the head to the cross-head guide housing, or "doghouse."

The plant's management decided to shut down operations to prevent further damage to the costly compressor, and begin a 24 hour a day "crash" program to rebuild the inlet cylinder, recast the concrete pedestal, and regrout the anchor bolts for the baseplate. The five to seven days usually required to dismantle equipment, restore the foundation, and reinstall the equipment had to be reduced as much as possible to minimize expensive downtime of the continuous ammonia processing system.

Solution

Cominco's engineering staff selected a firm that specializes in rapid on-site repairs with highly skilled and experienced machinists and general millwrights. The plant shut down all operations at 6:00 p.m., and the contractor's crews worked through the night to dismantle and remove the cylinder. Pneumatic chip hammers were used to break up the cracked concrete, which revealed that the $2' \times 3' \times 2\frac{1}{2}'$ high pedestal for the cylinder had been constructed without steel reinforcing bars (rebar) around the perimeter at the top and outside the anchor bolts. Restoring the foundation would require nearly 10" of concrete with additional ¾" rebar to assure structural integrity.

Compressor crosshead is installed on foundation just four hours after initial pour of epoxy grout

Because of the critical timing, the contractor selected a cement-based, non-shrink grout that can achieve a compressive strength of 6000 psi in only four hours. In addition, the material can be "adjusted" with a chemical additive to allow a working time of nearly 35 minutes during application in hot weather.

The old foundation and rebar, after sand blasting, were saturated with wet rags while the workmen were building the forms for the concrete. Protective sleeves were slipped around the large anchor bolts prior to pouring the concrete, to provide a deep cavity for grouting the cylinder head baseplate.

Fast setting cement-based concretes have an unusually high heat of hydration, so two precautions were taken to assure that the heat would not cause cracking. First, the grout was extended with ⅜" pea gravel. Secondly, the grout was poured in two "lifts," allowing the first to set for approximately one hour. Deep grooves

were scratched in the setting concrete before pouring the second lift to further enhance the mechanical bond between the layers. Wet rags were placed on the curing concrete of the second pour for approximately one hour.

A final layer of the epoxy-based grout, that reaches a high 6000 psi compressive strength in only two hours, was placed over the repaired foundation and in the cavity around the anchor bolts. The chemical-resistant grout provides protection against lubricant spillage, dampens vibration, and adapts to thermal changes in the steel baseplate. The epoxy grout was drawn into the pedestal for the doghouse with a vacuum to void any entrapped air.

Results

The cracked foundation was rebuilt in approximately 30 hours by using the fast-setting grouts, and the mechanics began repositioning the cross-head on the pedestal only four hours after the initial pour. The compressor was placed back in service just 48 hours after the start of the crash program, instead of five to seven days normally required with conventional methods and materials. Because of the significant reduction in costly downtime, the same contractor and fast-setting grouts were used to rebuild the foundation for another stage of the compressor during a scheduled turnaround in August 1985. ∎

Five Star® Instant Grout—U.S. Grout Corp., 401 Stillson Rd., Fairfield, CT 06430.

Five Star® Rapid Epoxy Grout—U.S. Grout Corp., 401 Stillson Rd., Fairfield, CT 06430.

On-site mechanical repairs and construction—Woods Service Corp., PO Box 389, Borger, TX 79007.

SECTION III
CONCRETE REPAIR
INTRODUCTION

The repair of concrete has received far too little attention from architects, engineers, contractors and owners. Since concrete was first used as a structural material, there have been continual failures in concrete repair and maintenance.

This is caused by lack of attention to procedures, inadequate training of skilled people, limited knowledge of materials, and the improper selection of the patching material to be used. The failure of the concrete can be caused by any one of a myriad of reasons, ranging from exposure conditions, wearing conditions and misuse of the structure, to poorly selected ingredients, mix design and/or improper placement of mixes.

When repairing a damaged section of concrete, all of these factors have to be taken into account. Recently, manufacturers of concrete products performed considerable research in this area and developed products specifically for the repair of structural concrete. These products have taken into account critical factors such as bonding capability, shrinkage, expansion, strength, thermal compatibility, ease of application, waterproofing, freeze/thaw and abrasion resistance. FIVE STAR STRUCTURAL CONCRETE was developed with the above criteria in mind.

Sand/cement mixes which have been used in the past should not be used as structural repair products. Such mixes do not provide acceptable performance under the criteria listed.

The purpose of this Section of the Handbook is to discuss materials available for repair and patching, their performance, use, and specifications.

CHAPTER 1
SELECTING A PATCHING MATERIAL

Repair and patching materials may be classified into two general groups: Cementitious and Polymer. Cementitious materials are those materials which require the addition only of potable water - they may also be termed "hydraulic materials". Polymer materials are those which require the use of a "setting agent" other than water. Both groups have advantages and disadvantages.

Cementitious Type: These generally are prepackaged materials requiring only the addition of potable water. Their physical properties are very similar to those of concrete. As opposed to the polymer types, cementitious products are considered "user-friendly" and users have had considerable experience with them.

The cementitious materials achieve strengths equal to or greater than the concrete being repaired. Most do not develop high exotherms and dimensional stability is better than the polymer types. Thermal coefficients of expansion are nearly identical to that of concrete.

The main disadvantage of most cementitious products is their lack of development of adequate bond strength. Sand/cement mixtures, with or without "bonding" admixtures, and gypsum-based products, exhibit this disadvantage and are usually classified as "temporary" patches. Of all the properties of cementitious repair materials, bond strength is *the* most important requirement.

There are two products on the market developed specifically to produce excellent bond strength and the other desirable properties of ideal repair materials. They are known as FIVE STAR STRUCTURAL CONCRETE and FIVE STAR HIGHWAY PATCH.

Polymer Type: These include epoxies, polyesters, and acrylics and are most commonly used where chemical resistance is required. Most of the polymer types achieve high strength and good bond to a properly prepared and dry substrate.

The disadvantages of these materials outnumber their few good features. They are difficult to work with and exhibit varying degrees of toxicity and flammability and must be used with extreme caution. Proportioning of the components and mixing are critical to proper curing. During and after cure, the polymer types exhibit greater shrinkage than the cementitious materials. In general, they develop high exotherms and exhibit much higher coefficients of expansion than the concrete being repaired. These disadvantages have led to field failures.

In addition to their many other disadvantages, all of the polymer types are very expensive compared to the cementitious materials.

Regardless of the type of repair material desired, an adequate inventory should be kept in stock. Situations that present a hazard to personnel safety and health and/or those which threaten the usefulness or life of equipment must be dealt with as quickly as possible. If repair and patching materials are not immediately available, there will be long delays and the possibility that inferior or inadequate (but available) materials will be used.

Any patching and repair materials chosen to be kept in stock *must* have an adequate "shelf life". These materials may remain in inventory for months and *must* retain their efficacy. A "shelf life" of a minimum of 6 months is highly recommended.

There are some companies, such as **FIVE STAR PROD-UCTS, INC.**, who are constantly doing research and development work in this field. It is recommended that individuals working in this area keep in touch with **FIVE STAR PROD-UCTS, INC.** in order to be current with the latest developments.

For example, almost every product manufactured under the **FIVE STAR** label is now being made available in a NOMIX™ formulation which results in a tremendous reduction in tools, installation time and costs. This major patented breakthrough in cementitious technology is rapidly spreading throughout the world. Contact the Engineering and Technical Center of **FIVE STAR PRODUCTS, INC.** for further information.

CHAPTER 2
PERFORMANCE PROPERTIES AND TESTS

The following properties must be considered when selecting a repair material.

A. BOND STRENGTH

Bond strength is the single most important and most ignored property of a repair material.

Generally, repairs (patches) do not fail in compression - they fail due to inadequate bond strength and excessive length change. Either of these conditions will ultimately result in failure of the repair. Inadequate bond strength will quickly result in the "pop-out" of the entire repair. Excessive length change will result in cracks with resulting deterioration due to freeze/thaw cycles or salt attack. A *combination* of inadequate bond and excessive length change is a guarantee of rapid failure. Attempts, occasionally successful, have been made to produce adequate bond by the use of lattices used integrally or as primers. Such additives usually introduce other, greater problems, and often have a limited life.

While ASTM has not yet published a test method for adequately determining the bond strength of cementitious products to a concrete substrate, the construction

industry, including highway departments, have been using for many years a modification of ASTM C 882 "Test Method for Bond Strength of Epoxy-Resin Systems Used with Concrete".

The modification consists of merely leaving out any prime coat and applying the repair (patching) material to a properly prepared substrate. To ensure adequate bond according to this test procedure, a minimum of 2,500 psi is required. In most cases this will eliminate the cold joint.

B. LENGTH CHANGE

With repair and patching products, length change (linear shrinkage) is more important than vertical volume change. Since the products are not being placed under baseplates, effective bearing area (EBA) is not a critical consideration. However, excessive length change (linear shrinkage) can result in cracking during and after the curing period and cause debonding. Cracks allow entrance of deleterious materials and water which may result in spalling and failure of the patch when freezing or corrosion occurs. Not all cracks are due to length change. (See Technical Bulletin #52 at the back of this section entitled "Cracking in Concrete".)

ASTM Method C 157, "Test Method for Length Change of Hardened Cement Mortar and Concrete" should be used to evaluate the length change properties of cementitious repair materials. Since most repair materials contain aggregate, it is recommended that 2" x 2" bars be used to determine the shrinkage or expansion of the repair material as described in ASTM C 157. Further, the measurement procedures should be modified to provide for an initial reading as soon as the bars can be demolded to reflect more accurately what happens in the field. For rapid setting materials, this is two hours after the addition of water. Curing should be in accordance with the manufacturer's recommended procedures. FIVE STAR STRUCTURAL CONCRETE should be moist cured for 30 minutes. Under these conditions, a repair material should exhibit between +0.05% and -0.05% length change to prevent cracking or stress build up.

C. COMPRESSIVE STRENGTH

Most quality repair and patching materials, polymer and cementitious, develop strengths equal to or greater than the concrete being repaired. There is no particular advantage in specifying or using a product based solely on the highest compressive strength. Bond strength and length change are better criteria for choosing a product.

In most concrete repair situations today, it is advantageous to have a fast strength gain material to minimize shut down time. Materials should be tested in accordance with ASTM C 109 (Test Method for Compressive Strength of Hydraulic Cement Mortars), and the two hour compressive strength after the addition of potable water should be a minimum of 2,500 psi, and 5,000 psi in 24 hours.

D. CONSISTENCY

This will determine whether a product can be successfully put in place without excessive effort. Horizontal repairs can usually be made with a flowable consistency. Pavement and bridge decks are seldom level and present the problem of the product trying to self-level, resulting in high areas at the lower edge of the patch and low areas at the higher edge. If this happens, added labor will be necessary to continually trowel the patch to conform to the required contour until the patching material stiffens sufficiently to maintain the shape desired. In such cases, it is desirable to use less water, resulting in a slightly stiffer consistency and less tendency to self-level.

For repair or patching of vertical or overhead surfaces, a plastic, trowelable consistency must be used. Even at a stiff plastic consistency there will be areas where the depth of repair will result in sagging of the repair material. While it is not generally good practice to install repair materials in layers, it may be necessary to do so with deep repairs. If so, successive layers should be applied immediately after the preceding layer has stiffened enough to prevent sagging, but has not yet hardened. Consideration should be given to forming and pouring deep pours.

There are no practical test methods to determine optimum consistency for a particular application. Experienced personnel will quickly determine the best consistency for use.

Where a range of water content is printed on the container, a good rule of thumb is to start at the low end of the range and adjust if necessary.

E. WORKING TIME

This is often confused with set time. Set time is measured by ASTM C 191 and generally is that time when the material can no longer be penetrated with a specific size needle. At this point, the material has usually passed its ability to be worked. Working time is generally much shorter than set time. For instance, a product with a set time of 16 minutes may have a useful working life of no more than ten minutes.

There are no reliable tests to determine working time. When the workmen are unfamiliar with a fast-setting material, they should take a small sample and mix it in accordance with manufacturer's instructions to determine the actual working time under the prevailing conditions.

F. THERMAL COEFFICIENT OF EXPANSION

A large difference in thermal coefficient between the concrete substrate and the repair material may often result in disruption and failure of many repaired areas. This is particularly true of many polymer materials which have thermal coefficients 3 to 5 times that of concrete. Higher coefficients mean that the patching materials will expand or contract faster and more than the concrete substrate. For example: concrete with a thermal coefficient of 5×10^{-6} in/in/°F is patched with an epoxy product having a thermal coefficient of 15×10^{-6} in/in/°F — with a radical temperature change (up or down) the epoxy product will expand or contract three times as fast and three times as much. The result is most often a cohesive failure of the concrete.

Most cementitious products have thermal coefficients very close to that of concrete and do not contribute to this problem.

ASTM C 531, "Test Method for Linear Shrinkage and Coefficient of Thermal Expansion of Chemical-Resistant Mortars, Grouts and Monolithic Surfacings" is used to determine thermal coefficient of expansion.

G. DURABILITY

Durability refers to the ability of a material to remain in service and afford protection to the substrate over an extended period of time. The following properties must be considered when evaluating the durability of the patch *and* the patched area:

Absorption - A low absorption rate will preclude damage to and deterioration of the patching material due to freeze/thaw cycling and salt or other chemical attack.

Permeability - Repair materials must have low permeability in order to minimize passage of water and salt solutions to the substrate. Highly permeable patches will result in saturation of the substrate with resulting freeze/thaw damage and potential corrosion of reinforcing steel.

Abrasion - Where subjected to vehicular traffic, patches must exhibit good resistance to abrasion or they will be worn away or worn through to the substrate.

Most outdoor repairs will be subjected to constant wetting from precipitation. Gypsum and gypsum-based products have shown poor resistance to wetting over the years that they have been used, and should only be considered for temporary patches.

H.   SELECTION CHART

To assist the reader in selecting the appropriate repair and patching material, a product selection chart follows. If a specific application is not covered in the chart, consult with the technical personnel at **FIVE STAR PRODUCTS, INC.**

CONCRETE REPAIR SELECTION CHART

USE/APPLICATION   PRODUCT

**Structural Repair/Patching
Of Horizontal And Vertical Concrete:**

• Foundations	• Abutments	• Tie-rod Holes
• Masonry Walls	• Walls	• Curbs
• Honeycombed Concrete	• Floors	• Pedestals
• Piers	• Decks	• Anchor Bolts
• Columns	• Airports	• Railings
	• Stair Treads	• Sidewalks

 FIVE STAR STRUCTURAL CONCRETE

**Structural Repair Of
Concrete Soffits (Nonmoving):**

• Beams   • Girders   • Floors

FIVE STAR STRUCTURAL CONCRETE V/O

Concrete Bridge and Pavement Repair:

• Permanently Bonded Repair

• Cold Weather/Low Temperature Repair

FIVE STAR HIGHWAY PATCH

• Temporary Patching

FIVE STAR CONCRETE PATCH

CHAPTER 3
QUALITY ASSURANCE PROGRAMS
FOR MANUFACTURER AND FIELD

Quality Assurance programs should be required for all repair and patching material manufacturers, and are required for many critical installations. There are two categories of Quality Assurance programs: manufacturer and field.

QUALITY ASSURANCE PROGRAM - MANUFACTURER

The repair and patching manufacturer must maintain records of all the cements, sands, aggregates, and chemicals used. All containers of raw materials and finished product should have a code marking so that the source of all materials can be traced and verified as meeting the manufacturer's standards. The manufacturer should regularly take samples from the plant and verify them in his own test laboratory as meeting his requirements, including bond properties. The manufacturer must maintain test records on production runs and should retain them for at least one year. Shipping tickets should be maintained at the plant and at the main office for all shipments.

Products stored beyond six months for cement-based products should not be shipped without the manufacturer's certification that the products meet the manufacturer's standards. The manufacturer should furnish written certification when required stating that the material is in accordance with the project and manufacturer's specifications.

The manufacturer should have instructions for normal placement conditions printed on the outside of the package. These instructions should include the maximum/minimum mixing water limits in quarts per unit.

The manufacturer should have posted instructions for manufacturing the material at the plant. The accuracy of the weighing scales at the plant must be checked every six months, as required in a good Quality Assurance program.

The manufacturer should provide access to his production facilities by the engineer upon receipt of adequate notice for the auditing of the Quality Assurance Program. If manufacturers cannot comply with this Quality Assurance Program verification, their products should not be approved.

QUALITY ASSURANCE PROGRAM - FIELD

The engineer should establish in his specifications a Field Quality Assurance Program to ascertain that the material he has specified meets his standards. This can be done by verifying the printed instructions on the package and also by performing simple field tests.

A small sample of the product should be taken from a randomly selected package and mixed with the recommended amount of water.

Fill a styrofoam drinking cup with some of the sample. Cast three cubes in accordance with ASTM C 109 with the remainder.

Check the set time of the material in the cup with a knife blade or screwdriver. Cure the cubes under the same conditions as the repair and test according to ASTM C 109.

CHAPTER 4
ESTIMATING AND PURCHASING
OF CONCRETE REPAIR MATERIALS

ESTIMATING

Estimating the quantity of repair and patching materials required is easily done by calculating the volume (length x width x average depth), converting to cubic feet, and then adding five percent for waste on large placements and ten percent waste for small placements.

Care should be taken to ensure that the published yield per unit is adjusted to a cubic foot basis. Many manufacturers market their materials in units of unusual weights and volumes.

PURCHASING

Unfortunately, repair materials are not all sold in cubic foot packages. To ensure that all prices are directly comparable, all requests for quotation should be made in cubic foot units. Repair materials must not be compared, bid, or purchased on a weight basis because there is no relationship to the volume. The customary unit of volume is the cubic foot. Requesting quotations in cubic foot units ensures direct price comparisons.

HIGHWAY REPAIR

STRUCTURAL CONCRETE REPAIR*

Permanent   Temporary   Magphos

CONCRETE REPAIR

*STRUCTURAL CONCRETE REPAIR/PATCHING OF HOR-IZONTAL, VERTICAL AND OVERHEAD CONCRETE - FOUNDATIONS - MASONRY WALLS - HONEYCOMBED CONCRETE - PIERS - COLUMNS - ABUTMENTS - WALLS - FLOORS - DECKS - TIE ROD HOLES - CURBS - PEDES-TALS - ANCHOR BOLTS - RAILINGS - STEPS - SIDE-WALKS - PERMANENTLY BONDED REPAIR - COLD WEATHER/LOW TEMPERATURE REPAIR - TEMPORARY PATCHING

NONSHRINK REPAIR AND PATCHING MATERIALS
ESTIMATING SHEET

From Premeasured Units

	FIVE STAR	PRODUCT "X"
A. Cost per Bag or Unit	_____	_____
B. Yield per Bag or Unit (Cubic feet/bag or unit)	_____	_____
C. Cost per Cubic Foot (A divided by B)	_____	_____
D. Total Cubic Feet Required (From field estimates)	_____	_____
E. Total Material Cost (C x D)	_____	_____

CHAPTER 5
DELIVERY AND STORAGE PROCEDURES

A. DELIVERY CONDITION

Cementitious repair and patching materials should be shipped from the plants palletized, shrink-wrapped, and delivered to the site in sound, dry packages. They should be stored in a dry area in accordance with ACI instructions. The temperature should be approximately 70°F, but not below 40°F, and not above 90°F.

B. STORAGE DAMAGE

Any material which becomes damp or otherwise defective should be immediately removed from the site.

C. STORAGE TIME

The total job storage time of cement-based repair and patching materials should be limited to six months, or the manufacturer's recommended storage limit, whichever is greater. For critical applications, it is recommended that a sample be sent to the manufacturer if the material has been stored for more than six months, for verification of the properties.

CHAPTER 6
PERMANENT CONCRETE REPAIR AND PATCHING

General structural repairs and patching include the following areas: walls, piers, abutments, columns, industrial and commercial floors.

FIVE STAR STRUCTURAL CONCRETE has been developed specifically for structural repair of horizontal and vertical (VO) concrete. FIVE STAR STRUCTURAL CONCRETE V/O is for repair of vertical and overhead concrete. They develop excellent bonds and high strengths for tough problems. They also have rapid strength gains so the patched area can be reopened to use with a minimum of delay.

A. VERTICAL AND OVERHEAD PATCHING

The procedures outlined below will suffice for most applications. Snap tie holes and the like are usually filled simply by troweling a waterproof patching material such as FIVE STAR STRUCTURAL CONCRETE or FIVE STAR STRUCTURAL CONCRETE V/O in and level with the surrounding concrete.

1. *SURFACE PREPARATION*

Surface preparation is extremely critical in all patching. In all structural patching, it is essential that all deleterious substances be removed from the existing concrete. This includes, but is not limited to, form oils, form coatings, curing agents, and similar products. Acid etchers, concrete cleaners, and degreasers may be required to properly clean the surface. All acid, chemical cleaners, and degreasers must be completely removed. The surface to be patched must not be smooth. It should be roughened by mechanical means such as chipping or bush hammering. All loose and excess material should be removed from the patch.

Use of 60 lb. jackhammers should be limited because of the possibility of causing additional cracking in the concrete.

"Properly Prepared Patch"

On deep, large or underside patching, consideration should be given to using forms, rib lathe, mesh or reinforcing bars, separately or in combination, depending on the circumstances. Due to the critical nature of surface preparation when applying a repair product, it is essential that the contractors and engineers carefully supervise the workmen and inspect the preparation to ensure that the surfaces are truly cleaned and roughened.

As a result of studies by the American Concrete Institute and the Portland Cement Association on whether concrete substrates should be soaked with water or dry at the time of placement of cementitious repair materials, the following procedure should be followed.

With a dry substrate in hot weather, the patching material may lose water too rapidly for proper hydration to take place. Conversely, if the substrate is too wet, cement may be washed from the bonding surface. Therefore, it is generally recommended that the substrate be moistened and any excess (visible accumulation) of water be removed. Under unusual circumstances, the manufacturer of the patch material should be contacted for guidance.

   a.   Outline the areas to be patched with chalk or crayon.
   b.   Chip out concrete within the outlines to a minimum depth of 1/2 inch. Keep all edges as vertical as possible. Avoid featheredges - they tend to dry rapidly, debond and break up.
   c.   Add steel or mesh for deep or large patches.
   d.   If rebar is exposed, chip to 1/2 inch below rebar.
   e.   All exposed rebar showing any oxidation should be water or sand-blasted.
   f.   Brush away any debris or dust in the chipped area.
   g.   Moisten the area to be patched.

2.   *FORMS*
   a.   Surface preparation should be as outlined above.
   b.   Forms should be lined with polyethylene or coated with paste wax or form release agent for easy release.

3.   *MIXING*
   a.   Mix the patching material in a mortar mixer to a trowelable consistency for all applications except those to be poured in place. Mix only the amount of material that can be placed within the working life of the material. For small applications, use a paddle type mixer.
   b.   For formed areas to be poured, use the patching material mixed to a pourable consistency. Do not exceed maximum water indicated on the container. Tap the forms while placing and after placing to eliminate entrapped air.
   c.   During hot weather, adjust set and working times with the admixture provided by the manufacturer.

4. *PLACING*
   a. TROWEL METHOD

   Use a trowel to place material and press it into contact with the chipped out substrate. If the entire depth cannot be placed in one lift without sagging or pulling away, trowel the material in layers, allowing each layer to stiffen before applying the next layer. Work from the bottom of the patch up or for overhead repairs from the edge toward the center. Finish off smooth and level with the surrounding concrete. For overhead patching, ask for **FIVE STAR STRUCTURAL CONCRETE V/O.**

   b. FORM & POUR METHOD

   A small opening or slot must be left at the top of the form to permit the material to be poured in place. The material may be poured directly from the pail or into a small chute inserted in the opening. Consolidate using a slightly bent bar to ensure good contact with the substrate and an absence of bubbles or voids.

   c. PNEUMATICALLY APPLIED PATCHES

   The pneumatically applied (shotcrete/gunite) method of patching is not covered since the method requires an experienced shotcrete contractor. It is an excellent method to use where very large total areas or overhead installations are involved. It does, however, require an experienced contractor with one or more highly skilled nozzle men. It is an excellent and most economical method to use for patching of very large horizontal, vertical or overhead areas. It has the additional advantage of producing a patch with the lowest possible water content (water/cement ratio).

   Technical Bulletin #49, "Structural Concrete Repair (Pneumatically Applied Mortar)," is enclosed at the end of this Section describing the entire procedure from Surface Preparation through Application.

5. *CURING*

   Follow manufacturer's instructions.

6. *FORM REMOVAL*

   If it was necessary to anchor the forms through the patch, form removal should be delayed until adequate bond of the patch to the old concrete has developed.

B. HORIZONTAL PATCHING

   This category covers mainly floors in plants, warehouses and other industrial and commercial structures.

1. *SURFACE PREPARATION*

   Surface preparation is extremely critical in all patching. In all structural patching, it is essential that all deleterious substances be removed from the existing concrete. This includes, but is not limited to, form oils, form coatings, curing agents, and similar products. Acid etchers, concrete cleaners, and degreasers may be required to properly clean the surface. All acid, chemical cleaners, and degreasers must be completely removed. The surface to be patched must not be smooth. It should be roughened by mechanical means such as chipping or bush-hammering. All loose material and excess material should be removed from the patch.

   Use of 60 lb. jackhammers should be limited because of the possibility of causing additional cracking in the concrete.

   On deep or large repairs, consideration should be given to using forms, rib lathe, mesh or reinforcing bars, separately or in combination, depending on the circumstances and as recommended in ACI standard practices for concrete. For very large pours, contact the manufacturer for installation instructions.

   As a result of studies by the American Concrete Institute and the Portland Cement Association on whether concrete substrates should be soaked with water or dry at the time of placement of cementitious repair materials, the following procedure should be followed.

With a dry substrate in hot weather, the patching material may lose water too rapidly for proper hydration to take place. Conversely, if the substrate is too wet, cement may be washed from the bonding surface. Therefore, it is generally recommended that the substrate be moistened and any excess (visible accumulation) of water be removed. Under unusual circumstances, the manufacturer of the patch material should be contacted for guidance.

    a.   Outline the area to be patched using chalk or crayon.

    b.   Make vertical saw cuts along outline.

    c.   Chip out concrete within the saw cut area. Chip deep enough to reach sound, *uncontaminated* concrete. This is important since many areas are subjected to saturation by fluids such as cutting oils.

    d.   Keep edges as vertical as possible. Avoid featheredging! It presents problems of rapid drying, cracking, debonding and abrasion from traffic.

    e.   Remove debris and dust using shovels, brooms and oil-free compressed air blowers.

2. *WETTING*

Premoisten the area, but remove any excess, standing water.

3. *MIXING*

    a.   Mix the patching material in a mortar mixer to a pourable consistency for most applications. Mix only the amount of material that can be placed within the working life of the material. For small applications, hand mix or use a paddle-type mixer.

    b.   For deep or large repairs, most materials may be extended with clean pea gravel to act as a heat sink and lower the cost. Consult the manufacturer for the amount that may be added.

    c.   During hot weather, adjust set and working times with the admixture provided by the manufacturer.

4. *PLACING*

Place patching material full depth from one side or end of patch to the other side or end. Puddle lightly to assure full contact with bottom and sides of patch. Screed level with surrounding concrete and finish as desired.

"Airport Project"

"Airport Project"

5. *CURING*
   Follow manufacturer's recommendations for curing.
6. *FORM REMOVAL*
   If it was necessary to anchor soffit forms through the patch, form removal should be delayed until adequate bond of the patch to the old concrete has developed.

C. REPAIR OF CONCRETE JOINT EDGES
   Joints in floors are often subjected to repeated heavy loads by steel-wheeled or hard rubber-wheeled equipment. With time, the edge of the joint breaks off and the process continues until a large gap or hole exists. These holes should be immediately filled to avoid hazardous conditions to people and equipment.

   Repair and patching material must be chosen to accommodate the type of traffic and loads to which the joint will be exposed. Light impact loadings and pneumatic-tired equipment often will not damage cementitious surfaces as severely as steel wheels. For light applications, repairs may be made with FIVE STAR STRUCTURAL CONCRETE. For heavy impact loadings or steel wheeled equipment, repairs should be made with one of FIVE STAR's epoxy grouts. Procedure is as follows:

1. *SURFACE PREPARATION*

    Proceed as outlined under "Horizontal Patching", except leave a minimum one inch vertical sawcut and chip down so the depth of the patch is at least two inches. If chipping exposes reinforcing, chip to a minimum of 1/2" below steel. If no reinforcing is present or if the patch will be deep or wide, the engineer should design reinforcement to be added prior to placement.

2. *WETTING*

    If **FIVE STAR STRUCTURAL CONCRETE** is being used, premoisten the area to be patched. If an epoxy grout is to be used, *do not* premoisten and be sure the substrate is dry.

3. *FORMING*

    Use a length of wooden board or rigid plastic foam having a thickness equal to width of joint as the form. Wrap the form with polyethylene to serve as form release. *Do not* use oil, grease or other release agents as they will prevent bond of any joint sealant used to fill the joint after repair is complete.

4. *MIXING*

    Mix the selected patching material as indicated on the package.

5. *PLACING*

    Place the material full depth from one end to the other end. Consolidate by puddling. Screed off level with surrounding concrete. Do not permit patched side of joint to be higher or lower than the other side! Finish epoxy with a steel trowel lightly moistened with solvent or diesel oil.

6. *CURING*

    As soon as **FIVE STAR STRUCTURAL CONCRETE** has hardened, keep all exposed surfaces wet for a minimum of 30 minutes after hardening.

    Epoxy grout requires *no curing* and should *not* be wet cured.

CHAPTER 7
CONCRETE PAVEMENT REPAIR
PLACEMENT PROCEDURES

The concrete pavement category includes bridge decks, highways, roads, parking garages and similar applications. All of these areas require products having specific properties.

The most important property is *bond to the substrate*. More repairs and patches have failed because of inadequate bond than from all other causes combined. As mentioned in Chapter 2, products which do not develop a minimum of 2,500 psi bond strength should not be considered for any permanent patching.

Length change (linear shrinkage or expansion) can result in cracking and debonding. Cracks will permit entry of water and salt solution and this will result in failure when freezing or corrosion occurs.

Most repair and patching materials develop strengths adequate for patching. Strength gain should be rapid in order to minimize shut-down time and the resulting inconvenience to the traveling public.

An efficient patching material should be formulated to be used at varying consistencies. Flowable-only materials present problems at any areas which are not absolutely level. Flowable patching materials tend to flow toward the low end and require constant troweling to make them conform to the levels of the surrounding concrete. If they start to set while being troweled, "rippling" of the patch surface may result.

Most patching is not done at carefully controlled temperatures. Hot weather presents problems of too rapid set and too short working time. Preferably the patching material manufacturer will have available admixtures to adjust set and working times. These admixtures should be capable of being using in varying amounts and should also be able to be used in the field to meet any job requirement. FIVE STAR HIGHWAY PRODUCTS, INC. has a product called SUMMERSET which will adjust the set and extend the working time.

FIVE STAR HIGHWAY PRODUCTS, INC. has manufactured three products for concrete pavement repair. They are listed in the order of the highest performance and desirability:

FIVE STAR HIGHWAY PATCH
FIVE STAR MAGPHOS
FIVE STAR CONCRETE PATCH

On the following page is a chart comparing the typical physical properties of the three leading types of rapid setting cementitious concrete repair materials. FIVE STAR HIGHWAY PRODUCTS, INC., although it did manufacture FIVE STAR MAGPHOS AND FIVE STAR CONCRETE PATCH, recommends that all specifiers and users upgrade their specifications and projects to the permanent FIVE STAR HIGHWAY PATCH to take full advantage of its far superior characteristics. Since all materials will vary by manufacturer, the data shown is based on the typical performance of the top selling brands of each type.

TYPICAL PHYSICAL PROPERTIES
@ 70°F and 70% R.H.

	FIVE STAR HIGHWAY PATCH		MAGNESIUM PHOSPHATE		PORTLAND-GYPSUM		
	Neat	60% Ext.	Neat	60% Ext.	Neat	100% Ext.	200% Ext.
Compressive Strength: psi							
ASTM C 109　　1 hr. + Set	3500	3000	3500	3000	2500	2000	1500
3 hr.	5000	4500	5000	4500	3500	2500	2000
1 day	7000	6500	5500	5000	6500	6000	5500
7 day	8500	8000	6000	5500	8000	8000	7500
Linear Length Change: Percentage							
ASTM C 157　　1 day	-0.005	-0.003	-0.070	-0.050	-0.005	-0.010	-0.015
(dry)　　　　　28 day	-0.007	-0.005	-0.070	-0.050	-0.015	-0.030	-0.035
Bond Strength: psi							
ASTM C 882　　1 day	2500	2000*	1500*(1)	1200*(1)	1000*	800*	600*
7 day	4000	3500	2000*(1)	1800*(1)	1800*	1400*	1000*
Thermal Coefficient of Expansion: in./in./°F							
ASTM C 531	5.0×10^{-6}		5.3×10^{-6}		4.5×10^{-6}		
Permeability: gallons/1000 sq. ft./day							
1 day	1.1	0.7	3.0	2.6	6.9	5.0	4.1
Set Time: minutes							
ASTM C 191	25	25	18	18	30	30	35
Yield per 50 lb. bag	0.43	0.62	0.42	0.59	0.46	0.80	1.05

*2500 psi needed to eliminate cold joint of 5000 psi concrete.
(1) Magnesium phosphates do not bond to damp or wet concrete.
£ 1988 by U. S. GROUT CORPORATION

A. EQUIPMENT

All tools, screeds, mixer, potable water, aggregate and product should be at the point of placement prior to start of mixing and placing.

B. SURFACE PREPARATION
1. The area(s) to be patched should be outlined with chalk or crayon.
2. Saw cut at least 1/2" deep at the outlines. This is to avoid "featheredges" and their potential for failure. "Featheredges" dry out rapidly with resulting cracking and debonding. They are also much more susceptible to break-out and abrasion.
3. Chip down at least 1 inch, but deeper if necessary to reach sound, uncontaminated concrete. If chipping exposes reinforcing bar, chip at least 1/2 inch below the reinforcing bar. There may be insufficient reinforcing bar at headers. The engineer should design reinforcing bar cages with top steel approximately (but not less than) 1-1/2" below the surface.

"Chipping"

4. Keep all outside edges as vertical as possible.
5. Remove all chipped out debris and dust using shovels, brooms and oil-free compressed air blowers.

C.   SUBSTRATE WETTING

Follow manufacturer's recommendations for substrate wetting. *Some products require a wet substrate; others do not.* When wetting a substrate be sure all standing water (puddles) is removed prior to placement.

D.   MIXING

1.   A mortar mixer (with moving blades) is preferred for most products.

2.   Wet all tools and the inside of the mixer and pour out all excess water.

3.   Measure out the quantity of potable water called for on the bag and pour into mixer. (Multiply by number of bags being mixed.) Start mixer. If product is being extended with clean, washed pea gravel, the pea gravel should be added after the water. Aggregate containing large (over 3/4") pieces should not be put into a mortar mixer. Large stones tend to wedge under the blades and stall the mixer.

4.   If it is necessary to extend the set or working time, add SUMMERSET to the water before the addition of the cementitious mixture.

5.   Dump contents of bag(s) into mixer and mix for time indicated on the product bags.

E.   PLACEMENT

1.   Most patching products will be pourable and self-leveling at the maximum recommended water and mixing time. As mentioned in the "Introduction", this can be troublesome. Products should have the capability of being mixed at *varying* water contents to produce consistencies appropriate to job requirements.

2.   Pour into patch area from one side and continue pouring across patch until filled. Do not place in lifts! Most patching and repair materials will function best if placed in a single layer. Where this is not practical, multiple layers (lifts) can be placed by allowing the previous layer to stiffen somewhat before placing additional layers (lifts). Puddle or rod first layer (lift) to ensure good contact with substrate.

3. Screed off level with surrounding concrete. Float, trowel, or broom to desired finish. Be sure to trowel edges of patch carefully to ensure edges are sealed.

F. CURING

Follow manufacturer's recommended procedures for curing of all repair and patching materials.

CONCLUSION

All of the foregoing assumes that patching and repair of surfaces in a horizontal plane are the main and only problems associated with bridge decks, highways, roads and parking decks. Unprotected surfaces such as piers, columns, and abutments along with retaining walls *must* be protected from water and salt penetration to avoid deterioration. Such areas can be effectively and economically protected by coating with **FIVE STAR WATERPROOFING**. This material, its properties and application are described in Section IV of this publication.

CHAPTER 8
TYPICAL APPLICATIONS
CONCRETE REPAIR

"Airport Runway"

"Loading Dock Repair"

"Pedestal Repair"

"Bridge Deck Repair"

CHAPTER 9
CONCRETE REPAIR SPECIFICATIONS

A general discussion of specifications and types is present in Section I, Chapter 9. The general discussion applies to specifications for repair and patching materials.

Repair and patching materials should not be specified based only on requirements for compressive strength and/or rate of strength gain. As mentioned in Chapter 2, these materials seldom, if ever, fail due to lack of sufficient compressive strength. They fail due to *inadequate bond strength and excessive length change*.

Any specification which does not take these considerations into effect will not ensure the use of a product which will give long-lived performance. A proprietary specification can assure the owner and specifier that the performance desired will be achieved. Where a proprietary specification is prohibited, for whatever reason, a performance specification should be written.

The performance specification should include requirements for bond strength, length change, and compressive strength. In order to demonstrate the level of performance expected, the specifier may add the name of a product and manufacturer that meets the performance requirements required.

Following are examples of the specification types discussed.

EXAMPLES OF SHORT FORM SPECIFICATIONS
1. *PROPRIETARY SPECIFICATION*

All repair and patching as called for on the drawings and/or in specifications shall be performed with FIVE STAR STRUCTURAL CONCRETE as manufactured by U. S. GROUT CORPORATION, a subsidiary of FIVE STAR PRODUCTS, INC. of Fairfield, Connecticut. No substitutions will be approved.

2. *OR APPROVED EQUAL WITH IDENTICAL PROPER-*
   TIES SPECIFICATION

   All repair and patching called for on the drawings
   and/or in the specifications shall be performed with
   FIVE STAR STRUCTURAL CONCRETE as manufactured by **U. S. GROUT CORPORATION,** a subsidiary of
   FIVE STAR PRODUCTS, INC. of Fairfield, Connecticut,
   or approved equal with identical properties. The repair
   and patching material must exhibit a minimum 2,500 psi
   bond strength when tested according to ASTM C 882
   (modified).

3. *PERFORMANCE SPECIFICATION*

   The short form cannot be used for this type of specification. See the following for performance specifications.

4. *OPEN LISTING - NAMING THREE OR MORE*
   MATERIALS IN A SPECIFICATION

   The short form cannot be used in this type of specification because standards have to be established to determine whether the products can meet the requirements.
   Only the long form specification should be used in this
   case.

SHORT FORM PERFORMANCE SPECIFICATION

All concrete repair and patching as called for on the drawings and/or in the specifications shall be performed with a material meeting the performance requirements that follow.

Permanent structural repair material must be a one component system that requires only the addition of water. It must meet the following performance requirements at maximum water.

A. Bond Strength: 1 Day   1,500 psi (min.)
    ASTM C 822*   7 Days   2,500 psi (min.)
B. Length Change: 28 Days Dry   −0.05% (max.)
    ASTM C 157*   28 Days Wet   +0.05% (max.)
C. Compressive Strength:
                         2 Hours   2,500 psi (min.)
    ASTM C 109   1 Day   5,000 psi (min.)
                         7 Days   7,000 psi (min.)

*Modified: Contact U. S. GROUT CORPORATION for details.

SECTION 03600
PERFORMANCE SPECIFICATION FOR PERMANENT STRUCTURAL CONCRETE REPAIR MATERIALS

PART I GENERAL

All permanent structural concrete repair as indicated in designer's specification and on drawings shall apply to this section. Generally, these products are supplied by the contractor installing repair material. They are used to rapidly and permanently repair spalled concrete on horizontal and vertical surfaces.

1.01 REFERENCES

ASTM C 109	Test Method for Compressive Strength of Hydraulic Cement Mortars.
ASTM C 157	Test Method for Length Change of Hardened Cement Mortar and Concrete.
ASTM C 882	Test Method for Bond Strength of Epoxy-Resin Systems Used with Concrete.

1.02 SUBMITTALS

The contractor must submit prior to installation, for designer's approval, manufacturer's literature and certified test data that material complies with requirements in Article 2.02. Designer should, at contractor's expense, buy any submitted material in the open marketplace, without the contractor's or manufacturer's knowledge, and test material at an independent laboratory to verify compliance with this specification.

1.03 DELIVERY, STORAGE AND HANDLING

All repair materials shall be preblended, prepackaged materials requiring only the addition of water. They must be packaged in original unopened packages, clearly labeled with the manufacturer's identification and printed instructions. All material shall be stored and handled in accordance with recommendations of the manufacturer and the American Concrete Institute.

1.04 ENVIRONMENTAL CONDITIONS

Refer to the manufacturer's literature for any physical or environmental limitations or contact the manufacturer directly.

PART II PRODUCTS
2.01 MANUFACTURER

The following manufacturers supply materials which meet this specification and offer field service:

Manufacturer	Products
U.S. GROUT CORPORATION	FIVE STAR STRUCTURAL CONCRETE

A Subsidiary of FIVE STAR PRODUCTS, INC.
Fairfield, Connecticut
800-243-2206 or 203-336-7900

Other materials which meet this specification must be submitted to the designer for approval by following procedures outlined in Article 1.02.

2.02 MATERIALS

Permanent structural repair material must be a one component system that requires only the addition of water. It must meet the following performance requirements at maximum water.

A.	Bond Strength:	1 Day	1,500 psi (min.)
	ASTM C 882*	7 Days	2,500 psi (min.)
B.	Length Change:	28 Days Dry	-0.05% (max.)
	ASTM C 157*	28 Days Wet	+0.05% (max.)
C.	Compressive Strength:		
		2 Hours	2,500 psi (min.)
	ASTM C 109*	1 Day	5,000 psi (min.)
		7 Days	7,000 psi (min.)

*Modified: Contact U. S. GROUT CORPORATION for details.

2.03 AGGREGATE

Aggregate shall consist of 3/8" clean, washed and dried gravel or crushed stone of reasonably uniform quality throughout.

PART III EXECUTION
3.01 INSPECTION

Inspect surfaces to receive structural repair material and verify the following:

(A) They are free of ice, frost, dirt, grease, oil, curing compounds, paints, impregnations, all loose material, and other foreign matters likely to affect the bond or performance of the material.

(B) Surfaces are sufficiently rough to ensure good cement bond and that the concrete is structurally sound and surfaces are sufficiently rough to ensure good bond.

(C) That provisions for expansion and control joints are consistent with specifications and sound engineering practices.

3.02 PREPARATION

(A) All grease, oil, dirt, curing compounds, laitance, and other deleterious materials must be completely removed from the concrete.

(B) Roughen the surfaces by chipping, sandblasting, or other mechanical means and provide a near vertical face on the edges of existing concrete to ensure bond. Loose or broken concrete shall be removed.

(C) If any existing reinforcing bars are exposed, they shall be sandblasted. Because of superior salt water resistance of FIVE STAR STRUCTURAL CONCRETE, no coating of rebars is necessary.

(D) All surfaces shall be thoroughly saturated, and free standing excess water shall be removed with clean compressed air before applying the structural repair material.

3.03 INSTALLATION

(A) Carefully read and understand the manufacturer's instructions as printed on the container.

(B) Mixing

The mixing operation shall be located close to the repair area. A mortar mixer is recommended. For smaller quantities, an electric drill and paddle mixer is recommended.

The mixing order for mortar type mixer shall be as follows:

(1) Clean water shall be placed in the mixer at the rate specified on the container instructions. Water content is critical; do not deviate from the rate specified.

(2) When temperatures exceed 90°F, a pre-packaged set retarder shall be used as recommended by the manufacturer. Add retarder to mixing water maximizing dispersion in the mix.

(3) For large pours, 3/8-inch clean washed pea gravel should be added to the mix at a rate not to exceed 30 lbs. per 50 lb. pail.

(4) Add the repair material. This sequence is important in order to produce a consistent mix and to reduce mixing time. Allow approximately 3 minutes mixing time.

(5) When pouring large volumes of material, special consideration should be given to maintaining a continuous flow of material, producing a plastic leading edge. More than one mixer may be necessary to deliver enough material to prevent cold joints.

(C) Placing

(1) Horizontal - Place the mixed material into the prepared area starting from one side of the repair and working to the other side. Do not place the repair material in lifts. Work the material firmly into the bottom and sides of the repair. Screed the material to the desired level. Close up edges of the repair with a trowel. Finish the material to the desired texture.

(2) Vertical - Using a trowel, move the material in an upward motion against the cut out substrate. Successive applications must be troweled against the previously placed material just prior to set. Build up the material to thickness desired. Finish the material to the desired texture.

(3) Do not re-temper the material. Clean the mixer and tools periodically with water to prevent build-up, especially in hot temperatures.

(D) Curing

As soon as the material sets, all exposed surfaces must be thoroughly saturated for 30 minutes.

(E) Clean-Up

Upon completion of placement, equipment and tools should be cleaned in such a manner as recommended by manufacturer.

SECTION 03000
PERFORMANCE SPECIFICATION
FOR
RAPID SETTING CEMENTITIOUS HIGHWAY REPAIR

PART I GENERAL

All concrete repair as indicated in designer's specification and on drawings shall apply to this section. Generally, these products are supplied by the contractor installing the repair material. They are used for repair of spalled concrete.

1.01 REFERENCES

ASTM C 109	Test Method for Compressive Strength of Hydraulic Cement Mortars.
ASTM C 157	Test Method for Length Change of Hardened Cement Mortar and Concrete.
ASTM C 882	Test Method for Bond Strength of Epoxy-Resin Systems Used with Concrete

1.02 SUBMITTALS

The contractor should submit, prior to installation, for designer's approval, manufacturer's literature and certified test data that material complies with requirements in Article 2.02. Designer should, at contractor's expense, buy any submitted material in the open marketplace, without the contractor's or manufacturer's knowledge, and test material at an independent laboratory to verify compliance with this specification.

1.03 DELIVERY, STORAGE AND HANDLING

All repair materials shall be preblended, prepackaged materials requiring only the addition of water. They must be packaged in original unopened packages, clearly labeled with the manufacturer's identification and printed instructions. All material shall be stored and handled in accordance with recommendations of the manufacturer and the American Concrete Institute.

1.04   ENVIRONMENTAL CONDITIONS

Refer to the manufacturer's literature for any physical or environmental limitations, or contact the manufacturer directly.

PART II   PRODUCTS

2.01   MANUFACTURER

The following manufacturer supplies materials which meet this specification and offers field service:

Manufacturer	Products
FIVE STAR HIGHWAY PRODUCTS, INC.	FIVE STAR HIGHWAY PATCH

A Subsidiary of FIVE STAR PRODUCTS, INC.
Fairfield, Connecticut
800-243-2206 or 203-336-7900

Other materials which meet this specification must be submitted to the designer for approval by following procedures outlined in Article 1.02.

2.02   MATERIALS

Rapid setting cementitious mortars shall be one component systems that require only the addition of water. They must meet the following performance requirements at maximum water.

A.	Bond Strength:	1 Day	1,500 psi (min.)
	ASTM C 882*	7 Days	2,500 psi (min.)
B.	Length Change:	28 Days Dry	-0.05% (max.)
	ASTM C 157*	28 Days Wet	+0.05% (max.)
C.	Compressive Strength:		
		1 Hour	2,500 psi (min.)
	ASTM C 109*	1 Day	6,000 psi (min.)
		7 Days	7,000 psi (min.)

*Modified: Contact **FIVE STAR HIGHWAY PRODUCTS, INC.** for details.

2.03   AGGREGATE

Aggregate shall consist of 3/8" clean, washed and dried gravel or crushed stone of reasonably uniform quality throughout.

PART III   EXECUTION

3.01   INSPECTION

Inspect surfaces to receive patch material and verify the following:

(A) They are free of ice, frost, dirt, grease, oil, curing compounds, paints, impregnations, all loose material, and other foreign matters likely to affect the bond or performance of the material.

(B) Surfaces are sufficiently rough to ensure good cement bond and that the concrete is structurally sound and surfaces are sufficiently rough to ensure good bond.

(C) That provisions for expansion and control joints are consistent with specifications and sound engineering practices.

3.02 PREPARATION

(A) All grease, oil, dirt, curing compounds, laitance materials, and other deleterious materials must be completely removed from the concrete.

(B) Roughen the surfaces by chipping, sandblasting, or other mechanical means and provide a near vertical face on the edges of existing concrete to assure bond. Loose or broken concrete shall be removed.

(C) If any existing reinforcing bars are exposed, they shall be sandblasted. Because of superior salt water resistance of FIVE STAR STRUCTURAL CONCRETE, no coating of rebars is necessary.

(D) All surfaces should be thoroughly saturated, and free standing excess water shall be removed with clean compressed air before applying the patching material.

3.03 INSTALLATION

(A) Carefully read and understand the manufacturer's instructions as printed on the unit.

(B) Mixing - The mixing operation shall be located close to the repair area. A mortar mixer is recommended for large jobs. For smaller quantities, an electric drill and paddle mixer is recommended. The mixing order for mortar type mixer shall be as follows:

(1) Clean water shall be placed in the mixer at the rate specified on the bag instructions. Water content is critical; do not deviate from the rate specified.

(2) When temperatures exceed 90°F, a pre-packaged set retarder shall be used as recommended by the manufacturer. Add retarder to mixing water maximizing dispersion in the mix.

(3) For large pours, 3/8-inch clean washed pea gravel should be added to the mix at a rate not to exceed 30 lbs. per 50 lb. bag.

(4) Add the patching material. This sequence is important in order to produce a consistent mix and to reduce mixing time. Allow approximately 3 minutes mixing time.

(5) When pouring large volumes of material, special consideration should be given to maintaining a continuous flow of material producing a wet leading edge. More than one mixer may be necessary to deliver enough material to prevent cold joints.

(C) Placing - Place the mixed material into the prepared area starting from one side of the repair and working to the other side. Do not place the patch material in lifts. Work the material firmly into the bottom and sides of the patch. Screed the material to the desired level. Close up edges of the patch with a trowel. Finish the material to the desired texture. Do not re-temper the material. Clean the mixer and tools periodically with water to prevent build-up, especially in hot temperatures.

(D) Curing - As soon as the material sets, all exposed surfaces must be thoroughly saturated for half an hour.

(E) Clean-Up - Upon completion of placement, equipment and tools should be cleaned in such a manner as recommended by the manufacturer.

CHAPTER 10
TECHNICAL DATA ON FIVE STAR
CONCRETE REPAIR PRODUCTS

FIVE STAR
CONCRETE
REPAIR
PRODUCTS

This chapter contains product literature, magazine re-
prints and technical bulletins on **FIVE STAR** concrete repair
products. **FIVE STAR** products are designed to provide a
higher level of performance.

FIVE STAR® STRUCTURAL CONCRETE

DESCRIPTION

Five Star Structural Concrete represents a major technological breakthrough in concrete repair materials. Five Star Structural Concrete is a high strength permanent concrete repair material which is dimensionally stable and forms an integral bond to existing concrete that restores structural integrity. Its unique properties also include a rapid development of strength so that industrial floors, walls and other structural members can be put back into use within the shortest possible time. Five Star Structural Concrete is formulated to be troweled vertically or flowed horizontally. Application thicknesses may run from 1/8 inch to 12 inches in thickness in a single pour. Five Star Structural Concrete has eliminated the objections most professionals have to present patching products—slow strength gain, cold joints, cracking and thermal incompatibility are eliminated. Five Star Structural Concrete provides waterproofing properties superior to any ready-mix concrete and will resist the penetration of most chemicals, oils and salts.

ADVANTAGES

- Permanent Concrete Repair
- Very Rapid Strength Development
- High Bond Strength
- Dimensionally Stable
- High Freeze/Thaw Resistance
- Variable Consistencies
- Variable Application Thicknesses
- Controllable Working Time[1]
- Economical
- Resealable Package

TYPICAL PHYSICAL PROPERTIES

Compressive Strength, ASTM C-109*	2 Hours	2500 psi
	3 Hours	4000 psi
	1 Day	5000 psi
	7 Days	7500 psi
	28 Days	8000 psi
Bond Strength, ASTM C-882*:	1 Day	2000 psi
	7 Days	3000 psi
Linear Length Change, ASTM C-157*:	28 Days Wet	0.00%
	28 Days Dry	0.00%
Thermal Coefficient of Expansion, ASTM C-531:	5.0×10^{-6} in/in/°F.	
Flexural Strength, ASTM C-78:	7 Days	1200 psi
Modulus of Elasticity, ASTM C-469:	7 Days	3.5×10^6 psi
Freeze/Thaw Resistance, ASTM C-666* (B):	300 cycles	94% durability
Scaling Resistance, ASTM C-672:	50 cycles	0
Set Time, ASTM C-191:	Initial	25 minutes
	Final	35 minutes
Yield per 50 lb. pail:	.42 cu. ft.	

Placement Properties

Five Star Structural Concrete provides approximately 20 minutes working time. This may be controlled by easily adding units of Summerset® directly to mixing water to reach the desired working time. Five Star Structural Concrete is formulated for a very rapid, economical placement while minimizing placement errors and material waste.

[1]Set Time can be easily controlled and increased using SUMMERSET® as a special retarder for the new patented cement.

*Modified for rapid setting material and recommended curing.

III.2

APPLICATIONS	• Repairing Concrete Columns, Floors, and Walls • Repairing Concrete Foundations • Repairing Honeycombed or Spalled Concrete • Repairing Concrete Piles and Seawalls • Setting Anchors, Railings • Leveling Floors • Filling Snap Tie Holes • Fast Turnaround Concrete Structures

PLACEMENT GUIDELINES

1. **Surface Preparation:** Existing concrete surface must be thoroughly cleaned of oil and any other deleterious substances. All unsound or damaged concrete should be removed until only sound, clean, roughened concrete is exposed within the perimeter of a ¼ inch minimum vertical saw cut. Feather edging is not recommended for structural repairs. All loose material should be removed by brushing, washing, and/or oil-free air jet. The existing concrete to be patched should then be thoroughly saturated with water. Standing water should be removed prior to patching.
2. **Mixing:** Five Star Structural Concrete may be used for both large and small repairs. For repairs where the entire contents of one or more pails will be used, a mortar mixer is recommended. Wet down the mixer before using and drain any excess water. While the mixer is running, add recommended minimum amount of water to the mixer, followed by Five Star Structural Concrete. Mix from 2 to 5 minutes. Add more water if required. Do not exceed maximum water. Do not mix more material than can be placed in ten minutes. For large pours, Five Star Structural Concrete should be extended 50% with clean, washed ⅜ inch pea gravel. Where smaller quantities are required, Five Star Structural Concrete may be hand mixed with a trowel or hoe. The mixing should be in a chopping and rolling motion for a full five minute duration until thoroughly mixed. For small batches, add the water slowly to avoid overwatering.
3. **Horizontal Placement:** Pour Five Star Structural Concrete from one side of the hole to the other side, filling the hole to the desired level. Do not place the patch in layers. After leveling, the surface may be finished to the desired texture with a steel trowel, wood float or brush.
4. **Vertical Placement:** For placement on walls, generally less flowability will be required. This is accomplished by using less water. Add additional water only after mixing for several minutes and adjust the water as required for troweling on the walls. When the desired consistency is achieved, apply by trowel from the bottom part of the cavity in an upward motion. Do not layer. Trowel the material firmly against the cut out substrate. For deep, vertical cavities, simple forming may be required. The rapid setting properties of Five Star Structural Concrete should eliminate the need for extensive forming.
5. **Special Conditions:** For large applications or applications during extreme temperatures, contact the Engineering and Technical Center of U.S. Grout Corp.
   For **COLD WEATHER** patching, Five Star Structural Concrete and the mixing water should be kept as warm as possible. Do not let Five Star Structural Concrete freeze before it has reached the desired strength.
   For **HOT WEATHER** patching, use cold water or iced water to extend the working time and keep the packaged material in a cool, dry place. Summerset® is also recommended for extending the working time.
6. **Curing:** As soon as the surface of the patch has hardened, soak the surface with sufficient water to keep the material wet for at least 30 minutes. For large pours, keep the material wet for at least 2 hours.

SPECIFICATION GUIDELINES

All concrete and masonry repairs shall be performed with Five Star Structural Concrete as manufactured by U.S. Grout Corporation, Fairfield, Connecticut. The material shall provide a minimum 2500 psi compressive strength in two hours and a bond strength of 2,000 psi in one day. Patching materials shall be mixed and installed in accordance with manufacturers recommendations. No substitutions will be permitted. Technical service shall be made available by manufacturer upon request.

PACKAGING, YIELD, ORDERING AND AVAILABILITY

Five Star Structural Concrete is packaged in heavy duty resealable plastic pails weighing 50 lbs. and producing .42 cubic feet and .57 cubic feet with 50% aggregate extension. For ordering, determine the total number of cubic feet required, add 5% waste, and contact U.S. Grout Corporation or one of your local Five Star dealers throughout the United States. Five Star products are manufactured in plants throughout the United States and are also manufactured and available worldwide.

STORAGE AND HANDLING

Five Star® Structural Concrete should be stored in a cool, dry place in accordance with the recommendations of the American Concrete Institute. The package may be easily resealed.

Warranty: U.S Grout Corporation stands behind its products when used by competent workmen in accordance with manufacturer's directions. No responsibility for product use is assumed or implied where inferior workmanship is encountered, or difficulty caused by other materials is evident. U.S. Grout Corporation's liability is limited to replacement of materials found to be defective. These recommended procedures are for normal field practice. They may be modified by the designer, specifier, purchaser or their authorized agent since only they are responsible for the design, installation and supervision of specific conditions and installations.

ENGINEERING & TECHNICAL CENTER, U.S. GROUT CORPORATION, SUBSIDIARY OF FIVE STAR PRODUCTS, INC.

401 STILLSON ROAD, FAIRFIELD, CONN. 06430 • (203) 336-7900 • CABLE FIVE STAR • FACSIMILE: (203) 336-7939 • TELEX 643857 • COPYRIGHT 1987 • 8875K

FIVE STAR STRUCTURAL CONCRETE™ V/O

DESCRIPTION

Five Star Structural Concrete V/O (Vertical/Overhead) represents a major technological breakthrough in concrete repair materials. Five Star Structural Concrete V/O is a high strength permanent concrete repair material which is dimensionally stable and forms an integral bond to existing concrete that restores structural integrity. Its unique properties also include a rapid development of strength so that industrial walls, ceilings and other structural members can be put back into use within the shortest possible time. Five Star Structural Concrete V/O is formulated to be troweled or gunited vertically or overhead. Application thicknesses may run from 1/8 inch to 12 inches in thickness by applying the material in layers. Five Star Structural Concrete V/O has eliminated the objections most professionals have to present patching products — slow strength gain, cold joints, shrinkage and thermal incompatibility are eliminated. Five Star Structural Concrete V/O provides waterproofing properties superior to any ready-mix concrete and will resist the penetration of most chemicals, oils and salts.

ADVANTAGES

- Permanent Concrete Repair
- Rapid Strength Development
- High Bond Strength
- Dimensionally Stable
- High Freeze/Thaw Resistance
- Economical
- Trowel Vertically Overhead
- Variable Application Thicknesses
- Just Add Water
- Controllable Working Time
- Resealable Package

TYPICAL PHYSICAL PROPERTIES

Compressive Strength, ASTM C-109*	2 hrs.	2000 psi
	1 day	4000 psi
	7 days	5000 psi
	28 days	6000 psi
Bond Strength, ASTM C-882*	1 day	1500 psi
	7 days	2500 psi
Linear Length Change, ASTM C-157*	28 days Wet	+0.00%
	28 days Dry	-0.00%
Thermal Coefficient of Expansion, ASTM C-531	5.0×10^{-6}	in/in/° F.
Set Time, ASTM C-191	Initial	30 minutes
	Final	40 minutes
Yield per 50 lb. pail	.42 cu. ft.	

Placement Properties

Five Star Structural Concrete V/O provides approximately 20 minutes working time. This may be increased easily by adding Summerset® directly to mixing water to reach the desired working time. Five Star Structural Concrete V/O is formulated for a very rapid, economical placement while minimizing placement errors and material waste.

Set time can be easily increased using SUMMERSET® as a special retarder for the new patented cement.

*Modified for rapid setting material and recommended curing.

III.4

APPLICATIONS

Repairing Concrete Columns, Walls
Repairing Concrete Ceilings, Tunnels
Repairing Honeycombed or Spalled Concrete
Repairing Concrete Piles and Seawalls
Repairing Concrete Pipe
Repairing Precast Concrete
Filling Snap Tie Holes
Fast Turnaround Concrete Structures

PLACEMENT GUIDELINES

1. **Surface Preparation:** Existing concrete surface must be thoroughly cleaned of oil and any other deleterious substances. All unsound or damaged concrete should be removed until only sound, clean, roughened concrete is exposed within the perimeter of a ¼ inch minimum vertical chipped edge. Feather edging is not recommended for structural repairs. All loose material should be removed by brushing, washing, and/or oil-free air jet. The existing concrete to be patched should then be thoroughly saturated with water. Surface should be saturated surface dry.

2. **Mixing:** Five Star Structural Concrete V/O may be used for both large and small repairs. For repairs where the entire contents of one or more pails will be used, a mortar mixer is recommended. Wet down the mixer before using and drain any excess water. While the mixer is running, add recommended minimum amount of water to the mixer, followed by Five Star Structural Concrete V/O. Mix from two to five minutes. Add more water if required. Do not exceed maximum water. Do not mix more material than can be placed in twenty minutes. Where smaller quantities of one unit or less are required, Five Star Structural Concrete V/O should be mixed with a drill and paddle mixer.

3. **Vertical and Overhead Placement:** For vertical placement apply Five Star Structural Concrete V/O by troweling the material firmly against the chipped out substrate working from the bottom part of the cavity in an upward motion. For deep patches apply the material in lifts. Before the first layer has taken set and after it has stiffened enough to support its weight proceed with the next layer. For overhead work simply trowel a thin layer of Five Star Structural Concrete V/O into the roughened substrate forcing material into the area to be repaired. Build up the material in layers to the desired thickness. Scratch each layer for better mechanical bond working from the outer edges of the repair towards the center. Put the next layer on before the first layer has taken final set and after it has stiffened enough to support its own weight. The depth of the repair should be built up as quickly as possible without sagging or slumping of the mortar. Reinforcing may be required to continue the structural continuity. The methods of reinforcement used must be approved by the designer. Finish to desired texture with steel trowel or sponge float. For deep pours, consideration should be given to forming and pouring or guniting with Five Star Structural Concrete.

4. **Special Conditions:** For large applications or applications during extreme temperatures, contact the Engineering and Technical Center of U.S. Grout Corporation.

   For **COLD WEATHER** patching, Five Star Structural Concrete V/O and the mixing water should be kept as warm as possible. Do not let Five Star Structural Concrete V/O freeze before it has reached the desired strength.

   For **HOT WEATHER** patching, use cold water or iced water to extend the working time and keep the packaged material in a cool dry place. Summerset® is also recommended for extending the working time.

5. **Curing:** As soon as the surface of the patch has hardened, spray the surface with sufficient water to keep the material wet for at least 30 minutes. For large pours, keep the material wet for at least 2 hours.

SPECIFICATION GUIDELINES

All concrete and masonry repairs shall be performed with Five Star Structural Concrete V/O as manufactured by U.S. Grout Corporation, Fairfield, Connecticut. The material shall provide a minimum 2000 psi compressive strength in two hours and a bond strength of 1500 psi in one day. Patching materials shall be mixed and installed in accordance with manufacturers recommendations. No substitutions will be permitted. Technical service shall be made available by manufacturer upon request.

PACKAGING, YIELD, ORDERING AND AVAILABILITY

Five Star Structural Concrete V/O is packaged in heavy duty resealable plastic pails weighing 50 lbs. and producing .42 cubic feet. For ordering, determine the total number of cubic feet required, add 5% waste, and contact U.S. Grout Corporation or one of your local Five Star dealers throughout the United States. Five Star products are manufactured in plants throughout the United States and are also manufactured and available worldwide.

STORAGE AND HANDLING

Five Star® Structural Concrete V/O should be stored in a cool, dry place in accordance with the recommendations of the American Concrete Institute. The package may be easily resealed.

Warranty: U.S. Grout Corporation stands behind its products when used by competent workmen in accordance with manufacturer's directions. No responsibility for product use is assumed or implied where inferior workmanship is encountered, or difficulty caused by other materials is evident. U.S. Grout Corporation's liability is limited to replacement of materials found to be defective. These recommended procedures are for normal field practice. They may be modified by the designer, specifier, purchaser or their authorized agent since only they are responsible for the design, installation and supervision of specific conditions and installations.

ENGINEERING & TECHNICAL CENTER, U.S. GROUT CORPORATION, SUBSIDIARY OF FIVE STAR PRODUCTS, INC

401 STILLSON ROAD, FAIRFIELD, CONN. 06430 • (203) 336-7900 • CABLE FIVE STAR • FACSIMILE (203) 336-7939 • TELEX 643857 • COPYRIGHT 1987 • 11/87 10K

FIVE STAR® HIGHWAY PATCH

DESCRIPTION

Five Star Highway Patch is a patented hydraulic cement material that is ideal for permanent repair and patching of concrete. It exhibits very high early strengths, very high bond strengths, and precision nonshrink performance while also providing very high abrasion scaling and freeze/thaw resistance. Five Star Highway Patch provides superior resistance to oil, grease, gasoline, salts and other chemicals found in the transportation environment. Unlike accelerated materials based on portland, gypsum, magnesium phosphate or polymer materials, it does not exhibit excessive volume change, excessive heat generation, poor bonding or contain any harmful or corrosive compounds. Five Star Highway Patch provides the unique advantage of adding up to 60% pea gravel (¼"–⅜") extension without significantly affecting early strength development or long term durability.

ADVANTAGES

- Very Rapid High Strengths
- High Bond Strengths
- Precision Nonshrink
- High Freeze/Thaw Resistance
- High Chemical Resistance

- Controllable Working Time[1]
- Variable Consistencies
- Most Economical
- Effective 60% Extension
- No Noxious Fumes or Odors

**TYPICAL PHYSICAL
PROPERTIES**

Compressive Strength, ASTM C-109*:

Time	Neat	60% Extension
1 Hour	2500 psi	2000 psi
3 Hours	4500 psi	4000 psi
1 Day	6500 psi	6000 psi
7 Days	8000 psi	7500 psi

Bond Strength, ASTM C-882*:

1 Day	2500 psi
7 Days	3500 psi

Length Change, ASTM C-157*:

28 Days Wet	0.00%
28 Days Dry	0.00%

Flexural Strength, ASTM C-78:

1 Day	1100 psi
7 Days	1300 psi

Modulus of Elasticity, ASTM C-469:

1 Day	3.0×10^6 psi
7 Days	3.5×10^6 psi

Freeze/Thaw Resistance, ASTM C-666* (B): 300 cycles — 96% durability

Scaling Resistance, ASTM C-672: 50 cycles — 0.1

Set Time, ASTM C-191:

Initial	25 minutes
Final	35 minutes

Yield Per 50 lb. Bag:

Neat	.43 cu. ft.
60% Extension	.62 cu. ft.

Placement Properties

Five Star Highway Patch provides approximately 20 minutes working time. This may be controlled by easily adding units of Summerset® directly to mixing water to reach the desired working time. Five Star Highway Patch is formulated for a very rapid, economical placement while minimizing placement errors and material waste.

[1]Working time can be easily controlled and increased using SUMMERSET® as a special retarder for the new patented cement.

*Modified for rapid setting material and recommended curing

APPLICATIONS **Very Rapid Permanent Patching of Concrete**

- Highways and Bridges
- Parking Decks and Ramps
- Airport Runways and Taxiways
- Floors and Joints
- Steps and Sidewalks
- Piers and Seawalls

PLACEMENT GUIDELINES

1. **Surface Preparation:** Existing concrete surface must be thoroughly cleaned of oil and any other deleterious substances. All unsound or damaged concrete should be removed until only sound, clean concrete is exposed within the perimeter of a two-inch minimum vertical saw cut. All loose material should be removed by brushing, washing, and/or oil-free air jet. The existing concrete to be patched should then be thoroughly saturated with water. Standing water should be removed prior to patching.

2. **Mixing:** Five Star Highway Patch should be mixed in a mortar mixer. Wet down the mixer before using and drain any excess water. With the mixer running, add the minimum recommended water to the mixer, followed by the Five Star Highway Patch, and if extending, then the aggregate. For water requirement, see front of bag. Mix from 2 to 5 minutes. Add more water only if required. Do not exceed the maximum water. Do not mix more material than can be placed in 10 minutes. Five Star Highway Patch may be extended with clean, washed, 3/8-inch pea gravel or crushed stone. Do not extend with sand.

3. **Placing:** Five Star Highway Patch may be troweled or poured into the area to be patched. After leveling, the patch can be broomed, brushed, or troweled to the desired finish. Do not place in lifts. Do not feather edge.

4. **Cold Weather:** When using at or near freezing temperatures, Five Star Highway Patch should be stored in as warm a place as possible. The patched area must be kept above 32°F until Five Star Highway Patch has set.

5. **Hot Weather:** Summerset® is recommended for extending the working time of Five Star Highway Patch in hot weather.
For applications during extreme weather conditions, contact the Engineering and Technical Center of Five Star Highway Products, Inc.

6. **Curing:** As soon as the surface of the patch has hardened, flood with sufficient water to keep the surface wet for at least 30 minutes.

ECONOMICS AND PURCHASING **Cost Per Cubic Foot with Extension**

Historically, purchasing of patching materials has been done on a per pound or per bag basis. This has always led to erroneous and costly purchasing decisions as every material has a different cubic footage yield even when extended. Thus, omitting the actual yield with proper aggregate extension will not reflect true costs. As an example, the cubic footage yield of Five Star Highway Patch is increased by approximately 50% through proper aggregate extension, resulting in high yield and large material cost savings.

All requests for quotations and bids should require manufacturers to provide material prices on the cubic footage basis with the recommended aggregate extension. This enables purchasing decisions to be made on true values, not just initial costs.

SPECIFICATION GUIDELINES

All very rapid high strength gaining nonshrink patching shall be performed with Five Star Highway Patch as manufactured by Five Star Highway Products Inc., Fairfield, Connecticut. The material shall provide a minimum 2000 psi compressive strength in one hour and 2500 psi bond strength in 1 day. Patching materials shall be mixed and installed in accordance with manufacturer's recommendations. No substitutions will be permitted. All quotations and bid evaluations will be based on material cost per cubic foot with maximum allowed aggregate extension. Technical service shall be made available by manufacturer upon request.

PACKAGING, YIELD, ORDERING AND AVAILABILITY

Five Star® Highway Patch is packaged in heavy duty polyethylene lined bags weighing 50 lbs. and producing .43 cubic feet when used neat and .62 cubic feet with 60% aggregate extension.
For ordering, determine the total *number of cubic feet* required, add 5% wastage, and contact Five Star Highway Products, Inc., 405 Stillson Road, Fairfield, Connecticut 06430.

STORAGE AND HANDLING

Five Star Highway Patch should be stored in a cool, dry place for hot weather patching in accordance with the recommendations of the American Concrete Institute. For cold weather use, keep the material stored in a warm dry place.

Warranty: Five Star Highway Products stands behind its products when used by competent workmen in accordance with manufacturer's directions. No responsibility for product use is assumed or implied where inferior workmanship is encountered, or difficulty caused by other materials is evident. Five Star Highway Products' liability is limited to replacement of materials found to be defective. These recommended procedures are for normal field practice. They may be modified by the designer, specifier, purchaser or their authorized agent since only they are responsible for the design, installation and supervision of specific conditions and installations.

FIVE STAR HIGHWAY PRODUCTS, INC., SUBSIDIARY OF FIVE STAR PRODUCTS, INC.

405 STILLSON ROAD, FAIRFIELD, CONN. 06430 • (203) 336-7930 • TELEX: 643857 • FACSIMILE: (203) 336-7939 • CABLE FIVE STAR • COPYRIGHT 1987 • 3875K

FIVE STAR® CONCRETE PATCH

DESCRIPTION Five Star Concrete Patch is a unique type of hydraulic cement developed for the very rapid concrete patching requirements demanded by D.O.T.'s. It provides high early strengths, ease of workability, and can be extended up to 200% (up to 100% of clean, washed sand plus up to 100% clean, washed gravel). This special extension formulation provides the unique advantage of adding tremendously to the volume of the finished product which results in significant cost savings without significantly affecting strength development.

ADVANTAGES
- Rapid Strengths
- High Ultimate Strength
- Freeze/Thaw Resistance
- Pourable, Self Levelling
- Very Economical
- Effective 0-200% Extension

TYPICAL PHYSICAL PROPERTIES

Compressive Strength, ASTM C-109*:

Time	Neat	200% Extension
1 Hour	2500 psi	1500 psi
3 Hours	3500 psi	2000 psi
1 Day	6500 psi	5500 psi
7 Days	8000 psi	7500 psi

Linear Length Change, ASTM C-157*:

28 Days Wet	+0.10%
28 Days Dry	−0.015%

Freeze/Thaw Resistance, ASTM C-666(B)*:

300 cycles	86% durability

Set Time, ASTM C-191:

Initial	25 minutes
Final	30 minutes

Yield Per 50 lb. Bag:

Neat	.46 cu. ft.
200% Extension	1.05 cu. ft.

Placement Properties

Five Star Concrete Patch has approximately 20 minutes working time. This may be delayed or accelerated by impurities in the aggregate when the material is extended. Mixing and placing procedures are on each bag. Five Star Concrete Patch is formulated for a very rapid, economical placement while minimizing placement errors and material waste.

*Modified for rapid setting material and recommended curing

III.8

APPLICATIONS
Very Economical Rapid Patching of Concrete

- Bridges
- Highways
- Roads
- Driveways
- Sidewalks
- Curbs

PLACEMENT GUIDELINES

1. **Surface Preparation:** All surfaces to be in contact with Five Star Concrete Patch shall be entirely free of oil, grease, laitance, or other foreign materials. Roughen surfaces to ensure good bond to existing concrete. Clean thoroughly with liberal quantities of water, leaving concrete saturated, but free of standing water.
2. **Mixing:** Five Star Concrete Patch is a unique cementitious material which may be extended 100% with D.O.T.-approved, clean, washed and well-graded sand, and an additional 100% with D.O.T.-approved, clean, washed and well-graded gravel. The maximum size gravel shall not be greater than one-third the depth of the patch. The mixing instructions are on the back of each bag.
3. **Methods of Placing:** Five Star Concrete Patch may be screeded, troweled or flowed into place. Finishing should begin immediately after placing as material sets rapidly.
4. **Post-Placement Procedures:** Five Star Concrete Patch should be protected from severe weather conditions and from any traffic use for approximately 45 minutes after set.

ECONOMICS AND PURCHASING

Cost Per Cubic Foot with Extension

A bag of Five Star Concrete Patch which yields .46 cubic foot per 50 lbs. may be extended with 100% sand and 100% gravel. All requests for quotations and bids should require manufacturers to guarantee that their products can be extended with 100% sand and 100% gravel, and all bids shall be based on a one cubic foot yield. This will enable purchasing agents to make their decisions based on true values, not just initial costs, and be able to compare actual volumes of materials purchased. A pound basis for purchasing should never be used.

SPECIFICATION GUIDELINES

All rapid high strength gaining nonshrink patching shall be performed with Five Star Concrete Patch as manufactured by Five Star Highway Products, Inc., Fairfield, Connecticut. The material may be extended with 100 lbs. of sand and 100 lbs. of pea gravel which meets the manufacturer's and D.O.T.'s requirements. The neat Five Star Concrete Patch shall have a minimum one hour compressive strength after set of 2,000 psi. Patching materials shall be mixed and installed in accordance with manufacturer's recommendations. No substitutions will be permitted. All quotations and bid evaluations will be based on material cost per cubic foot. Technical service shall be made available by manufacturer upon request.

PACKAGING, YIELD, ORDERING AND AVAILABILITY

Five Star Concrete Patch is packaged in heavy-duty, polyethylene-lined bags designed to meet D.O.T. job conditions. This product is manufactured in both 50 and 100 lb. bags, the 50 lb. bags being used primarily for small patching. The 100 lb. bags provide considerably more economy in purchasing and installation and are usually preferred by contractors. The yield of Five Star Concrete Patch is .46 cubic foot per 50 lbs. For ordering or bidding, determine the total number of cubic feet required, add 5% wastage, and contact Five Star Highway Products Inc., Fairfield, Connecticut.

STORAGE AND HANDLING

Five Star Concrete Patch should be stored in a cool, dry place in accordance with the recommendations of the American Concrete Institute. For cold weather use, keep the material stored in a warm, dry place.

Warranty: Five Star Highway Products stands behind its products when used by competent workmen in accordance with manufacturer's directions. No responsibility for product use is assumed or implied where inferior workmanship is encountered, or difficulty caused by other materials is evident. Five Star Highway Products' liability is limited to replacement of materials found to be defective. These recommended procedures are for normal field practice. They may be modified by the designer, specifier, purchaser or their authorized agent since only they are responsible for the design, installation and supervision of specific conditions and installations.

FIVE STAR HIGHWAY PRODUCTS, INC. SUBSIDIARY OF FIVE STAR PRODUCTS, INC.

405 STILLSON ROAD, FAIRFIELD, CONNECTICUT 06430 • (203) 336-7930 • TELEX: 643857 • FACSIMILE: (203) 336-7939 • CABLE FIVE STAR • ©COPYRIGHT 1987 3875K

III.10

TECHNICAL ★5★ BULLETIN
FIVE STAR

```
Physical Performance
Five Star Structural Concrete
When Extended 50% With 3/8" Pea Gravel
```

Five Star Structural Concrete will accept a 50% extension of clean, washed, 3/8" pea gravel. The addition of aggregate effectively transforms Structural Concrete from a sand/cement mortar to what can be appropriately considered a prepackaged high early strength, high bond, non-shrink concrete. Many engineering firms and material divisions at various D.O.T.'s have approved extended Five Star Structural Concrete as an acceptable substitution for engineered field mixed concrete. The use of Five Star's Structural Concrete, a prepackaged mix necessitating only water and aggregate, ensures the engineer and owner, specified high performance results while eliminating unnecessary difficulties for the contractor in the field. The following Physical Performance values were found for a random sample from a production batch of Structural Concrete and will approximate subsequent field values. The actual certified test report is available.

```
================================================================
```
Water Added For Test: 3 quarts / 50 lbs.   Pea Gravel: 50% by weight

Bond Strength	1 Day	7 Day
ASTM C - 882 (Modified)	2,100 psi	3,070 psi

Compressive Strength
ASTM C - 109

2 Hour	3 Hour	1 Day	7 Day	28 Day
2,730	4,200	5,800	6,730	9,200

Linear Length Change	Dry	0.00%
ASTM C - 157 (Modified)	Wet	0.00%

Yield: per 50 lb. pail = 0.57 cu. ft.

Time of Set	Initial:	18 minutes
ASTM C - 191	Final:	30 minutes

Coefficient of Thermal Expansion
ASTM C - 531 5.2×10^{-6} in./in./F°
```
================================================================
```

Technical Bulletin #45 5/29/87

U. S. GROUT CORPORATION, 401 STILLSON ROAD, FAIRFIELD, CONNECTICUT 06430 ● (203) 336-7900

RAPID SETTING CEMENTITIOUS CONCRETE REPAIR MATERIALS

COMPARISON CHART

This bulletin highlights the typical physical properties of the three leading types of rapid setting cementitious concrete repair materials. The three leading types are Five Star Highway Patch, magnesium phosphate and portland-gypsum. Uniquely, U. S. Highway Products, Inc. manufactures the premier versions of all three types since each type has its unique benefits and drawbacks. Because all materials will vary by manufacturer, the data shown is based on the typical performance of the top selling brands of each type. Below are brief descriptions of the critical physical properties and related test methods. These should be investigated by a Licensed Professional Engineer before deciding upon a concrete repair material. Particular attention should be paid to elevated structures and through deck patching. It is recommended that a Licensed Professional Engineer approve the application, design, reinforcement, patching procedures, etc.

Compressive Strengths – Compressive strength is a basic structural property, and the repair material should at least reach the compressive strength of the concrete being repaired. ASTM C-109 is one test method used to measure compressive strength and should be modified to reflect the manufacturer's recommended curing procedures.

Length Change – A repair material should not exhibit significant length change in the hardened state or it will crack or pull away from the surrounding substrate. ASTM C-157 is one method to measure length change. This test should be modified to reflect manufacturer's recommended curing procedures and measurements should begin at set plus 10 minutes to reflect actual hardened length change of these rapidly setting materials. A 4" x 4" x 11" bar should be used to reflect depth of most patches.

Bond Strength – Bond strength is a critical property for any structural application, especially for elevated structures. Bonding agents and slurries are not recommended because of timing and usual field problems. Without adequate bond (above 2500 psi) to concrete, a patch will usually breakout and will serve no structural purpose which may result in failure of a structure. ASTM C-882 is used to test bond strength provided the procedures are modified to reflect the substrate preparation procedures recommended by the manufacturer.

Thermal Coefficient of Expansion – A repair material should exhibit a thermal coefficient of expansion similar to the substrate. The thermal coefficient of expansion of concrete has been reported between 2×10^{-6} to 11×10^{-6} inch per inch per $^{\circ}F$. ASTM C-531 is the method for measuring this.

Permeability – The permeability of the repair material is critical because it is a measure of durability. If a material is very permeable to water, then salts and other ingredients will penetrate the material. Ultimately this will lead to the degradation of the material and areas surrounding the material.

Set Time – Set time is a relative measure of working time. Generally, the longer the set time the longer the working time. ASTM C-191 measures set time.

Yield – Yield is a critical feature in purchasing material because you are filling a void. Buying by bag or pound can be costly since not all materials have the same yield.

TYPICAL PHYSICAL PROPERTIES
@ 70°F and 70% RH

	Five Star Highway Patch		Magnesium Phosphate		Portland-Gypsum		
	Neat	60% Ext.	Neat	60% Ext.	Neat	100% Ext.	200% Ext.
Compressive Strength: psi							
ASTM C-109 1 Hr. + Set	3500	3000	3500	3000	2500	2000	1500
3 Hr.	4500	4000	4200	4000	3500	2500	2000
1 Day	6500	6000	5500	5000	6500	6000	5500
7 Day	8000	7500	6000	5500	8000	8000	7500
Linear Length Change: Percentage							
ASTM C-157							
(Wet) 28 Day	+0.005	+0.005	+0.080	+0.060	+0.100	+0.060	+0.050
(Dry) 28 Day	-0.007	-0.005	-0.070	-0.050	-0.015	-0.030	-0.035
Body Strength: psi							
ASTM C-882 1 Day	2500	2000*	1500*(1)	1200*(1)	1000*	800*	600*
7 Day	3500	3500	2000*(1)	1800*(1)	1800*	1400*	1000*
Thermal Coefficient of Expansion: in/in/°F							
ASTM C-531	5.0×10^{-6}	—	5.3×10^{-6}	—	4.5×10^{-6}	—	—
Permeability: gal/sq ft							
1 Day	1.1×10^{-3}	0.7×10^{-3}	3.0×10^{-3}	2.6×10^{-3}	6.9×10^{-3}	5.0×10^{-3}	4.1×10^{-3}
Set Time: minutes							
ASTM C-191	35	25	18	18	30	30	35
Yield per 50 lb. bag	0.43	0.62	0.41	0.59	0.46	0.80	1.05

*2500 psi needed to eliminate cold joint of 5000 psi concrete.
(1) Magnesium phosphates do not bond to damp or wet concrete.

Technical Bulletin #41
5872.5k

III.14

STRUCTURAL CONCRETE REPAIR
(Pneumatically Applied Mortar)

DESCRIPTION:

This item shall consist of removing all deteriorated, disintegrated, soft or honey–combed concrete and replacing it with sound concrete (or mortar) at locations shown on the plans, or as directed by the engineer and as specified herein. Repairs shall include, but not be limited to: removal and disposal of damaged concrete, cleaning and preparing of bonding surface, cleaning of existing reinforcing steel, placing of additional reinforcing steel where required, and placement of new concrete or mortar to restore the structural elements to the original line and grade.

MATERIALS:

Material for repairing concrete structures shall be a ready to use, pre-mixed, pre–packaged material, marketed under the trade name "FIVE STAR STRUCTURAL CONCRETE^{TM}" by U. S. GROUT CORPORATION, 401 Stillson Road, Fairfield, Connecticut. Minimum compressive strength (ASTM C 109) shall be 2,500 psi @ 2 hours, and 5,000 psi @ 24 hours.

Water shall be potable water.

All wire mesh, reinforcing bars and mechanical anchors shall be of a size and spacing as directed by the engineer or shown on or described in the plans and specifications.

If the depth of concrete repair exceeds one and one half (1–1/2) inches and existing reinforcement is encountered, the engineer shall determine the condition of the reinforcement and order the contractor to either replace the reinforcement with steel of equal area at the same spacing as the original reinforcement, or to clean and reuse the existing reinforcing.

If any of the reinforcement is damaged by the contractor in his operations, the bars shall be replaced as required by the engineer at the contractor's expense.

Storage: It is recommended that the dry material be stored in a controlled environment to maintain a temperature of approximately 70°F.

Technical Bulletin #49

–1–

U. S. GROUT CORPORATION, 401 STILLSON ROAD, FAIRFIELD, CONNECTICUT 06430 ● (203) 336-7900

CONSTRUCTION METHODS:

Surface Preparation: All deteriorated or honey-combed concrete shall be removed from the areas to be repaired, by suitable methods, to sound material, and to provide at least one (1) inch clearance around the exposed reinforcing bars. Power tools that cause overbreakage of concrete will not be permitted. Any damage caused by the contractor to the existing structure that is designated to remain in place shall be repaired or replaced by the contractor at his own expense to the satisfaction of the engineer.

The existing concrete to be patched should then be thoroughly saturated with water. Standing water should be removed prior to concrete application.

The boundaries of areas to be repaired shall be square cut or slightly undercut to a depth of not less than one (1) inch. Feathered edges will not be permitted.

Corroded reinforcing bars shall be cleaned by suitable methods to remove all rust.

All chipped areas and surfaces to be repaired shall be thoroughly cleaned by means of oil-free compressed air, sandblasting, air and water blasting, steam, wire brushing or by other methods approved by the engineer. The contractor may use one or all of the various means of cleaning chipped areas as approved by the engineer.

Care shall be taken during the removal of the designated portions of the structure to avoid damaging the portions that are to remain in place.

Wire mesh held with mechanical anchors shall be used on repairs over 1-1/2" deep.

Application: The following procedure shall be used in applying the pneumatic mortar.

Retardant: SUMMERSET^R may be needed to allow enough working time to finish the surface to the original contour as closely as practicable. The small amounts of water used in the mix decreases the set time and SUMMERSET will offset this to a certain degree.

Mixing: FIVE STAR STRUCTURAL CONCRETE shall be loaded into approved equipment and placed under pneumatic pressure with a machine satisfactory to the engineer. The structural concrete shall be carried by a stream of compressed air to a nozzle approximately at the point of deposit. Water shall be introduced into the suspended stream of air and material at the nozzle. The material should be pre-dampened with water and mixed a minimum of three minutes with a mortar mixer. The material should be extended with sand as recommended by the manufacturer. The pre-dampening procedure steps are as follows: water, aggregate, FIVE STAR STRUCTURAL CONCRETE, and then mixed for the recommended time.

Water: The water used in placement shall be potable and maintained at a temperature of 60°F maximum. Uniform water pressure must be maintained at the nozzle.

-2-

III.16

The concrete (mortar) shall be placed by pneumatic means. The contractor shall do this work only with competent operators, experienced in the technique of placing concrete pneumatically.

Mixing and water content shall be strictly in accordance with the manufacturer's instructions. The disintegrated areas shall be restored to their original lines and contours with the outer edge being square and true to lines. This shall be done by placing guide strips or wires in such a manner as to allow the free escape of all rebound material and at the same time maintain the dimensions and areas necessary to produce an acceptable finish. Provide minimum 3/4" cover on all reinforcing (depart from original contour if required making smooth transition to existing dimensions). High spots shall be removed by troweling, sandblasting, or other approved means. The surface texture of the new concrete shall be the same as that of the surrounding existing concrete. Excessive troweling or working of the concrete shall be avoided.

Air pressure and nozzle velocity shall be as recommended by the gun manufacturer for the particular application.

The stream of FIVE STAR STRUCTURAL CONCRETE material from the nozzle shall impinge as nearly as possible at right angles to the surface being covered in order to maintain uniform coverage behind the reinforcement steel. Care should be taken to thoroughly wash down all previously hardened concrete with water and compressed air before shooting new material. The pressure and nozzle velocity shall be adjusted to minimize the amount of rebound. Rebounded material shall not be reused.

Finish: The final finish shall have a steel trowel, wood float, wet sponge float, or other finish approximating the existing, adjacent concrete surfaces. An exposed aggregate finish has become quite appealing from an appearance standpoint by many designers. This can be accomplished first by guniting or shotcreting the concrete or concrete block wall with FIVE STAR STRUCTURAL CONCRETE. Just before the structural concrete reaches its final set, 1/4" colored aggregate, no greater than twice the depth, is shotcreted or gunited into the structural concrete surface, giving an exposed aggregate finish.

Curing: Once the FIVE STAR STRUCTURAL CONCRETE has reached final set, all exposed surfaces must be cured as called for on the package.

Technical Bulletin #49
870929

-3-

III.17

TECHNICAL ★ BULLETIN
FIVE STAR

CRACKING IN CONCRETE

Ever since the first discovery of cementitious mixtures by the Egyptians, there has been cracking in concrete. Some of the world's greatest concrete experts have written many papers and given many talks about the causes of concrete cracking.

There are many ways to bracket the types of cracking. In the following paragraphs is a simple, concise approach to various causes of concrete cracking. This is not meant to be the total explanation for any particular crack or the absolute answer to the exact cause of the crack.

Common types of cracking can be broken down into two Force categories: External Force and Internal Force.

External Force includes movement due to temperature changes. (Cementitious materials will shrink on cooling and expand on heating.) External force concrete cracking may be caused by:

    Load factors
    Horizontal pressures (tension or compression)
    Vertical forces causing deflection or positive bending

Internal Force cracking can be caused by:

    Plastic shrinkage
    Hardened shrinkage
    Hardened expansion
    Rapid evaporation
    Internal heat build up
    High ambient temperatures
    High material temperatures
    High water temperatures
    High internal heat of reaction temperatures
    Freezing
    Sudden temperature changes (particularly downward)
    Use of chemical additives (which often increase shrinkage)
    Internal shear stresses
    Internal tensile stresses
    Improper formulations of the cementitious mixture
    Overwatering
    Overfinishing (bringing the fines to the surface)
    Segregation
    Internal rebar corrosion
    Length of the pour
    Depth of the pour
    Mass of the pour
    Inability of the concrete materials to keep a low heat of hydration
    Inability of the concrete materials to dry out and cool off on an even basis
    Improper curing

U. S. GROUT CORPORATION, 401 STILLSON ROAD, FAIRFIELD, CONNECTICUT 06430 ● (203) 336-7900

The above does not explain any particular reason for a crack on a specific project. For example, a fast-setting product could develop a high heat during setting. Thus, in a deep pour, excessive internal heat build up would cause cracking at the surface, and possibly well into the mass, due to the rapid loss of heat. This can be often alleviated by assuring reasonable ambient temperatures, reasonable water temperatures, reasonable material temperatures, pouring in layers (before each layer hardens), or even adding reinforcing bars to help dissipate heat (temperature bars). Sometimes extending with aggregates is helpful.

Another example would be a situation in which a long, vibrating machine is grouted with a cement grout. The anchors are relatively close to the edge of the machine. Usually, a crack in the grout will occur because the anchors are too close to the edge of the machine or the machine vibration caused the anchors to vibrate, cracking the grout. Also, if it was a long pour and no expansion joints were provided in the grout, machine temperatures, vibration, or unusual drying could cause cracking in the grout.

All FIVE STAR products are designed not to crack when used with the proper installation procedures. If concrete has broken off a wall, if grout has broken out, or if a new structural patch or highway patch is cracked, it will almost always be for one of the internal or external force reasons stated above. Sometimes engineers and owners, public and private, do not want to do the technical testing to determine the specific cause of the cracking, partially because of the high cost of this testing, and secondly, because of the possible embarrassment to the people involved in selecting the existing system.

If a FIVE STAR product cracks on a project, take photographs, get samples, and talk to our Technical Service Department immediately. FIVE STAR PRODUCTS' Engineering and Technical Center, through its quarter-century of experience, will make every effort to advise the client as to the cause of the cracking and how to correct the problem. As has often been said in the concrete industry, "We wrote the book on grouting and patching."

No contractor or design firm can be expected to supervise every minute of every workman's time, nor can every workman be expected to be thoroughly educated in every product. The famous FIVE STAR handbook, the standard of the industry, should be used for any normal problems arising in the field. If your client is lacking one, please contact the main office.

Technical Bulletin #52 – 9/23/87

Copyright (c) 1987 by U. S. GROUT CORPORATION

1781P

TECHNICAL ✪ BULLETIN
FIVE STAR

SUMMERSET®

DESCRIPTION

SUMMERSET is an additive which extends the working time and retards the set of certain FIVE STAR® rapid setting hydraulic cement products. SUMMERSET should be used when working in hot weather or placing a large amount of material at one time to provide ample working time to place and finish the material.

SUMMERSET should only be used with FIVE STAR hydraulic cement products that call for it by name in their mixing instructions.

INSTRUCTIONS

The working time and set time of certain FIVE STAR rapid setting hydraulic cement products may be extended by adding SUMMERSET to the mixing water, allowing it to fully dilute, and then adding the dry material. Total dispersion of SUMMERSET in the mixing water will result in a consistent working time and set time for the entire batch. Do not add SUMMERSET to the dry material.

Each tube of SUMMERSET will extend the working time by 50 percent. A general guide for the use of SUMMERSET is that one tube per unit should be used for every ten degrees Fahrenheit increase in temperature above 70°F. That is, use one tube if FIVE STAR product, water, and air temperature are at 80°F. Use two tubes if material, water, and air are at 90°F. Up to 3 tubes per unit may be added.

Remember SUMMERSET extends the set time and thus slows down the rate of strength gain. SUMMERSET does not reduce the ultimate compressive strength or compromise any other properties.

Technical Bulletin #28   © U. S. Grout Corporation 10/862.5K

U. S. WATERPROOFING, 425 STILLSON ROAD, FAIRFIELD, CONNECTICUT 06430 ● (203) 336-7970

SECTION IV
CEMENTITIOUS WATERPROOFING SYSTEMS
INTRODUCTION

"WATERPROOF", like "nonshrink", is a misused and misunderstood term. ASTM D 1079 (Definitions of Terms Relating to Roofing, Waterproofing, and Bituminous Materials) defines "waterproofing" as: "Treatment of a surface or structure to *prevent* the passage of water under hydrostatic pressure." Unfortunately, most waterproofing materials do not *prevent* passage of water, even without hydrostatic pressure. In fact, many do not even meet the ASTM description for "dampproofing" - "Treatment of a surface or structure to *resist* the passage of water in the *absence* of hydrostatic pressure."

There are very few situations without hydrostatic pressure. Even walls above grade are subjected to wind driven rain - with pressures equivalent to up to a nine inch head of water!

The specifier and user must know the difference between the definitions. Prevent means "to stop" the passage of water; resist means "to hinder" the passage of water. Stopping passage of water results in dry areas. Hindering passage only delays mopping up or pumping!

In addition to stopping passage of water, waterproofing materials must exhibit sufficient bond to the substrate to resist being pushed off by hydrostatic pressure. Some waterproofings may also exhibit dimensional instability resulting in cracking and leaking.

This section discusses performance, testing, application and specification of cementitious waterproofing materials.

CHAPTER 1
SELECTING A WATERPROOFING MATERIAL

Externally applied waterproofing can be classified into two general categories - rigid and flexible. Cementitious waterproofing is always a rigid material and may be applied by trowel, brush, spray or gunite (shotcrete). Flexible waterproofing includes all the liquid applied and pre-formed sheet elastomeric products as well as the natural clay systems.

Cementitious waterproofing has many advantages over the flexible systems and has one *exclusive* advantage - it can be applied on the "negative" side (away from the water source)! The sketch below illustrates the difference between "positive" and "negative" side treatment.

Positive side waterproofing means that the fluid is in direct contact with the waterproofing material, such as the outside of a basement.

Negative side waterproofing is applied on the side opposite the fluid, such as the inside of a basement or tunnel wall.

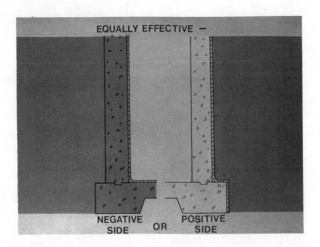

"Cementitious waterproofing, unlike flexible systems, can waterproof from either the inside or the outside."

Cementitious waterproofing used on the negative side has the advantage of being accessible during and after construction, it can be easily repaired, and continues to permit the concrete to cure from moisture in backfill or water in tanks. Properly applied to suitable substrates, cementitious materials give long and trouble-free service. Cementitious waterproofing materials should have low permeability under hydrostatic pressure, exhibit good chemical resistance, be breathable and resistant to freeze/thaw damage. They do not require a dry substrate for application and do not require protection board.

All cementitious systems are not equal in performance, however. The chart on the following page compares performance of the principal types of cementitious waterproofing, and Chapter 2 discusses important performance properties.

Flexible waterproofing, because of its nature, can be applied to "positive" side only. This complicates the location of leaks due to rips, tears or faulty laps and makes repairs time-consuming and expensive. Longevity is only fair as is fungus resistance. Permeability and hydrostatic pressure resistance range from poor to excellent, depending on product and method of application. Most flexible materials exhibit shrinkage over time and most are emulsifiable or degraded in water. Most flexible systems *require* some type of protection board if below grade and must have a traffic-bearing topping applied if in a horizontal plane.

One of the most recent discoveries has been that vermin in the ground often will eat through flexible materials, leaving large holes which are no longer accessible for repair.

CEMENTITIOUS WATERPROOFING COMPARISON CHART

Material Type	Five Star[1] Waterproofing		Crystalline	Water Repellent Cement	Metallic Oxide
Method of Application	Trowel—1 coat	Brush—2 coats	Brush—2 coats	Brush—2 coats	Brush—3 coats
Initial Absorption gal/1000 ft² First 24 hrs.	8	24	132	108	33
Permeability gal/1000 ft³/day	0.16	0.60	130	30	11.4
Shear Bond Strength ASTM C 882	2710 psi	2490 psi	470 psi	920 psi	2160 psi
Plastic Volume Change ASTM C 827	+0.20%	+0.20%	-2.10%	-1.00%	-2.60%
Hardened Volume Change					
Wet - 21 days ASTM C 157	+0.032%	+0.031%	+0.122%	+0.026%	+0.058%
Dry - 21 days ASTM C 596	-0.003%	-0.025%	-2.160%	-0.360%	-0.228%
Differential	0.035%	0.056%	2.282%	0.386%	0.286%
Compressive Strength ASTM C 109					
1 day	7000 psi	4800 psi	25 psi	2150 psi	1400 psi
7 days	7800 psi	6400 psi	1600 psi	3300 psi	4600 psi

[1]Total Application Thickness: For Trowel 1/8"; For Brush 1/16"

FIVE STAR WATERPROOFING PRODUCTS
PRODUCT/APPLICATION METHOD SELECTION CHART
(In Order Of Increasing Effectiveness)

HORIZONTAL SURFACES	
No traffic	FIVE STAR WATERPROOFING 2 brush coats; spray coat
Foot traffic	FIVE STAR WATERPROOFING dry shake method; trowel FIVE STAR WATERPROOFING HG trowel
Pedestrian and light rubber wheel traffic	FIVE STAR WATERPROOFING 1/8" trowel coat FIVE STAR WATERPROOFING gunite application FIVE STAR WATERPROOFING HG
Pneumatic wheel traffic	FIVE STAR WATERPROOFING HG trowel or gunite 1/8" minimum thickness

VERTICAL SURFACES
FIVE STAR WATERPROOFING 2 brush coats (1/16" total thickness)
FIVE STAR WATERPROOFING trowel, spray or gunite coat (1/8" thickness)

CHAPTER 2
PERFORMANCE PROPERTIES AND TESTS

In order to perform satisfactorily, cementitious waterproofing must exhibit definite physical properties. The most important property is low permeability or low rate of water transmission through the coating. Initial absorption is also very important where the coating is subject to intermittent wetting due to varying heights of groundwater or rain. Products with low rates of initial absorption will usually show excellent freeze/thaw resistance.

Bond strength is vitally important with cementitious waterproofing. Debonding results in cracks and water passage. Another major cause of cracks and debonding is length change in both plastic and hardened states.

As a measure of wear resistance, high compressive strength is desirable. High and early compressive strength reduces the need for prolonged protection and permits the coating to be put in service against hydrostatic pressure sooner.

The following paragraphs discuss test methods and desired performance characteristics of cementitious waterproofing.

A. PERMEABILITY

A good waterproofing should have very low permeability. The permeability shows you the level of protection you are buying. No waterproofing should be purchased without this vital piece of information. The permeability is the long term steady state rate of water transmission through the coating (per unit area), and is therefore the most important property of any waterproofing product. The permeability is a function of the water pressure encountered.

Permeability can be expressed as a volume of water passing through a given area of coating in a given period of time. It may also be expressed as a velocity of water through the coating. The permeability may be expressed in many units such as perms, cm/sec, or gallons per 1,000 square feet per day.

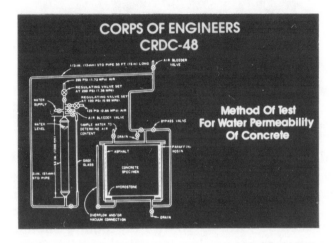

Many manufacturers report values such as "percentage absorption", "no leaks visible", "100% waterproof", "perms", or "cm/sec". This leaves the owner or specifier with little comparable data to judge the effectiveness and value of the waterproofing being selected. No standardized test has yet been accepted by the industry for measuring the permeability of waterproofing.

The Army Corps of Engineers has developed a test method CRD C-48, Method of Test for Water Permeability of Concrete. This method measures the permeability of a bonded waterproofing with 200 psi of water pressure against it (equivalent to a 461 ft. head). This pressure is more than sufficient to separate the true waterproofing materials from the dampproofing materials. CRD C-48 can be used to measure the permeability of a material placed on the negative side or positive side.

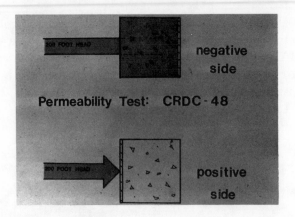

negative side

Permeability Test: CRDC-48

positive side

It can also be easily modified to measure the permeability at other water pressures.

The permeability of well placed concrete is typically of the order of 10^{-8} cm/sec as measured by CRD C-48. To be considered waterproof, a coating should exhibit a permeability of between 10^{-12} cm/sec and 10^{-14} cm/sec as measured by the Army Corps of Engineers test method CRD C-48. Waterproofing should not be specified or used unless it meets the above requirement.

Another test to measure the permeability is the CPR Funnel Absorption Test. (See end of this section for test method.) It is used to measure the permeability of the waterproofing on the positive side only at low (6 in.) water pressures. It does have the advantage of being able to judge the effectiveness of the waterproofing as placed on the site. The test is easy and inexpensive to run. The values reported from this test method are expressed as gallons of water passed per 1,000 sq. ft. per day. These units are much easier to visualize than cm/sec.

B. INITIAL ABSORPTION

A waterproof coating should exhibit little initial absorption. Initial absorption is defined as the amount of water absorbed (per unit area) by the coating in the first 24 hours of exposure. The rate of water absorption during this period has been found to be higher than the permeability.

The initial absorption is measured by the CPR Funnel Absorption Test. The initial absorption is very important where the coating is only subjected to intermittent water conditions. The initial absorption also gives an indication of the freeze/thaw durability of the coating. Initial absorption should not exceed 25 gallons per 1,000 square feet for the first 24 hours.

"Funnel Absorption Test Results"

C. BOND STRENGTH

A good waterproof coating must have a high bond strength to concrete. Debonding of the coating usually results in cracking and thus a loss of coating integrity. Cracks are an easy way for water to find its way through the coating.

While ASTM has not yet published a test method for adequately determining the bond strength of cementitious products to a concrete substrate, the construction industry, including highway departments, have been using for many years a modification of ASTM C 882 "Test Method for Bond Strength of Epoxy-Resin Systems Used with Concrete". The modification consists of merely leaving out any prime coat and applying the waterproofing material to a properly prepared substrate. To ensure adequate bond of a coating according to this test procedure, a minimum of 2,000 psi is required.

The "dummy" section of C 882 should be prepared as called for in the manufacturer's published instructions for surface preparation. The "dummy" should then be inserted into lightly oiled 3" × 6" steel cylinders.

The waterproofing should be mixed according to the manufacturer's published instructions.

The waterproofing should be placed in the mold in three lifts, making sure to consolidate each lift, leaving the waterproofing free of voids. The specimen should then be cured according to the manufacturer's published instructions for curing.

The specimens shall be removed from the molds when hardened, at 1 day and 7 days, capped and then broken.

D. LENGTH CHANGE

A good cementitious waterproofing should not exhibit significant length change (shrinkage or expansion) in either the plastic or hardened state. Plastic length change is measured using the ASTM C 827 Standard Test Method for Change in Height at Early Ages of Cylindrical Specimens from Cementitious Mixtures. Hardened length change is measured by ASTM C 157, (Test Method for Length Change of Hardened Cement Mortar and Concrete).

SHRINKAGE

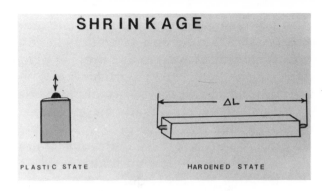

PLASTIC STATE   HARDENED STATE

"ASTM Shrinkage Test for Grouts"

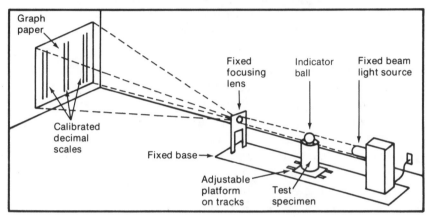

Graph paper

Calibrated decimal scales

Fixed focusing lens

Indicator ball

Fixed beam light source

Fixed base

Adjustable platform on tracks

Test specimen

Length change is very important because cementitious materials are rigid and essentially inelastic. When the coating shrinks or expands, stress is placed on the coating and the bond interface. This stress can only be relieved in one of two ways - cracking or debonding. Either of these events results in an ineffective waterproofing system.

Length change of cementitious waterproofing should be within the following limits:

Plastic State (ASTM C 827)
0.0 to +0.4%

Hardened State Wet (ASTM C 157)
0.0 to +0.05%

Hardened State Dry (ASTM C 157 modified*)
0.0 to -0.05%

*ASTM C 157 (Test Method for Length Change of Hardened Cement, Mortar, and Concrete) modified:

Instead of beginning the dry bar measurement at the end of 28 days of curing as called for in the C 157 method, take the initial reading one day after molding the bars (just the same as the wet method). After taking the initial reading, store and read the dry bar as called for in 10.1.2 of ASTM C 157.

E. COMPRESSIVE STRENGTH

A good cementitious waterproofing should have a high compressive strength and attain that strength rapidly.

Compressive strength is measured using ASTM C 109 (Test Method for Compressive Strength of Hydraulic Cement Mortars). Rapid strength gain means that the coating can be subjected to hydrostatic pressure earlier and does not need to be protected for as long. Further, the coating is less sensitive to variations in curing. The compressive strength also provides an indication of the wear resistance of the coating.

A minimum of 4,000 psi at one day and 6,000 at seven days is required for all types of applications.

F. OTHER PROPERTIES
    1. *ABRASION RESISTANCE*
            FIVE STAR WATERPROOFING PRODUCTS
        offer the advantage of superior abrasion resistance
        in a cementitious waterproofing. While other wa-
        terproofing must use sandwich-type construction,
        FIVE STAR offers the only line of cementitious wa-
        terproof coatings resistant to abrasion.
            Applications where this is required are parking
        garages, warehouse floors, loading ramps, working
        aisles, industrial floors, entrance areas and bays.
        Abrasion resistance may be measured by ASTM C
        501 (Test Method for Relative Resistance to Wear of
        Unglazed Ceramic Tile by the Taber Abraser).
    2. *BREATHABILITY*
            All cementitious or film coatings should pro-
        vide breathability to eliminate the possibility of
        moisture build-up and break-out during freeze/
        thaw, causing debonding. A good test for the
        breathability of a waterproofing is ASTM E 96 Pro-
        cedure B (Test Method for Water Vapor Transmis-
        sion of Materials).
    3. *CHEMICAL RESISTANCE*
            In many waterproofing applications, the coat-
        ing will come in contact with a variety of chemicals.
        Outdoor applications have a good possibility of
        coming in contact with deicing salts and acid rain.
        In industrial applications, the waterproofing may
        typically come in contact with acids, oils, greases,
        solvents, bases, paints, sewage and detergents. The
        waterproofing's ability to be resistant to these types
        of chemicals will increase the variety of applica-
        tions where the coating can be used successfully.
        The test for chemical resistance is ASTM C 267 (Test
        Method for Chemical Resistance of Mortars).

4. *FREEZE/THAW RESISTANCE*

A coating that has very low absorption will exhibit excellent freeze/thaw resistance. It is amazing how many "waterproofings" have poor freeze/thaw resistance. The test for freeze/thaw resistance is ASTM C 672 (Test Method for Scaling Resistance of Concrete Surfaces Exposed to Deicing Chemicals).

5. *CHLORIDE ION RESISTANCE*

The ability of materials to block the penetration of chlorides has come under close scrutiny in the last few years. Chloride ion penetration of reinforced concrete structures has been found to be a major cause of failure in those structures.

The chlorides penetrate into the concrete, attacking the reinforcing steel, causing corrosion of the steel. This results in expansion of the reinforcing steel leading to cracking of the slab and eventual loss of structural integrity.

FIVE STAR WATERPROOFING has been shown to be an excellent barrier to chloride penetration. This property has been verified by tests run by Wiss, Janney & Elstner, Law Engineering, and the Federal Highway Administration.

CHAPTER 3
WATERPROOFING OF HIGHWAYS AND WATERFRONT AREAS WHERE CONCRETE IS EXPOSED TO CHLORIDE ATTACK

There has been much discussion for many years about chloride attack on reinforced concrete and the underlying reinforcing bars. Many chemicals have been looked at, as well as many membranes. All have had various advantages and disadvantages.

Almost ten years ago, a product was developed in the cementitious area which has branched out into many different formulations and different applications to specifically solve this problem of preventing chloride damage.

As discussed previously, there are several test procedures and reports which are presently being used as "the method" of evaluating various products. The cementitious formulations of FIVE STAR WATERPROOFING have turned out to provide adequate protection from chloride damage for almost all types of installations.

At the end of this section are the technical bulletins showing the results of the AASHTO Test T277-831 performed by the Federal Highway Administration in which the leading types of products are rated, including four of the FIVE STAR WATERPROOFING products. This test data clearly shows that bridge decks, bridge abutments and sea walls should be coated with FIVE STAR WATERPROOF TOPPING 1/4″ thick for maximum effectiveness, economy, wearability, abrasion resistance and long product life.

One of the nation's leading test laboratories, Wiss, Janney, Elstner & Associates, prepared a test report on FIVE STAR WATERPROOFING and many other products in accordance with the National Cooperative Highway Research Program Report 244. Once again, for bridge decks, salt water exposure and chloride protection, FIVE STAR WATERPROOF TOPPING 1/4″ thick turned out to be the most effective for economy, wearability, abrasion resistance and long product life.

In 1984, Law Engineering of Atlanta, Georgia, one of the leading test laboratories in the Southeast, performed the U. S. Army Corps of Engineers CRD C-48 using a 115 foot head of pressure to determine the reduction of chloride content based on a pressure test using a 15% salt solution and comparing it with a highly dense concrete with a permeability of 7.1×10^{-10} cm/sec. All **FIVE STAR WATERPROOFING** products showed a superior reduction in chlorides.

It is, therefore, recommended that for heavy wearing surfaces such as bridge decks, **FIVE STAR WATERPROOF TOPPING** 1/4" thick be used for its effectiveness, economy, wearability, abrasion resistance, salt resistance and long product life. The walls and other areas exposed to water or chloride will reduce penetration with the use of **FIVE STAR WATERPROOFING**.

FIVE STAR WATERPROOFING Dry Shake can be used on newly poured concrete floors.

CHAPTER 4
QUALITY ASSURANCE PROGRAMS
FOR MANUFACTURER AND FIELD

Quality Assurance programs should be required for all waterproofing manufacturers, and are required for many critical installations. There are two categories of Quality Assurance programs: manufacturer and field.

QUALITY ASSURANCE PROGRAM - MANUFACTURER

The waterproofing manufacturer must maintain records of all the cements, sands, aggregates, and chemicals used. All containers of raw materials and finished product should have a code marking so that the source of all materials can be traced and verified as meeting the manufacturer's standards. The manufacturer should regularly take samples from the plant and verify them in his own test laboratory as meeting his requirements, including shrinkage, strength and permeability properties. The manufacturer must maintain test records on production runs and should retain them for at least one year. Shipping tickets should be maintained at the plant and at the main office for all shipments.

Products stored beyond six months should not be shipped without the manufacturer's certification that the products meet the manufacturer's standards. The manufacturer should furnish written certification when required stating that the material is in accordance with the project and manufacturer's specifications.

The manufacturer should have instructions for normal placement conditions printed on the outside of the container. These instructions should include the maximum/minimum mixing water limits in quarts per unit.

The manufacturer should have posted instructions for manufacturing the material at the plant. The accuracy of the weighing scales at the plant must be checked every six months, as required in a good Quality Assurance program.

The manufacturer should provide access to his production facilities by the engineer upon receipt of adequate notice for the auditing of the Quality Assurance Program. If a manufacturer cannot comply with this Quality Assurance Program verification, his products should not be approved.

QUALITY ASSURANCE PROGRAM - FIELD

The engineer should establish in his specifications a Field Quality Assurance Program to ascertain that the waterproofing he has specified meets his standards. This can be done by verifying the printed instructions on the bag and also by performing two field tests.

Permeability should be tested according to the "Funnel Absorption Test" (enclosed at the back of this Section).

In addition, compressive strength tests should be run according to the applicable portions of ASTM C 109.

CHAPTER 5
ESTIMATING AND PURCHASING OF
WATERPROOFING MATERIALS

ESTIMATING AND PURCHASING

Estimate the quantity of waterproofing required by measuring the total area (length and width) to be treated and adding 10% for waste on small jobs and 5% on large jobs.

All purchasing should be based on cost per square foot. This may be calculated by using the following chart. All cost comparisons must be calculated on an equivalent "Waterproofing Efficiency Basis".

CEMENTITIOUS WATERPROOFING ESTIMATING SHEET
FIVE STAR   *PRODUCT "X"*

A.   Cost per unit[1]   _____   _____

B.   Application rate
     sq. ft./unit   _____   _____

C.   Cost per sq. ft.
     (A divided by B)   _____   _____

[1] Include cost of all additives and components.

The unit coverage for 50 lbs. of FIVE STAR WATERPROOFING is 85 square feet (7.9m²) when brushed to a 1/16 inch (1.6 mm) total thickness in a two coat application and 42 square feet (3.9 m²) when applied in a 1/8 inch (3 mm) trowel coat. FIVE STAR WATERPROOFING-HG will cover 40 square feet (3.7 m²) when applied at 1/8 inch (3 mm) thickness.

FIVE STAR WATERPROOFING is available throughout the United States from a network of FIVE STAR WATERPROOFING PRODUCTS' dealers. For technical information and the source nearest you, contact FIVE STAR WATERPROOFING PRODUCTS' main office in Fairfield, Connecticut or your local FIVE STAR WATERPROOFING representative. For international availability, contact INTERNATIONAL CONSTRUCTION PRODUCTS RESEARCH, INC.

WATERPROOFING PRODUCTS

FIVE STAR WATERPROOFING PRODUCTS

* PATENTED * SELF-CURING * HIGH BOND * HIGH STRENGTH * WATERPROOF BARRIER * OIL RESISTANT * NONFLAMMABLE * SALT RESISTANT * NONMETALLIC * NONCRYSTALLINE TYPE * RAPID CURING * BRUSH * TROWEL * SPRAY * GUNITE * DRYSHAKE * UV RESISTANT * EXCELLENT FREEZE/THAW RESISTANCE * PROTECTION FOR MOISTURE SENSITIVE COATINGS * LOWEST INSTALLATION AND TOTAL COST * USE INSIDE OR OUTSIDE * MANUFACTURED AND AVAILABLE WORLDWIDE

CHAPTER 6
WATERPROOFING DELIVERY AND STORAGE PROCEDURES

A. DELIVERY CONDITION

FIVE STAR WATERPROOFING should be shipped from the plant and delivered to the site in sound, unopened condition. It should be stored, unopened until use, in a dry area. The temperature should be approximately 70°F, but not below 45°F, and not above 90°F.

B. STORAGE DAMAGE

Any material which becomes damp, congealed, or otherwise defective should be immediately removed from the site.

C. STORAGE TIME

The total job storage time of FIVE STAR WATERPROOFING should be limited to six months, or the manufacturer's recommended storage limit, whichever is less. For critical applications, it is recommended that a sample be sent to the manufacturer if the material has been stored for more than six months, for verification of the properties.

CHAPTER 7
WATERPROOFING PLACEMENT PROCEDURES

A. SURFACE PREPARATION

1. All concrete, concrete block, brick, stone and other masonry surfaces to which the product will be applied must be clean and sound. Wet or dry sand-blasting and/or concrete cleaners and degreasers may be required to properly clean the surface. All grease, oil, dust, laitance, paint, coatings, curing compounds, chemicals, cleaners, degreasers, and/or etchers and all other deleterious materials must be completely removed.

2. All surfaces must be roughened. The desired surface finish can be achieved by chipping, bush-hammering, sand-blasting or other approved methods. Steel-troweled or form finishes should be mechanically roughened.

3. All surfaces must be structurally sound. Repair all large cracks, holes and spalled areas, etc., with FIVE STAR WATERPROOFING, leaving a rough surface. For treatment of moving cracks and joints, contact FIVE STAR WATERPROOFING PRODUCTS.

4. All surfaces to which the waterproofing will be applied must be damp at the time of application. Wet down surfaces thoroughly with potable water, leaving surface free of excess water. No gloss should be visible.

5. Do not apply FIVE STAR WATERPROOFING on frozen surfaces or where frost is suspected in the substrate. Surfaces should be between 45°F and 90°F. Do not apply waterproofing when freezing temperatures are expected within 24 hours.

6. Active leaks should be plugged with a stable, quick-setting waterproof plug before applying FIVE STAR WATERPROOFING.

7. Due to the critical nature of surface preparation when applying a waterproofing product, it is essential that the contractors and the owner's representative approve the surface preparation to ensure that the surfaces are truly cleaned and roughened.

B. MIXING PROCEDURES

1. All cementitious waterproofing materials and potable water should be at a temperature between 45°F and 90°F at the time of mixing.

2. Use a mortar mixer (with moving blades) or heavy-duty drill and paddle mixer. Pre-wet all tools and mixer before mixing and pour out excess water.

3. Add the recommended amount of potable water and/or liquid to the mixer as directed in the manufacturer's instructions. Then add the dry powder slowly while mixing. Never exceed the maximum water limits printed on the container.

4. Mix in the manner and for the length of time as directed in the manufacturer's published instructions.

5. Never retemper the mix. Never add more water to bring back the consistency after material has begun to stiffen. Once material has been placed, do not overwork or over-trowel.

6. All equipment and tools should be thoroughly flushed clean with water before the waterproofing material has reached its initial set.

C. APPLICATION PROCEDURES

The following procedures are those normally used at the time of the writing of this handbook. See manufacturer's packages for any variations.

FIVE STAR WATERPROOFING is a very versatile product that allows a variety of application techniques. This versatility enables the best application technique for each project to be chosen, ensuring optimum performance and economy.

FIVE STAR WATERPROOFING can be applied by brush, trowel, wet spray, gunite/shotcrete, and using the dryshake/power trowel method (new slab construction only). The details of each of these techniques are described as follows.

1. *BRUSH*

　　To apply **FIVE STAR WATERPROOFING** by brush, the contents of the pail (50 lbs. powder and 2 qts. of **FIVE STAR WATERPROOFING** Liquid) are mixed with 2 to 2-1/2 qts. of potable water. The consistency should be varied slightly to adjust for the degree of roughness of the surface, with rougher surfaces requiring a looser consistency for ease of installation.

　　After the waterproofing has been properly mixed and the concrete or masonry prepared, the cementitious waterproofing should be applied in the manufacturer's recommended number of coats. Metallic and crystalline materials generally require three to five brush coats. **FIVE STAR WATERPROOFING** is applied in two thick brush coats, resulting in tremendous labor savings. Masonry brushes (sometimes known as whitewash brushes) are recommended. (Do not use a paint brush.) It has been found that nylon bristle brushes (maximum bristle length 3 inches) work well. The thickness of the total application should be at least 1/16 inch. Care should be taken to ensure that there are no pinholes, voids, or uncovered areas.

　　Before applying any additional coats of **FIVE STAR WATERPROOFING**, the previous coat should be checked to make sure the coating has fully set. After approximately four hours, under normal conditions, sprinkle the first coat with water; after the waterproofing surface is washed off, the second brush coat of waterproofing may then be applied. Moisten the first coat with a fine spray of water before applying the second coat. Differences in temperature and humidity will affect the time between coats. Most of the other cementitious waterproofings require moist curing for 24 hours between coats.

Brushing does not require highly trained workers and can produce good results where normal protection (up to 25 ft. of water pressure) is required.

2. *TROWEL APPLICATION*

The trowel is one of the most popular tools for applying **FIVE STAR WATERPROOFING**. Trowel application gives the contractor the opportunity to apply the waterproofing in a single 1/8" coat. No bond coats or long curing periods between coats are necessary. This option can be very important on small jobs.

"Trowel Application"

The dry material should be mixed with the **FIVE STAR WATERPROOFING** Liquid and up to two quarts of water (just enough to bring the material to a trowelable consistency). The waterproofing should be applied in a single 1/8 inch thick coat. Care should be taken to ensure that all holes and voids are completely filled. Standard concrete finishing techniques should be used to achieve the finish required, whether that be a smooth steel trowel or rough sponge float finish.

"Sponge Float Finishing
FIVE STAR WATERPROOFING (foreground)."

It must be noted that the ability to achieve a desired finish is totally dependent on the skill of the applicator, as the material is a waterproofing product and not an architectural coating.

3. *GUNITE/SHOTCRETE*

Guniting (or shotcreting) is a spray method where essentially dry cement powder is fed through a line to a nozzle where it is mixed with water and/or liquid and then sprayed. Gunite is the most economical way to apply **FIVE STAR WATERPROOFING.** Using the gunite spray technique, application rates of 1,000 sq. ft. per hour are common on large projects.

Guniting has many advantages over spraying or troweling on large projects because the walls can first be sandblasted with a gunite machine for roughening and preliminary cleaning, then washed down and cleaned for final application of gunited waterproofing. Because it is applied so rapidly, it permits additional time for special finishing. Gunite is excellent for applying the waterproofing over rough and uneven surfaces such as fieldstone foundations.

"Guniting FIVE STAR WATERPROOFING"

To use the best and most economical method, use gunite and ask for FIVE STAR WATERPROOFING, gunite grade, or extend it 30% by weight with a mortar sand. The waterproofing and the sand should be mixed and then dampened slightly (one to three quarts of water per 100 lbs. of dry mix) to keep the dust down. Over-dampening will result in jammed lines. Consult the manufacturer on the recommended amount of water. The addition of sand and dampening will ensure a good, steady feed rate of waterproofing to the nozzle. A steady material feed rate is essential to getting a uniform application of waterproofing.

The waterproofing should be sprayed on in a single 1/8" coat, making sure to fill all pores, holes and voids. No more than 200 ft. of line should be used. It is also advisable to find a gunite contractor that has had experience applying rapid setting specialty cement products.

4. *WET SPRAY*

FIVE STAR WATERPROOFING may be sprayed using plaster (insulation type) spray equipment. Best results with FIVE STAR WATERPROOFING have been obtained using carousel type pumps and 1-1/2 inch diameter (minimum) hose. A mortar mixer (with moving blades) should be positioned so that it empties directly into the hopper of the spray equipment.

A fine screen with openings smaller than the orifice in the spray nozzle must be placed on top of the sprayer's hopper to remove any lumps which can cause clogging. (If the nozzle jams, it is important to resume spraying as quickly as possible to prevent the waterproofing from setting up in the pump. It is advisable to have a spare spray gun to avoid long delays.)

After about every five batches, the pump and line should be flushed out to remove the buildup of material that occurs.

"Spraying FIVE STAR WATERPROOFING"

Provisions for disposing of the water used to clean the mixer between batches should be made. Hose length should not exceed 100 ft.

Each pail of **FIVE STAR WATERPROOFING** should be mixed with 2 qts. of **FIVE STAR WATERPROOFING** Liquid and approximately 2 qts. of water. Mix according the the manufacturer's recommendation. The consistency can be varied slightly by adjusting the amount of mixing water to compensate for changes in ambient temperature.

Wet spray may be used whenever the project is sufficiently large and is laid out so that uninterrupted spraying can take place. Spray is best suited to surfaces which are uneven and must only be attempted by workmen experienced in the use of plaster sprayers.

5. *DRYSHAKE/POWER TROWEL*

This method of application can be used to waterproof concrete slabs at the time the slabs are placed.

After the concrete has been placed, screeded, bull floated, and is ready to be floated with a power trowel, the cementitious waterproofing should be broadcast onto the slab at a rate recommended by the manufacturer. **FIVE STAR WATERPROOFING** powder is broadcast onto the slab at a rate of 3/4 to 1.0 lb./sq. ft. (see following photograph).

"Broadcasting **FIVE STAR WATERPROOFING** on freshly placed slab."

It is important not to broadcast the waterproofing before the concrete is capable of supporting a person's weight, leaving only a slight impression.

Broadcasting FIVE STAR WATERPROOFING too soon or onto a slab which has undergone "crusting" (premature hardening of the top layer of a slab usually caused by wind evaporation of surface moisture) can result in tearing of the waterproofing by the power trowel.

Since FIVE STAR WATERPROOFING has a working time of approximately 20 minutes, the product should not be broadcast too far ahead of the power trowel. The correct timing will allow a few minutes for the dry powder to soak up moisture from the concrete before the power trowel reaches it.

"Power Troweling the Dry Shake Powder"

Immediately after the power troweling has been finished in a given area, a high solids (minimum 28% solids) resin-based curing compound should be applied to protect the waterproofing.

The dryshake/power trowel method provides an economical means of applying FIVE STAR WATERPROOFING to a newly placed slab that requires mechanical finishing. Due to the importance of timing and the special techniques involved, an experienced finishing crew is required and special precautions (e.g., spare power trowels) are prudent.

6. CONSTRUCTION JOINTS

Proper treatment of the construction joints in the slab consists of sealing them with **FIVE STAR WATERPROOFING**, or if movement is expected at these joints, sealing them with an elastomeric sealant. To create an opening or notch that straddles the construction joint, a "block out" strip is used at the edge of each bay.

When the construction joint is to be filled with **FIVE STAR WATERPROOFING**, the dimensions of the notch should be approximately one inch deep and extend one-half inch into each bay, centered on the construction joint (creating a 1″ x 1″ notch). The concrete is then allowed a 28 day period in which to dry out and undergo shrinkage, further widening the construction joint. After roughening of the notch, the **FIVE STAR WATERPROOFING** is then mixed to a trowelable consistency and used to fill the notch. (See sketches below.)

TYPICAL NONMOVING CONSTRUCTION JOINT DETAIL

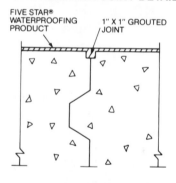

FIVE STAR®
WATERPROOFING
PRODUCT

1″ X 1″ GROUTED
JOINT

TYPICAL MOVING CONSTRUCTION JOINT DETAIL

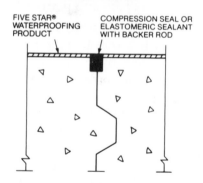

FIVE STAR®
WATERPROOFING
PRODUCT

COMPRESSION SEAL OR
ELASTOMERIC SEALANT
WITH BACKER ROD

D. RELATIVE COST OF APPLICATION

The following graph compares the relative cost of the different methods of application.

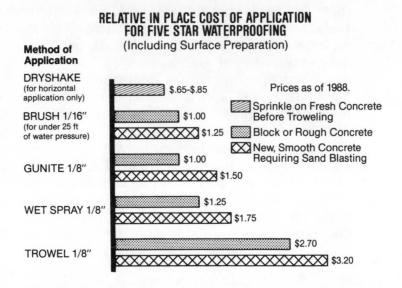

RELATIVE IN PLACE COST OF APPLICATION FOR FIVE STAR WATERPROOFING
(Including Surface Preparation)

Method of Application

DRYSHAKE
(for horizontal application only) — $.65-$.85

Prices as of 1988.

BRUSH 1/16"
(for under 25 ft of water pressure) — $1.00 / $1.25

GUNITE 1/8" — $1.00 / $1.50

WET SPRAY 1/8" — $1.25 / $1.75

TROWEL 1/8" — $2.70 / $3.20

Sprinkle on Fresh Concrete Before Troweling
Block or Rough Concrete
New, Smooth Concrete Requiring Sand Blasting

E. PROTECTION

FIVE STAR WATERPROOFING must be protected from freezing, rain, water, rapid evaporation and traffic until it reaches its normal strength. This can be accomplished by covering with plastic film. Cure according to manufacturer's recommended procedures. Under normal conditions, FIVE STAR WATERPROOFING reaches its normal strength in 24 hours and moist curing and curing compounds are not recommended. This results in significant cost savings and permits the waterproofed area to be put into operation quickly. When the dry shake method is used, a high solids content curing compound should be applied immediately after power troweling. For unique situations, contact the Engineering and Technical Center of FIVE STAR WATERPROOFING PRODUCTS DIVISION.

F. FIELD QUALITY CONTROL

1. Twenty-four hours after application, the FIVE STAR WATERPROOFING should be inspected to ensure that the product has cured to a hard finish, showing no softness or dusting. This can be done by randomly rubbing the cured material with your thumb.

2. If inadequate coverage is suspected, the area should be chipped out to determine if the minimum thickness has been applied. Chipped out areas must be carefully patched.
3. Visual inspection should be made to ensure that all holes, cracks, and voids have been sealed, leaving no pinholes or uncovered areas.
4. Adequacy of bond should be determined by tapping the cured material to ensure no hollow areas exist and a completely bonded installation has been achieved.
5. Any unacceptable areas must be outlined, removed, the surface prepared, and the material reapplied and reinspected.

G. RECOMMENDED ARCHITECTURAL DETAILS
   Recommended architectural details can be found at the back of this section.

CHAPTER 8
TYPICAL WATERPROOFING APPLICATIONS

"Parking Garage"

"Entire Bridge Sprayed with
FIVE STAR WATERPROOFING"

"Sewage Treatment Plant"

"Underground Vault to Contain Fuel Oil Tanks"

"Rehabilitation of a Settling Tank at a Paper Mill"

"Waterproofed Reflecting Pool/UV Resistance"

"Chloride Protection"

"Traffic Bearing"

"Protection for Moisture Sensitive Coatings"

"Waterproofing of Power Plant Scrubber Area"

"Gunited Stone Foundation"

"Foundation Waterproofed on Negative Side"

"Dry Shake/Power Trowel Method
Used to Waterproof Warehouse Floor"

"FIVE STAR WATERPROOFING Troweled On
to Waterproof Settling Tank at Paper Mill"

"Dam (Before Waterproofing)"

"Dam (After Waterproofing)"

CHAPTER 9
WATERPROOFING SPECIFICATIONS

Due to the critical nature of waterproofing, it is important that a proprietary specification be written to ensure the highest quality of waterproofing. The discussion on types of specifications in Section I, Chapter 8 is applicable to waterproofing as well as grout. Since there are a variety of materials which can be called cementitious waterproofing, it is imperative that the specifier be specific in describing what he wants. The proprietary specification will leave no doubt in anyone's mind as to what quality waterproofing is desired. If this cannot be done, a performance specification must preclude unqualified and non-performing materials.

Following are samples of various types of specifications for cementitious waterproofing.

Examples of Short Form Specifications:
1. *Proprietary Specifications*
   a. *Vertical Applications*

   All negative and positive side waterproofing as called for on the drawings and in the specifications shall be performed with **FIVE STAR WATERPROOFING** as manufactured by **FIVE STAR WATERPROOFING PRODUCTS,** a division of **FIVE STAR PRODUCTS, INC.,** Fairfield, CT. The waterproofing shall be mixed and installed according to the manufacturer's recommendations. No substitutions will be permitted. Technical service is provided by manufacturer upon request.

b. *Horizontal Applications*

All negative and positive side waterproofing on horizontal surfaces as called for on the drawings and in the specifications shall be performed with **FIVE STAR WATERPROOFING HG** as manufactured by **FIVE STAR WATERPROOFING PRODUCTS**, a division of **FIVE STAR PRODUCTS, INC.**, Fairfield, CT. The waterproofing shall be mixed and installed according to the manufacturer's recommendations. No substitutions will be permitted. Technical service is provided by manufacturer upon request.

2. *Or Approved Equal with Identical Properties*

All waterproofing called for on the drawings and/or in the specifications shall be performed with **FIVE STAR WATERPROOFING** (or **FIVE STAR WATERPROOFING HG**) as manufactured by **FIVE STAR WATERPROOFING PRODUCTS**, or approved equal with identical properties. The contractor must submit laboratory data verifying identical performance.

3. *Open Listing*

Naming three or more products in a specification.

The short form cannot be used for this type of specification because standards must be established to determine whether the products named can meet the requirements. Only the long form performance specification should be used in this case.

EXAMPLE OF SHORT FORM
PERFORMANCE SPECIFICATION

All cementitious waterproofing as called for on the drawings and/or in the specifications shall be performed with a material meeting the performance requirements that follow.

Cementitious membrane waterproofing shall consist of a self-curing, nonshrink cementitious membrane and job site material shall exhibit the following properties when applied in a single, self-curing coat at 1/8 inch thickness.

PROPERTY	TEST METHOD	TEST VALUE
A. Permeability	CRD C-48	1×10^{12} cm/sec (min.)
B. Shear Bond Strength	ASTM C 882	2,400 psi (min.)
C. Tensile Bond Strength	ASTM C 321	Substrate failure (min.)
D. Volume Change		
Plastic State	ASTM C 827	0.0% (min.) +0.4% (max.)
Hardened State (moist)	ASTM C 157	0.0% (min.) +0.05% (max.)
Hardened State (dry)	ASTM C 596	−0.05% (max.)
E. Compressive Strength		
1 day	ASTM C 109	4,000 psi (min.)
7 day	ASTM C 109	6,000 psi (min.)

CSI SECTION NO. 07100
PERFORMANCE SPECIFICATION
FOR
FIVE STAR CEMENTITIOUS
MEMBRANE WATERPROOFING

PART I - GENERAL
All positive and negative side waterproofing for concrete or masonry where indicated in specifications or on drawings as cementitious membrane waterproofing or cementitious waterproofing, shall apply to this section. This section also includes crack repair and sealing of active leaks.

WORK INCLUDED
(A) Clean and prepare surface to receive waterproofing in accordance with manufacturer's instructions.

(B) Apply cementitious membrane complete with cants, coves, fillets, construction and control joint treatment, sealing concrete penetrations and cracks.

1.01 REFERENCES
CPR Funnel Absorption Test:
Construction Products Research, Inc. is listed in the ASTM Directory of Testing Laboratories.

Corps of Engineers:
CRD C-48, Method of Test for Water Permeability of Concrete.

American Society for Testing and Materials:

ASTM C 109	Test Method for Compressive Strength of Hydraulic Cement Mortars (Using 2-in. or 50-mm Cube Specimens.)
ASTM C 157	Test Method for Length Change of Hardened Cement Mortar and Concrete.
ASTM C 321	Test Method for Bond Strength of Chemical-Resistant Mortars.
ASTM C 596	Test Method for Drying Shrinkage of Mortar Containing Portland Cement.

ASTM C 827   Standard Test Method for Change in Height at Early Ages of Cylindrical Specimens from Cementitious Mixtures.

1.02   SUBMITTALS

The contractor shall submit, prior to installation, for designer's approval, manufacturer's literature and test data from a laboratory listed in the ASTM Directory of Testing Laboratories that material complies with requirements in Sections 1.06 and 2.02. Designer should, at contractor's expense, buy any submitted material in the open marketplace, without the contractor's or manufacturer's knowledge, and test material at an independent laboratory to verify compliance with this specification.

1.03   QUALITY ASSURANCE

(A)   *Material Qualification*:
   1.   Conform to performance criteria in Section 2.02.

(B)   *Applicator Qualifications*:
   1.   Minimum of two years in application of cementitious waterproofing materials.
   2.   Experience with application by trowel, gunite, and/or spraying (as applicable) of cementitious materials.

(C)   *Sample Application:*
   1.   A sample application consisting of not less than 30 square feet shall be installed by the applicator in accordance with this section. The same application shall be examined in accordance with Section 3.06 of this specification entitled Field Quality Control. Work shall not proceed until acceptance of sample application has been obtained.
   2.   The sample application shall remain as a standard for all cementitious membrane waterproofing on this project.

1.04 DELIVERY, STORAGE AND HANDLING

(A) All waterproofing must be delivered to the job site in original, unopened packages, clearly labeled with the manufacturer's identification and printed instructions. All material shall be stored and handled in accordance with recommendations of the manufacturer and the American Concrete Institute. Do not store in temperatures below 45°F or above 90°F. Protect from freezing.

1.05 ENVIRONMENTAL CONDITIONS

Refer to the manufacturer's literature for any physical or environmental limitations or contact the manufacturer directly.

1.06 WARRANTY

The Applicator shall submit a written copy of manufacturer's warranty as part of Applicator's written warranty to cover workmanship and materials.

PART II - PRODUCT

2.01 MANUFACTURER

The following manufacturer supplies materials which meet this specification and offers field service:

Manufacturer	Products
Five Star Waterproofing	Five Star Waterproofing
Products, Division of	Five Star Waterproofing HG
Five Star Products, Inc.	
Fairfield, Connecticut	
800-243-2206 or 203-336-7970	

Other materials which meet this specification must be submitted to the designer for approval with the prime contractor's original bid documents by following the procedures outlined in Section 1.02.

2.02 MATERIALS

(A) Cementitious membrane waterproofing shall consist of a self curing, nonshrink cementitious membrane and job site material shall exhibit the following properties when applied in a single, self-curing coat at 1/8 inch thickness.

PROPERTY	TEST METHOD	TEST VALUE
A. Permeability	CRD C-48	1×10^{12} cm/sec (min.)
B. Shear Bond Strength	ASTM C 882	2,400 psi (min.)
C. Tensile Bond Strength	ASTM C 321	Substrate failure (min.)
D. Volume Change		
Plastic State	ASTM C 827	0.0% (min.) +0.4% (max.)
Hardened State (moist)	ASTM C 157	0.0% (min.) +0.05% (max.)
Hardened State (dry)	ASTM C 596	−0.05% (max.)
E. Compressive Strength		
1 day	ASTM C 109	4,000 psi (min.)
7 day	ASTM C 109	6,000 psi (min.)

PART III - EXECUTION

3.01 INSPECTION

(A) Inspect surfaces to receive waterproofing and verify the following:

1. They are free of ice, frost, dirt, grease, oil, curing compounds, form release agents, paints, impregnations, all loose material, and foreign matter likely to affect the bond or performance of the waterproofing.

2. That provisions for cants, coves, fillets, penetrations and construction joint strips are coordinated with concrete formwork.

3. That provisions for expansion and control joints are consistent with specifications and drawings.

4. Surfaces are sufficiently rough to comply with the requirements of Section 3.02 of this specification.

5. That surfaces/substrates to receive a positive side application have completed a minimum 28 day curing period in order that drying shrinkage cracks have nearly reached their maximum width.

6. That concrete is structurally sound, and all cracks have been repaired.

3.02 PREPARATION

(A) Cleaning:

All concrete, masonry and rock surfaces to which the cementitious membrane waterproofing will be applied must be clean. All grease, oil, dust, laitance, paint, coatings, curing compounds, unsound and weak concrete and all other foreign materials must be completely removed. Wet or dry sandblasting and/or acids, concrete cleaners and degreasers may be required to properly clean the surface.

(B) Surfaces to be waterproofed must be *rough*. Suitable mechanical roughening methods shall be used to produce a firm *granular* surface that must have the profile of medium grade sandpaper at a minimum.

(C) Repairing cracks, spalled areas, and patching holes.

1. All cracks not subject to movement shall be routed out to a minimum width and depth of 1 inch and patched with **FIVE STAR WATERPROOFING**.

2. All cracks subject to movement shall be treated as indicated in specifications and on drawings.

3. All cracks with active leaks shall be sealed with a waterproof plug per Section 3.05.

4. All honeycombed or spalled concrete areas and holes shall be patched with **FIVE STAR WATERPROOFING**.

(D) Surface Wetdown:

1. All surfaces shall be thoroughly saturated (using potable water), saturated and all freestanding and excess water shall be removed before applying waterproofing. No water gloss shall be visible at the time of application.

3.03 INSTALLATION

(A) Mix and apply materials in accordance with manufacturer's instructions and recommendations.

(B) Thoroughly mix waterproofing, using mortar mixer or electric drill and paddle mixer, leaving no lumps or unmixed materials. Do not use a concrete mixer. Add only enough water to reach the desired consistency. Do not exceed manufacturer's recommendations.

(C) *For Normal Protection* (up to 25 feet of water pressure for FIVE STAR WATERPROOFING only)

Apply a minimum of two thick brush coats to obtain a total application thickness of 1/16 inch minimum, leaving no pinholes or voids.

For Maximum Protection

Apply waterproofing in one coat, no less than 1/8″ thick, completely filling voids, holes, cracks, leaving no pinholes or uncovered areas.

    a. For small areas, waterproofing may be applied by trowel.

    b. For large areas, waterproofing may be applied with gunite equipment.

(D) Apply waterproofing in one application, at minimum dimensions of 1″ × 1″ strips for cants, coves, fillets, construction joints, and penetrations.

(E) Waterproofing must be protected from freezing, rain, hydrostatic pressure, and traffic until it reaches its normal 24 hour strength. Moist curing and curing compounds are not recommended. Consult the manufacturer for specific recommendations on proper curing.

3.04 PROTECTION COURSES

(A) Under normal nontraffic or nonabrasive conditions, the cementitious membrane waterproofing may not require a protection course.

(B) FIVE STAR WATERPROOFING HG does not require a protection course.

3.05 SEALING OF ACTIVE LEAKS

(A) Open crack or holes by cutting to a minimum depth of one inch; for severe leaks, one and one-half to two inches.

(B) Mix and apply waterproof plug in accordance with manufacturer's instructions.

(C)   Finish off surface and render flush with a minimum 1/8" coat of FIVE STAR WATERPROOFING per Section 3.03.

3.06   FIELD QUALITY CONTROL

(A)   Twenty-four hours after application, the cementitious membrane waterproofing shall be inspected to ensure that coating has cured to a hard finish, showing no softness or dusting. This can be done by rubbing the cured membrane to ensure that it is hard.

(B)   The cured membrane shall be chipped and patched to determine if the required minimum thickness has been applied in those areas where inadequate coverage is suspected.

(C)   Inspection for complete coverage shall be made to ensure all holes, cracks, and voids have been filled, leaving no pinholes or uncovered areas, and all joints and cracks have been properly treated.

(D)   The bond can also be inspected by tapping the cured, rigid membrane to ensure no hollow sounds occur and a tight, strong bond has been achieved.

(E)   Any improperly applied cementitious membrane waterproofing material shall be removed and surfaces shall be properly prepared, patched with cementitious membrane waterproofing and reinspected.

CHAPTER 10
TECHNICAL DATA ON FIVE STAR
WATERPROOFING PRODUCTS

FIVE STAR
WATERPROOFING
PRODUCTS

This chapter contains product literature, magazine re-
prints and technical bulletins on **FIVE STAR WATERPROOF-
ING** products. **FIVE STAR** products are designed to provide
a higher level of performance.

Use Five Star®Waterproofing Products And You'll Never Have To Worry About Water Penetration Again.

Five Star Waterproofing is a unique waterproofing cement that can be applied to concrete, brick, block, or stone to provide complete, foolproof protection against water penetration. One coat forms a cementitious barrier that withstands up to 200 feet (61.0 m) of water pressure. Because it can be applied to either the inside or outside of a structure, Five Star Waterproofing can protect both new and existing concrete structures from water damage.

The Advantages of Waterproofing over Dampproofing

The terms "dampproofing" and "waterproofing" are often confused. A dampproofing material will "resist" the passage of water where there is no hydrostatic pressure, i.e. moist soil or wind-driven rain. Used in hydrostatic applications, dampproofing products are ineffective.

In contrast, a "waterproofing" material must completely block the passage of water under pressure. As a true waterproofing product, Five Star Waterproofing blocks water penetration under hydrostatic pressures encountered with a holding tank or a high water table. It forms a waterproof barrier that even works on porous surfaces such as cement block.

Use Five Star Waterproofing Inside or Out

Five Star Waterproofing may be applied to either side of a concrete structure with equal effectiveness. Five Star Waterproofing's unique "negative side" capability makes waterproof protection available from the inside, even after construction is completed. Large holding tanks, equipment pits, basements, structures and even dams can be effectively protected by applying Five Star Waterproofing products.

Versatility Means Economy

Five Star Waterproofing can be installed by a wide range of application methods. By selecting the appropriate degree of protection and the most efficient application method, you'll secure maximum performance with minimum cost.

BRUSH
For smaller applications or where maximum protection may not be required, Five Star Waterproofing can be easily applied in brushed coats to 1/16 inch (1.6 mm) thickness offering protection for up to 25 feet (7.6 m) of water pressure.

TROWEL
Five Star Waterproofing can also be applied in a single 1/8 inch (3 mm) trowel coat which provides protection up to 200 feet (61.0 m) of water pressure.

SPRAY/GUNITE
For larger installations, a 1/8 inch (3 mm) coat may be sprayed on for maximum protection at maximum economy. This is particularly effective on irregular surfaces.

DRY SHAKE
Five Star Waterproofing may be broadcast onto freshly placed concrete and then power trowelled to waterproof a slab or deck.

For High Traffic Areas, Use Five Star Waterproofing-HG

Five Star Waterproofing-HG is a "self-leveling" system that applies easily to offer maximum water protection at 1/8 inch (3 mm) thickness for floors, parking garages, and other traffic-bearing surfaces.

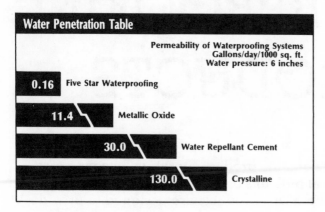

Water Penetration Table

Permeability of Waterproofing Systems
Gallons/day/1000 sq. ft.
Water pressure: 6 inches

0.16	Five Star Waterproofing
11.4	Metallic Oxide
30.0	Water Repellant Cement
130.0	Crystalline

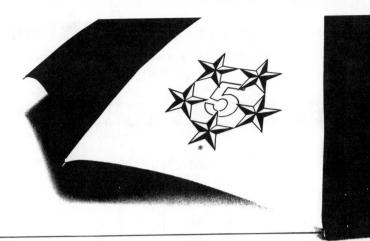

Easy Application Under Many Conditions

Five Star Waterproofing can be reliably applied in temperatures from 45°F (7°C) to 90°F (32°C). Five Star's unique self-curing composition eliminates most curing problems which saves time and money. Five Star Waterproofing will bond to sound concrete no matter which application method you choose. And newly protected surfaces may be put in service in as little as 24 hours.

Five Star Support

The Five Star Engineering and Technical Center has a qualified staff of professionals on hand to answer your questions. Whether you're looking for advice on writing a specification, or looking for field technical support, the people at Five Star's Engineering and Technical Center are available to assist you.

Five Star Waterproofing has been providing effective water protection for years. Project profiles are available on a wide variety of waterproofing applications.

Specification Guidelines

All negative and positive side waterproofing shall be performed with Five Star Waterproofing as manufactured by Five Star Waterproofing Products in Fairfield, CT. The job-shipped material must exhibit a permeability rate of no more than 1×10^{-12} cm/sec when tested per CRD C-48 at 1/8 inch (3 mm) thickness.

Packaging and Availability

Five Star Waterproofing is packaged in a 5 gallon weatherproof plastic pail containing 50 lbs. of dry material and a ½ gallon plastic container of Five Star Waterproofing liquid.

The unit coverage for Five Star Waterproofing is 85 square feet (7.9 m²) when brushed to a 1/16 inch (1.6 mm) total thickness in a two coat application and 42 square feet (3.9 m²) when applied in a 1/8 inch (3 mm) trowel coat. Five Star Waterproofing-HG will cover 40 square feet (3.7 m²) when applied at 1/8 inch (3 mm) thickness.

Five Star Waterproofing is available throughout the United States from a network of Five Star Waterproofing Products' Dealers. For technical information and the source nearest you, contact Five Star Waterproofing Products main office in Fairfield, Conn. or your local Five Star Waterproofing representative. For international availability contact International Construction Products Research, Inc.

Sample Applications

FIVE STAR WATERPROOFING	FIVE STAR WATERPROOFING-HG (HORIZONTAL GRADE)
Wastewater Treatment Tanks Elevator/Escalator Pits Tanks Tunnels Building Foundations Vaults, Pits Dams Bridges	Parking Decks Bridge Decks Mechanical Rooms Slabs Floors High Traffic Aisles

Typical Physical Properties

Plastic Shrinkage ASTM C-827	0.00% Shrinkage
Hardened Shrinkage ASTM C-157(Wet) ASTM C-596(Dry)	0.00% Shrinkage 0.05% Shrinkage
Compressive Strength ASTM C-109	4,000 PSI (27.6 MPa) 1 Day 7,000 PSI (48.3 MPa) 28 Days
Shear Bond Strength ASTM C-882	2,400 PSI (16.5 MPa)
Tensile Bond Strength ASTM C-321	Substrate Failure
Permeability CRD C-48	
1/8″ (3mm) Thickness	7.16×10^{-13}cm/sec (Neg. side) 7.96×10^{-14}cm/sec (Pos. side)

The Five Star Family of Quality Products

The Five Star name has always been associated with quality, high performance products.

Five Star manufactures:

PRECISION NON-SHRINK CEMENTITIOUS GROUTS	APPLICATION
FIVE STAR GROUT	Premier all-purpose grout for setting equipment, structural columns, anchor bolts, and pre-cast work.
FIVE STAR INSTANT GROUT	Rapid-strength-gain grout for four-hour machinery start-up and cold weather grouting.
FIVE STAR SPECIAL GROUT 100	Fluid grout for applications with tight clearances.
FIVE STAR SPECIAL GROUT 110	Pumpable grout for large placements and limited access applications.
FIVE STAR SPECIAL GROUT 120	Saltwater-resistant grout for saltwater-attack areas.
FIVE STAR SPECIAL GROUT 130	White or special-colored cement grout for architectural structural grouting.
FIVE STAR SPECIAL GROUT 150	Sulfate-resistant grout for sulfate-attack areas or deep placements.
FIVE STAR SPECIAL GROUT 160	High-density grout for radiation shielding.
FIVE STAR SPECIAL GROUT 200	High-temperature-resistant grout for high-temperature applications.
FIVE STAR SPECIAL GROUT 400	Fluid, high-bond-stength grout for small annular spaces or cable grouting.
FIVE STAR SPECIAL GROUT 550	Excellent hot-weather grout for grouting at mix temperatures up to 115° F without cold water.

PRECISION NON-SHRINK EPOXY GROUTS	APPLICATION
FIVE STAR EPOXY GROUT	Premier, all-purpose epoxy grout for high-impact vibration, and chemical-attack applications.
FIVE STAR ET EPOXY GROUT	High-temperature-resistant epoxy grout for applications with operating temperatures up to 250° F.
FIVE STAR RAPID EPOXY GROUT	Very fast strength gain for two-hour start-up of heavy equipment.
FIVE STAR SPEED EPOXY CHOCK	A very flowable rapid setting epoxy grout for tight clearances.

WATERPROOFING	APPLICATION
FIVE STAR WATERPROOFING	A high performance system for horizontal and vertical surfaces capable of withstanding 200 feet of water pressure. Applied by brushing, troweling, spraying, guniting, or dry shake.
FIVE STAR WATERPROOFING—HG (HORIZONTAL GRADE)	A reliable waterproofing system for traffic-bearing and heavy-duty surfaces.

CONCRETE REPAIR MATERIALS	APPLICATION
FIVE STAR STRUCTURAL CONCRETE	A permanent patch material suitable for both horizontal and vertical surfaces.
FIVE STAR HIGHWAY PATCH	A permanent fast setting patch for road and bridge repair.
FIVE STAR MAG-PHOS	A magnesium phosphate for patching dry concrete substrates.
FIVE STAR CONCRETE PATCH	An easy to use, fast setting patch for temporary patching of concrete.

Division of Five Star Products, Inc.
425 Stillson Road, Fairfield, CT 06430
(203)336-7970 Outside Connecticut (800)243-2206
Telex: 643857   Cable: Five Star   Facsimile: (203)336-7939
Marketed Internationally By:
International Construction Products Research, Inc. (203)336-7950

WARRANTY

FIVE STAR WATERPROOFING PRODUCTS warrants its products to be free from defects in the material shipped. Should a defect be proven in the material within four years from the date of sale, Five Star Waterproofing Products' sole liability shall not exceed the cost of defective material on a pro-rated basis. The warranty extends to the original purchaser only for the waterproofing performance of the material when applied in accordance with Five Star Waterproofing's written instructions. These recommended procedures are for normal field practice. They may be modified by the designer, specifier, purchaser or their authorized agent since only they are responsible for the design, installation and supervision of specific conditions and installations. Five Star Waterproofing Products' warranty shall be exclusive and in lieu of any other warranty or guarantee expressed or implied, including the implied warranties of merchantability and fitness for a particular purpose and all other warranties otherwise arising by operation of law, course of dealing, custom of trade or otherwise. No labor costs or any claims for consequential or other damages of any kind shall be allowed or recognized. Any questions regarding complete installation guarantee or warranty should be directed to the installer contracting the work.

Printed in U.S.A.
201086

©Five Star Waterproofing Products 1986

THE **APPLICATOR**

SEALANT & WATERPROOFERS INSTITUTE

1800 PICKWICK AVENUE ● GLENVIEW, ILLINOIS 60025 ● (312) 724-7700   Fall 1984

Waterproofing or Dampproofing? What Does Your Guaranty or Warranty Offer?

by Warner K. Babcock – Summary of Fall Meeting Presentation

ASTM D-1079 defines *Waterproofing* as treatment of a surface or structure to *prevent* passage of water under *hydrostatic pressure* and *Dampproofing* as treatment of a surface or structure to *resist* the passage of water in *the absence of hydrostatic pressure*. Unfortunately, there are no clear practical or functional distinctions made between prevent and resist in dictionaries or in other references. Furthermore, the majority of conditions that have been associated with dampproofing do create some level of pressure.

Examples of conditions which can create a nominal or significant pressure are (1) ponding water, (2) wind driven rain (1"-9" head), (3) tire traffic (60-120 ft head), (4) waves, (5) snow and water being thrown by plows or cars, (6) water dripping or falling from deck, ledge or spillway, (7) saturated soil from rain, (8) water trapped under tile, slabs, asphalt toppings or overlays (transferring the loads due to traffic—60 ft head), and (9) water and water vapor trapped behind paint, flooring and adhesives. It is actually quite rare in practice to find an application where no pressure will ever exist, either intermittently or constantly.

Many of the commonly used standard test methods and federal specifications do not take into consideration significant or practical pressures for true waterproofing applications in the field. Federal Specification TT-P-001411 (9 ft head) does take into account a pressure, but the specification allows droplets of water to show through the coating after 48 hours of pressure. The Corps of Engineers CRD-C48 test method (0-460 ft head) may provide the best test method and apparatus for evaluating materials under pressure, with either a negative or positive side application. However, the numerical results of the CRD-C48 test method (in cm/sec) are not easily understood. From the numerical results of this test method, and others mentioned, it is difficult to answer questions such as: When will dampness show? How much loss of water from a retaining structure will actually occur? What amount of salt will intrude into the concrete under pressure and how deep will salts penetrate? How much moisture and pressure will cause paints, coatings, floor coverings and insulation to be damaged, debond or blister? What permeability level will increase the relative humidity in a below grade useable space? Will water actually go completely through the wall?

These are not only performance level questions, but also cost/benefit questions that have to be decided based on test data with an appropriate test method and test condition.

Contractors, architects, engineers and owners who merely accept a material's performance based on terms and data such as "100% waterproof," "seals," "waterproof coating," "protects from water or salt," "prevents water," "withstands hydrostatic pressure," "plugs or stops leaks," "water resistant," "no visible leaks after 30 minutes," "resists hydrostatic pressure," "permeability—nil," "low absorption," "1.0 perms," "permeability coefficient 1x10⁻⁸ cm/sec," and "it is waterproof," may get into trouble. These claims can be deceptive and may not give the whole story. What may be worse is that an owner may pay for the application of a material described as above and later find his parking deck corroding and falling apart. What happens to the architect or engineer who specifies that material, thinking he is getting a "waterproofing," or the contractor who risks his money and reputation with a "waterproofing" guaranty, when they find out that the material did not stop the water or salt from penetrating into the concrete, through the concrete, into useable space, or worse, contaminated ground water due to a leaking tank.

The vagueness of industry definitions and the confusing usage of the terms "waterproofing" and "dampproofing," in addition to the inadequate test standards and known levels of performance required for each application, could cause problems for SWI contractors. Contractors are the first line of defense in a "failure."

SWI has an opportunity to take the leadership. We can clearly and practically differentiate between dampproofing and waterproofing, educate our membership on this problem, and assist in developing appropriate standards of performance which are acceptable to the members who guaranty or warranty installed systems.

[1]For example, ASTM E96 procedure BW (approximately 1/4" – 1/2" head), ASTM C642 or C67 (% absorption of cubes submerged), ASTM E514 (4" head spray simulation), AASHTO T-259 (1/2" head), NCHRP Report 244 (1" head), Federal Specifications TT-P-0035 (5" head spray)

 SYSTEM

FIVE STAR® WATERPROOFING

DESCRIPTION

Five Star Waterproofing is a patented cementitious waterproofing system that creates a waterproof barrier which can resist extremely high water pressures on either the negative or positive sides of a structure. This unique high performance product utilizes a liquid polymer which ensures reliable application under a wide variety of field conditions. Five Star Waterproofing is applied in one coat by trowel or spray, or in a two coat brush application, onto concrete, masonry or rock. Dry-shake application of Five Star Waterproofing onto freshly poured concrete slabs is also possible to create a rigid waterproof membrane that can be used as a traffic-bearing system.

ADVANTAGES

- Excellent Waterproof Barrier
- Effective on Negative or Positive Side
- High Bond Strength
- Excellent Freeze/Thaw Resistance
- Excellent Resistance to Chloride Ion Penetration
- Brush, Trowel, Gunite or Spray Applied
- Reliable Application
- Self-Curing
- Low in-Place Cost

APPLICATIONS

- Concrete, Masonry or Rock
- Negative/Positive Side Application
- Base for Moisture-Sensitive Coatings
- Wastewater Treatment Plants
- Elevator/Escalator Pits
- Tanks
- Tunnels
- Foundations
- Manholes and Vaults
- Dams

TYPICAL PHYSICAL PROPERTIES

Plastic Shrinkage
ASTM C-827

0.00% Shrinkage

Hardened Shrinkage
ASTM C-157 (Wet)
ASTM C-596 (Dry)

0.00% Shrinkage
0.05% Shrinkage

Compressive Strength
ASTM C-109

4,000 PSI (27.6 MPa) 1 Day
7,000 PSI (48.3 MPa) 28 Days

Shear Bond Strength
ASTM C-882

2,400 PSI (16.5 MPa)

Tensile Bond Strength
ASTM C-321

Substrate Failure

Permeability
CRD C-48
1/8″ (3mm)Thickness

7.16×10^{-13}cm/sec (Neg side)
7.96×10^{-14}cm/sec (Pos side)

IV.6

PLACEMENT GUIDELINES

Surface Preparation: Before applying Five Star Waterproofing all surfaces must be clean, structurally sound, free of oil, grease, laitance, loose material and other foreign contaminants. Mechanically roughen smooth surfaces to ensure good bonding (medium sandpaper profile or rougher). Clean thoroughly with liberal quantities of potable water, leaving surface damp.

Mixing: Thoroughly mix Five Star Waterproofing using all the Five Star Waterproofing Liquid provided and only enough water to reach desired consistency. Never exceed the maximum allowable mixing water stated on the container. Do not mix more material than can be applied in 20 minutes.

Application:

■ **Normal Protection - Brush Application**
Apply a minumum of two thick brush coats. Total application thickness should be a minumum of 1/16″ (1.6mm) with no pinholes or voids. Allow Five Star Waterproofing to completely harden (4-8 hrs.) before applying next coat. Thoroughly dampen hardened waterproofing before applying additional coats.

■ **Maximum Protection - Trowel, Gunite and Spray Application**
Apply Waterproofing in one coat by trowel or spray to at least 1/8″ (3mm) thickness, completely filling all holes, pores and voids.

Curing and Protection: Five Star Waterproofing is a self-curing product under normal field conditions. Five Star Waterproofing must be protected from freezing, rain, hydrostatic pressures and traffic until it reaches its normal 24 hr. strength.

TECHNICAL SERVICES

Five Star Waterproofing Products offers technical service covering specifications, architectural details, and on-site service. For guidance and recommendations in the proper selection and use of our products, call 203-336-7970.

SPECIFICATION GUIDELINES

All negative and positive side waterproofing shall be performed with Five Star Waterproofing as manufactured by Five Star Waterproofing Products, a Division of Five Star Products, Inc., Fairfield, Connecticut. The waterproofing shall be mixed and installed according to the manufacturer's recommendations. No substitutions will be permitted. Technical service is provided by manufacturer upon request.

PACKAGING, ORDERING AND AVAILABILITY

Five Star Waterproofing is packaged in 5 gal. weatherproof plastic pails with 50 lbs. of dry material and a 1/2 gallon plastic container of Five Star Waterproofing Liquid enclosed.

The unit coverage for Five Star waterproofing is 85 sq. ft. (7.9m²) when brushed in a 1/16″ (1.6mm) thickness and 42 sq. ft. (39m²) when troweled in a 1/8″ (3mm) thickness. No allowance has been made for surface roughness, irregularities, waste or spillage.

Five Star Waterproofing products are available throughout the U.S. from a network of Five Star Waterproofing Products Dealers. For the source nearest you, contact Five Star Waterproofing Products' main office in Fairfield, Connecticut, 203-336-7970 or your local representative. For international availability contact International Construction Products Research at 203-336-7950.

STORAGE AND HANDLING

Five Star® Waterproofing should be stored in a cool, dry place in accordance with the recommendations of the American Concrete Institute. Do not store in temperatures below 45°F (7°C). Protect from freezing. Extended storage may affect performances. Please contact manufacturer for further information.

WARRANTY

Five Star Waterproofing Products warrants its products to be free from defects in the material shipped. Should a defect be proven in the material within four years from the date of sale, Five Star Waterproofing Products' sole liability shall not exceed the cost of defective material on a pro-rated basis. The warranty extends to the original purchaser only, for the waterproofing performance of the material when applied in accordance with Five Star Waterproofing Products' written instructions. These recommended procedures are for normal field practice. They may be modified by the designer, specifier, purchaser or their authorized agent since only they are responsible for the design, installation and supervision of specific conditions and installations. FIVE STAR WATERPROOFING PRODUCTS' GUARANTEE SHALL BE EXCLUSIVE AND IN LIEU OF ANY OTHER WARRANTY OR GUARANTEE EXPRESSED OR IMPLIED, INCLUDING THE IMPLIED WARRANTIES OF MERCHANTABILITY AND FITNESS FOR A PARTICULAR PURPOSE AND ALL OTHER WARRANTIES OTHERWISE ARISING BY OPERATION OF LAW, COURSE OF DEALING, CUSTOM OF TRADE OR OTHERWISE. No labor costs or any claims for consequential or other damages of any kind shall be allowed or recognized.

Any questions regarding complete installation guarantee or warranty should be directed to the installer contracting the work.

FIVE STAR WATERPROOFING PRODUCTS

DIVISION OF FIVE STAR PRODUCTS, INC.
MARKETED INTERNATIONALLY BY INTERNATIONAL CONSTRUCTION PRODUCTS RESEARCH
425 STILLSON ROAD, FAIRFIELD, CONNECTICUT 06430
(203) 336-7970 • CABLE: FIVE STAR • FACSIMILE: (203) 336-7939
TELEX: 643857 • COPYRIGHT 1987 • 8875K

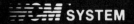
FIVE STAR® WATERPROOFING HG
(Horizontal Grade)

DESCRIPTION

Five Star Waterproofing HG is a patented traffic-bearing cementitious waterproofing system that forms a waterproof barrier which is effective against high water pressures, and provides an excellent resistance to chloride ion penetration. This unique high performance product utilizes a liquid polymer to insure reliable application under a wide variety of field conditions. Five Star Waterproofing HG eliminates the need to sandwich waterproofing since it can be applied on the top surface of a slab or deck and does not require protection from normal traffic due to its high strength and abrasion resistance. Having a flowable consistency, this material is easily spread in a minimum 1/8 inch (3mm) thickness and finished with a hand float. Five Star Waterproofing HG creates a tough abrasion resistant waterproof barrier that naturally provides a textured surface.

ADVANTAGES

- Excellent Waterproof Barrier
- Effective on Negative or Positive Side
- High Bond Strength
- Excellent Freeze/Thaw Resistance
- Excellent Resistance to Chloride Ion Penetration

- High Abrasion Resistance
- Reliable One Coat Application
- Flowable Consistency
- Self-Curing

APPLICATIONS

- Horizontal Concrete Surfaces
- Negative/Positive Side Application
- Base for Moisture-Sensitive Coatings
- Rapid Floor Leveling and Paching
- Parking Decks

- Mechanical Rooms
- Base for Carpet and Tile
- Slabs
- Roofs
- Floors

TYPICAL PHYSICAL PROPERTIES

Plastic Shrinkage
ASTM C-827

0.00% Shrinkage

Hardened Shrinkage
ASTM C-157 (Wet)
ASTM C-596 (Dry)

0.00% Shrinkage
0.05% Shrinkage

Compressive Strength
ASTM C-109

4,000 PSI (27.6 MPa) 1 Day
7,000 PSI (48.3 MPa) 28 Days

Shear Bond Strength
ASTM C-882

2,400 PSI (16.5 MPa)

Tensile Bond Strength
ASTM C-321

Substrate Failure

Permeability
CRD C-48
1/8″ (3mm)Thickness

7.16×10^{-13}cm/sec (Neg side)
7.96×10^{-14}cm/sec (Pos side)

PLACEMENT GUIDELINES

Surface Preparation: Before applying Five Star Waterproofing HG all surfaces must be clean, structurally sound, free of oil, grease, laitance, loose material and other foreign contaminants. Mechanically roughen smooth surfaces to ensure good bonding (medium sandpaper profile or rougher). Clean thoroughly with liberal quantities of potable water, leaving surface damp.

Mixing: Thoroughly mix Five Star Waterproofing HG using all the Five Star Waterproofing Liquid provided and only enough water to reach desired consistency. Never exceed the maximum allowable mixing water stated on the container. Do not mix more material than can be applied in 20 minutes.

Application: Apply HG in one coat by spreading and hand floating to at least 1/8″ (3mm) thickness, completely filling all holes, pores and voids.

Curing and Protection: Five Star Waterproofing HG is a self-curing product under normal field conditions. Five Star Waterproofing HG must be protected from freezing, rain, hydrostatic pressures and traffic until it reaches its normal 24 hr. strength.

TECHNICAL SERVICES

Five Star Waterproofing Products offers technical service covering specifications, architectural details, and on-site service. For guidance and recommendations in the proper selection and use of our products, call 203-336-7970.

SPECIFICATION GUIDELINES

All negative and positive side waterproofing on horizontal surfaces shall be performed with Five Star Waterproofing HG as manufactured by Five Star Waterproofing, a Division of Five Star Products, Inc., Fairfield, Connecticut. The waterproofing shall be mixed and installed according to the manufacturer's recommendations. No substitutions will be permitted. Technical service is provided by manufacturer upon request.

PACKAGING, ORDERING AND AVAILABILITY

Five Star Waterproofing HG is packaged in 5 gal. weatherproof plastic pails with 50lbs. of dry material and a 1/2 gallon plastic container of Five Star Waterproofing Liquid enclosed.

The unit coverage for HG is 40 sq. ft. (3.7m²) when applied in a 1/8″ (3mm) thickness. No allowance has been made for surface roughness, irregularities, waste or spillage. Five Star Waterproofing products are available throughout the U.S. from a network of Five Star Waterproofing Products Dealers. For the source nearest you, contact Five Star Waterproofing Products' main office in Fairfield, Connecticut, 203-336-7970 or your local representative. For international availability contact International Construction Products Research at 203-336-7950.

STORAGE AND HANDLING

Five Star® Waterproofing HG should be stored in a cool, dry place in accordance with the recommendation of the American Concrete Institute. Do not store in temperatures below 45°F (7°C). Protect from freezing. Extended storage may affect performance. Please contact manufacturer for further information.

WARRANTY

Five Star Waterproofing Products warrants its products to be free from defects in the material shipped. Should a defect be proven in the material within four years from the date of sale, Five Star Waterproofing Products' sole liability shall not exceed the cost of defective material on a pro-rated basis. The warranty extends to the original purchaser only, for the waterproofing performance of the material when applied in accordance with Five Star Waterproofing Products' written instructions. These recommended procedures are for normal field practice. They may be modified by the designer, specifier, purchaser or their authorized agent since only they are responsible for the design, installation and supervision of specific conditions and installations. FIVE STAR WATERPROOFING PRODUCTS' WARRANTY SHALL BE EXCLUSIVE AND IN LIEU OF ANY OTHER WARRANTY OR GUARANTEE EXPRESSED OR IMPLIED, INCLUDING THE IMPLIED WARRANTIES OF MERCHANTABILITY AND FITNESS FOR A PARTICULAR PURPOSE AND ALL OTHER WARRANTIES OTHERWISE ARISING BY OPERATION OF LAW, COURSE OF DEALING, CUSTOM OF TRADE OR OTHERWISE. No labor costs or any claims for consequential or other damages of any kind shall be allowed or recognized.

Any questions regarding complete installation guarantee or warranty should be directed to the installer contracting the work.

FIVE STAR WATERPROOFING PRODUCTS

DIVISION OF FIVE STAR PRODUCTS, INC.
MARKETED INTERNATIONALLY BY INTERNATIONAL CONSTRUCTION PRODUCTS RESEARCH
425 STILLSON ROAD, FAIRFIELD, CONNECTICUT 06430
(203) 336-7970 • CABLE: FIVE STAR • FACSIMILE: (203) 336-7939
TELEX: 643857 • COPYRIGHT 1987 • 8875K

TECHNICAL ⬟5⬟ BULLETIN
FIVE STAR

FIVE STAR® WATERPROOFING PRODUCTS
DESIGN DETAILS

The following Design Details are to be used as guidelines for preparing plans and drawings. They must be coordinated with the specification documents indicating which FIVE STAR WATERPROOFING product should be used for each area. The designer should review the FIVE STAR WATERPROOFING literature for performance properties, recommendations, use, and limitations prior to selecting the proper product.

Please note that either FIVE STAR WATERPROOFING or FIVE STAR WATERPROOFING HG (horizontal grade) can be used on horizontal surfaces. FIVE STAR WATERPROOFING HG has a higher abrasion resistance but can only provide a textured surface. If a smoother finish is required or if the application is on a vertical surface, FIVE STAR WATERPROOFING must be used.

If unique or special conditions are encountered that are not covered in these Details, contact FIVE STAR WATERPROOFING PRODUCTS' Engineering and Technical Center at the main office in Fairfield, Connecticut, (203) 336-7970.

TYPICAL MANHOLE DETAIL

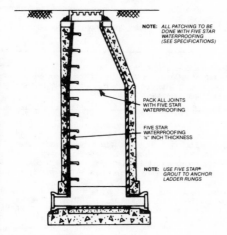

NOTE: ALL PATCHING TO BE DONE WITH FIVE STAR WATERPROOFING (SEE SPECIFICATIONS)

PACK ALL JOINTS WITH FIVE STAR WATERPROOFING

FIVE STAR WATERPROOFING ½" INCH THICKNESS

NOTE: USE FIVE STAR® GROUT TO ANCHOR LADDER RUNGS

TYPICAL ELEVATOR PIT DETAIL

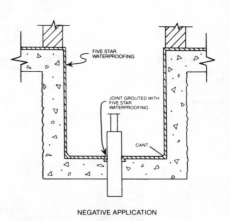

FIVE STAR WATERPROOFING

JOINT GROUTED WITH FIVE STAR WATERPROOFING

CANT

NEGATIVE APPLICATION

Technical Bulletin #50 9/87
1800P/1

©1987 by FIVE STAR WATERPROOFING
PRODUCTS

FIVE STAR WATERPROOFING PRODUCTS (Div. of Five Star Products, Inc.)
425 Stillson Road, Fairfield, Connecticut 06430 (203) 336-7970

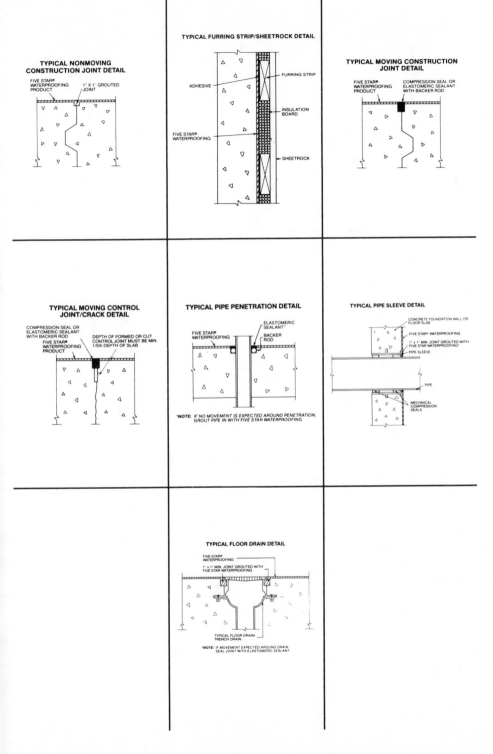

TYPICAL NONMOVING CONSTRUCTION JOINT DETAIL

FIVE STAR® WATERPROOFING PRODUCT

1" X 1" GROUTED JOINT

TYPICAL FURRING STRIP/SHEETROCK DETAIL

ADHESIVE

FURRING STRIP

INSULATION BOARD

FIVE STAR® WATERPROOFING

SHEETROCK

TYPICAL MOVING CONSTRUCTION JOINT DETAIL

FIVE STAR® WATERPROOFING PRODUCT

COMPRESSION SEAL OR ELASTOMERIC SEALANT WITH BACKER ROD

TYPICAL MOVING CONTROL JOINT/CRACK DETAIL

COMPRESSION SEAL OR ELASTOMERIC SEALANT WITH BACKER ROD

FIVE STAR® WATERPROOFING PRODUCT

DEPTH OF FORMED OR CUT CONTROL JOINT MUST BE MIN. 1/5th DEPTH OF SLAB

TYPICAL PIPE PENETRATION DETAIL

FIVE STAR® WATERPROOFING

ELASTOMERIC SEALANT*

BACKER ROD

*NOTE: IF NO MOVEMENT IS EXPECTED AROUND PENETRATION, GROUT PIPE IN WITH FIVE STAR WATERPROOFING.

TYPICAL PIPE SLEEVE DETAIL

CONCRETE FOUNDATION WALL OR FLOOR SLAB

FIVE STAR® WATERPROOFING

1" x 1" MIN JOINT GROUTED WITH FIVE STAR WATERPROOFING*

PIPE SLEEVE

PIPE

MECHANICAL COMPRESSION SEALS

TYPICAL FLOOR DRAIN DETAIL

FIVE STAR® WATERPROOFING

1" x 1" MIN JOINT GROUTED WITH FIVE STAR WATERPROOFING

TYPICAL FLOOR DRAIN/ TRENCH DRAIN

*NOTE: IF MOVEMENT EXPECTED AROUND DRAIN SEAL JOINT WITH ELASTOMERIC SEALANT

IV.11

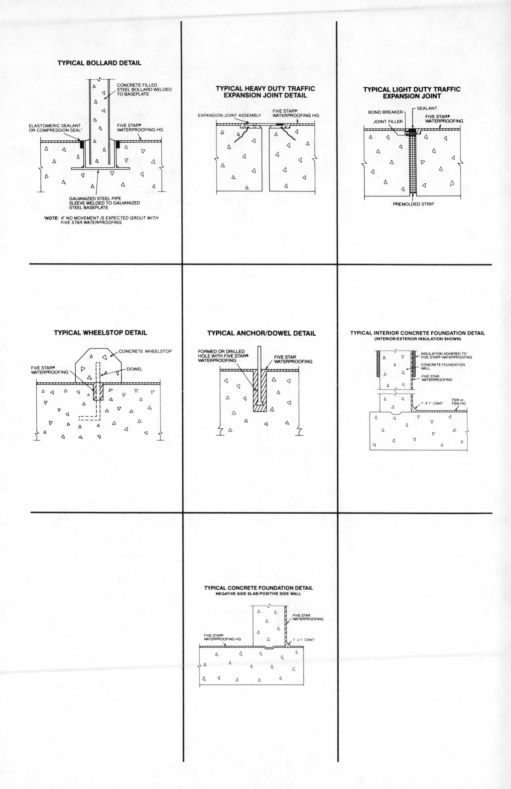

TYPICAL BOLLARD DETAIL

CONCRETE FILLED STEEL BOLLARD WELDED TO BASEPLATE

ELASTOMERIC SEALANT OR COMPRESSION SEAL*

FIVE STAR® WATERPROOFING HG

GALVANIZED STEEL PIPE SLEEVE WELDED TO GALVANIZED STEEL BASEPLATE

*NOTE: IF NO MOVEMENT IS EXPECTED GROUT WITH FIVE STAR WATERPROOFING.

TYPICAL HEAVY DUTY TRAFFIC EXPANSION JOINT DETAIL

EXPANSION JOINT ASSEMBLY

FIVE STAR® WATERPROOFING HG

TYPICAL LIGHT DUTY TRAFFIC EXPANSION JOINT

BOND BREAKER

SEALANT

JOINT FILLER

FIVE STAR® WATERPROOFING

PREMOLDED STRIP

TYPICAL WHEELSTOP DETAIL

CONCRETE WHEELSTOP

FIVE STAR® WATERPROOFING

DOWEL

TYPICAL ANCHOR/DOWEL DETAIL

FORMED OR DRILLED HOLE WITH FIVE STAR® WATERPROOFING

FIVE STAR WATERPROOFING

TYPICAL INTERIOR CONCRETE FOUNDATION DETAIL
(INTERIOR/EXTERIOR INSULATION SHOWN)

INSULATION ADHERED TO FIVE STAR® WATERPROOFING

CONCRETE FOUNDATION WALL

FIVE STAR WATERPROOFING

1" X 1" CANT

FSW or FSW HG

TYPICAL CONCRETE FOUNDATION DETAIL
NEGATIVE SIDE SLAB/POSITIVE SIDE WALL

FIVE STAR WATERPROOFING

FIVE STAR® WATERPROOFING HG

1" x 1" CANT

IV.12

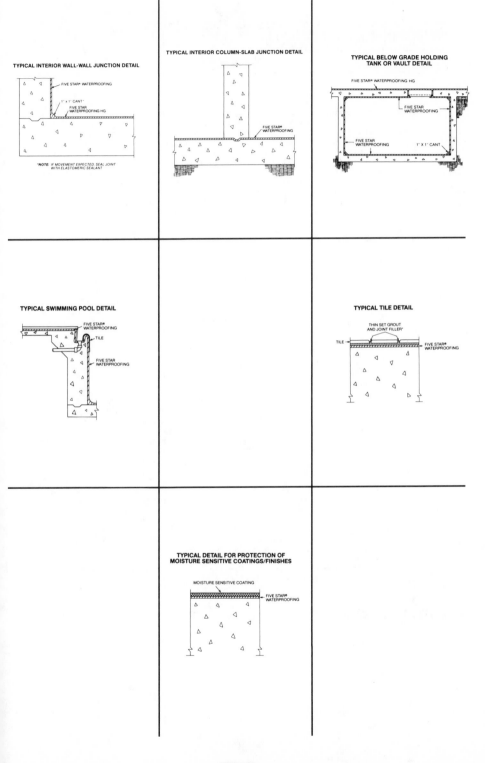

TYPICAL INTERIOR WALL-WALL JUNCTION DETAIL

FIVE STAR® WATERPROOFING

1" x 1" CANT*

FIVE STAR WATERPROOFING HG

*NOTE: IF MOVEMENT EXPECTED, SEAL JOINT WITH ELASTOMERIC SEALANT

TYPICAL INTERIOR COLUMN-SLAB JUNCTION DETAIL

FIVE STAR® WATERPROOFING

TYPICAL BELOW GRADE HOLDING TANK OR VAULT DETAIL

FIVE STAR® WATERPROOFING HG

FIVE STAR WATERPROOFING

FIVE STAR WATERPROOFING

1" X 1" CANT

TYPICAL SWIMMING POOL DETAIL

FIVE STAR® WATERPROOFING

TILE

FIVE STAR WATERPROOFING

TYPICAL TILE DETAIL

THIN SET GROUT AND JOINT FILLER*

TILE

FIVE STAR® WATERPROOFING

TYPICAL DETAIL FOR PROTECTION OF MOISTURE SENSITIVE COATINGS/FINISHES

MOISTURE SENSITIVE COATING

FIVE STAR® WATERPROOFING

IV.13

CEMENTITIOUS WATERPROOFING COMPARISON

This bulletin compares the typical physical properties of the four major types of cementitious waterproofing products. The major types of cement-based waterproofing materials are the cementitious membranes, crystalline, water repellent and metallic oxide. Five Star® Waterproofing, a cementitious membrane, uses a patented cement composition to provide a waterproof barrier. In contrast, the other three types are portland cement based coatings which use an additive to make them "waterproof". Since products of a given type all vary from manufacturer to manufacturer, the data shown is based on the typical performance of a top selling brand of each type. Therefore, the data provided represent the level of performance that can be expected from a given type of waterproofing. This data should be used for general comparative purposes only.

Brief descriptions of the important physical properties and their related test methods are listed below.

Initial Absorption

A waterproof coating must exhibit little initial absorption. Initial absorption is defined as the amount of water absorbed (per unit area) by the coating in the first 24 hours of exposure. The rate of water absorption during this period has been found to be higher than the permeability. The initial absorption is measured by a Funnel Absorption Test[1]. The initial absorption is very important where the coating is only subjected to intermittent water conditions. The initial absorption also gives an indication of the freeze/thaw durability of the coating.

Permeability

A waterproofing must have a very low permeability. The permeability is the rate of water transmission through the coating (per unit area), and is, therefore, the most important property of any waterproofing product. Permeability can be expressed as a volume of water passing through a given area of coating in a given period of time. It is reported here in terms of gallons of water per 1,000 square feet of coating per day. This property was measured using the Funnel Absorption Test[1].

The permeability shows you the level of long-term protection you are buying. No waterproofing should be purchased without this vital piece of information.

---

[1] A copy of the Funnel Absorption Test method is available on request. This test method was developed and used due to its simplicity and the lack of any applicable American Society of Testing and Materials (ASTM) method. The initial absorption and permeability are both functions of the water pressure they encounter. A 6 in. column of water was used to obtain the values reported.

Another test of the permeability is the U. S. Army Corps of Engineers test CRD-C 48. In this test the permeability of the concrete sample is measured at a water pressure of 462 ft. using special testing apparatus. The permeability is reported in terms of centimeters per second (cm/sec) which represents a permeability coefficient. When tested according to this standard procedure, Five Star® Waterproofing (one coat, 1/8" thick) has a permeability coefficient on the order of 1.0×10^{-12} cm/sec. In comparison, a leading manufacturer of crystalline waterproofing has published a permeability coefficient of 1.7×10^{-8} cm/sec for their products and concrete typically has a coefficient of approximately 4.0×10^{-8} cm/sec.

In contrast to their performance in the Funnel Test, the permeability of the water repellent cement products under higher water pressures will be equivalent to that of an ordinary sand/cement mortar. Since the hydrophobic force of the repellent will be overwhelmed by water pressure, this type of product is only suitable for dampproofing applications.

Bond Strength

A waterproof coating must have a high bond strength to concrete. The ASTM[2] C-882 test method is used to measure the bond strength. Debonding of the coating results in cracking and thus a loss of coating integrity. Cracks are an easy way for water to find its way through the coating.

Volume Change

A cementitious waterproofing must not exhibit significant volume change (shrinkage or expansion) in either the plastic or hardened state. Plastic volume change is measured using the ASTM C-827 standard test method. Hardened volume change is measured by ASTM C-596 (in the dry state) and ASTM C-157 (in the wet state). Volume change is very important because cementitious materials are rigid and essentially inelastic. When the coating shrinks or expands, stress is placed on the coating and the bond interface. This stress can only be relieved in one of two ways--cracking or debonding. Either of these events results in an ineffective waterproofing system.

Compressive Strength

A cementitious waterproofing must have a high compressive strength and attain that strength rapidly. Compressive strength is measured using the ASTM C-109 procedure. Rapid strength gain means that the coating can be subjected to hydrostatic pressure earlier, does not need to be protected for as long, and also means that the coating is less sensitive to variations in curing. The compressive strength also provides an indication of the wear resistance of the coating.

The physical properties for the four major types of cementitious waterproofing can be found on the attached chart and graph.

---

(2) American Society of Testing and Materials

Technical Bulletin #36   © 1987 Five Star Waterproofing Products.
5872.5K

CEMENTITIOUS WATERPROOFING COMPARISON CHART

Material Type	Five Star®(1) Waterproofing		Crystalline	Water Repellent Cement	Metallic Oxide
Method of Application	Trowel – 1 coat	Brush – 2 coats	Brush – 2 coats	Brush – 2 coats	Brush – 3 coats
Initial Absorption gal/1000 ft² First 24 hrs.	8	24	132	108	33
Permeability gal/1000 ft²/day	0.16	0.60	130	30	11
Shear Bond Strength ASTM C-882	2710 psi	2490 psi	470 psi	920 psi	2160 psi
Plastic Volume Change ASTM C-827	+0.20%	+0.20%	-2.10%	-1.00%	-2.60%
Hardened Volume Change Wet – 21 days ASTM C-157	+0.032%	+0.031%	+0.122%	+0.026%	+0.058%
Dry– 21 days ASTM C-596	-0.003%	-0.025%	-2.160%	-0.360%	-0.228%
Differential	0.035%	0.056%	2.282%	0.386%	0.286%
Compressive Strength ASTM C-109 1 day 7 days	7000 psi 7800 psi	4800 psi 6400 psi	25 psi 1600 psi	2150 psi 3300 psi	1400 psi 4600 psi

(1) Total Application Thickness: For Trowel 1/8"; For Brush 1/16"

FUNNEL ABSORPTION TEST

CEMENTITIOUS WATERPROOFING COMPARISON

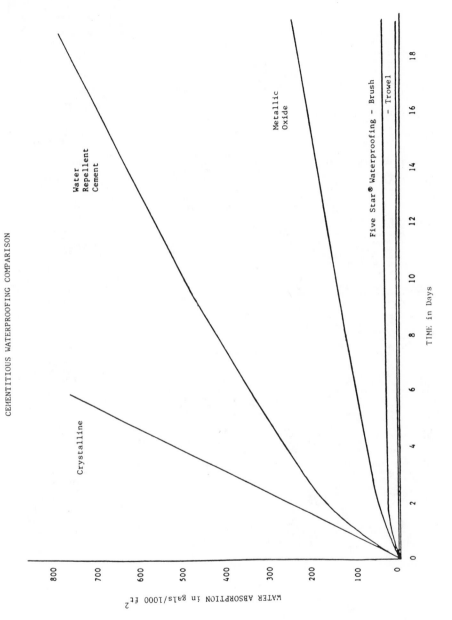

IV.17

This Spec-Data Sheet conforms to editorial style prescribed by The Construction Specifications Institute. The manufacturer is responsible for technical accuracy.

1. PRODUCT NAME

Five Star® Waterproof Topping with Kemblok™
WCM™ System
Heavy Duty Traffic Bearing
Cementitious Membrane

2. MANUFACTURER

U.S. WATERPROOFING, INC.
425 Stillson Road
Fairfield, CT 06430
203-336-7970
Telex: 643857
Telecopier: 203-336-7939
Cable: Five Star

3. PRODUCT DESCRIPTION

Basic Use: Five Star Waterproof Topping is a heavy duty waterproof traffic bearing cementitious membrane. It can be expected to outlast thin mil applied urethane based traffic toppings. It is applied as a thick coating, minimum 1/4 inch (250 mils), eliminating the chance for pinholing or thinly applied areas. In addition, being a cementitious membrane, it will not break down under ultraviolet or ozone attack and is nonflammable and nontoxic. It is not a vapor barrier and will not bubble, blister, rip or tear and cannot be punctured like elastomeric materials.

Unlike clear "sealers", Five Star Waterproof Topping resists hydrostatic pressure, and can be easily inspected for damage, proper coverage and performance over the life of the structure. It can be applied to damp and rough surfaces unlike thin mil liquid applied membranes. Five Star Waterproof Topping provides a rough finish for good traction with greater wear and abrasion resistance. It is recommended for use on concrete surfaces subjected to heavy duty traffic.

With Kemblok Emulsion, it is used to protect concrete structures from chemical or salt penetration and attack. Five Star Waterproof Topping also protects the slab from moisture penetration and thus prevents freeze/thaw deterioration.

Five Star Waterproof Topping with Kemblok Emulsion is a completely premeasured, two component system that only requires mixing. It is applied with a screed and trowel in a single, self-curing coat. It does not require a dry surface, primers, top coat or broadcasting of grit or aggregates. Special tough abrasion resistant aggregates are premixed into Five Star Waterproof Topping to provide a more uniform and integral application for reliable performance.

Five Star Waterproof Topping is recommended for use in the following areas:

Heavy duty traffic areas.
Concrete floors, decks, roofs, ramps, docks and sidewalks.
Concrete marine structures.
Thin overlays for resurfacing roads and bridges.
Concrete parking structures.
Salted and salt water areas.
Freeze/thaw areas.
Many chemical attack areas.
Running water areas.
Damp surfaces.
Rough sufaces.
Rapid patching and repairs.
Potentially flammable areas.
Alternating wet/dry areas.

Limitations: Do not use Five Star Waterproof Topping over moving joints or cracks. Apply Five Star Waterproof Topping up to such joints and cracks and seal with an appropriate elastomeric sealant. Five Star Waterproof Topping is self-leveling and therefore cannot be troweled onto walls or overhead surfaces. For active leaks, use Five Star Waterproof Plug.

Composition and Materials: Five Star Waterproof Topping is a prepackaged, dry, nonflammable and nontoxic patented cementitious membrane formulation with a patented waterproof cement and a special abrasion resistant aggregate. Kemblok Emulsion is a special polymer emulsion specifically formulated to maximize the resistance to chemical and salt penetration and attack. Upon mixing, it yields a loose, screedable/trowelable consistency. Five Star Waterproof Topping cures to a very hard abrasion/erosion resistant waterproof protective coating.

Color: Brown. Special Colors available upon request at additional cost.

Coverage: 68.5 lb. unit of Five Star Waterproof Topping and Kemblok Emulsion yields approximately 24 square feet applied at a ¼" thickness.

4. TECHNICAL DATA

See Table on page below.

PROPERTY	TEST METHOD	TEST VALUE
SINGLE 1/4" (Minimum)	APPLICATION. NO MOIST CURING	
Permeability		
Positive Side — 692 foot head	CRD-C-48	7.96×10^{-14} cm/sec
Negative Side — 230 foot head		7.16×10^{-13} cm/sec
Bond Strength		
6,000 psi concrete surface	ASTM C-321	85 psi minimum
Shrinkage		
Plastic State	ASTM C-827	0.0%
After Hardening — Moist	ASTM C-157	0.0%
After Hardening — Dry	ASTM C-596	300 millionths maximum
Compressive Strength		
3 Hours		3,000 psi minimum
1 Day	ASTM C-109	6,000 psi minimum
28 Day		7,000 psi minimum
RESISTANCE TO SALT PENETRATION AND ATTACK		EXCELLENT
RESISTANCE TO FREEZE/THAW CYCLING		EXCELLENT
RESISTANCE TO OIL, GAS, GREASE, ANTIFREEZE		EXCELLENT
NON FLAMMABLE, NON TOXIC		

WATERPROOF CEMENT MEMBRANE™ SYSTEM
Single Coat Application on Positive or Negative Side

Other Products	Use
Five Star Waterproofing	Walls and overhead areas; Trowel, spray. Traffic bearing areas; Dry Shake/Power Trowel
Five Star Waterproofing HG	Horizontal Grade—Traffic bearing membrane for slabs, roofs and decks. Trowel, pour or spray, self-leveling.
Five Star® PTP™ Cement Mix	Moisture Protection: Plaster, Topping, Tile Grouting, Resurfacing, Finishing, and Patching. Absolutely no shrinkage cracking.
Five Star Waterproof Plug	Hydrostatic pressure active leak sealer. Hand apply.

07570

5. INSTALLATION

Surface Preparation: Before applying Five Star Waterproof Topping, all surfaces must be clean, structurally sound, free of oil, grease, laitance, loose material and other foreign contaminants. Leave fresh concrete surfaces rough, otherwise roughen existing smooth surfaces to ensure good bonding. Clean thoroughly with liberal quantities of water, leaving surface damp, but free of all standing water.

Mixing: Thoroughly mix Five Star Waterproof Topping in accordance with written instructions on the bag. Do not exceed mixing instructions printed on bag.

FIVE STAR® WATERPROOF TOPPING

250 mils (1/4" thick)
ACTUAL THICKNESS

Application

- Leave Surface Rough
- Cure Concrete 28 days minimum
- Clean Surface
- Wet Down Surface
- Mix and Apply One Coat

"HEAVY DUTY" URETHANE TRAFFIC TOPPINGS

50-52 mils (1/20" thick)
ACTUAL THICKNESS

Application

- Float Using a Power or Hand Steel Trowel
- Finished with Fine Hair Broom
- Cure Concrete 28 days minimum
- Clean Surface (sandblasting or acid etching)
- Surface Must Be Dry (mat test)
- Prime Surface (8 hours prior to application maximum)
- Apply Base Coat — 1st Coat
- Apply Heavy Duty Coat with Grit Broadcast — 2nd Coat
- Apply Top Coat with Grit Broadcast — 3rd Coat

Placing: Five Star Waterproof Topping may be screeded and troweled onto horizontal surfaces. Five Star Waterproof Topping must be applied in one coat to a thickness of no less than 1/4", completely filling all holes, pores and voids.

Curing and Protection: Under normal conditions, Five Star Waterproof Topping is self-curing. Traffic may commence in 3 hours under normal conditions. For hot, windy or cold conditions, follow WCM System Hot or Cold Weather Application Procedure Technical Bulletin. Five Star Waterproof Topping does not require any post-curing protection.

TYPICAL FIVE STAR WATERPROOF TOPPING DETAILS

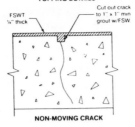

NON-MOVING CRACK

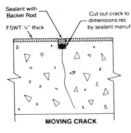

MOVING CRACK

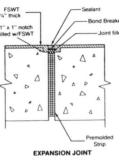

EXPANSION JOINT

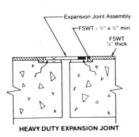

HEAVY DUTY EXPANSION JOINT

6. AVAILABILITY AND COST

Availability: Five Star Waterproof Topping is available throughout the U.S.A. Call U.S. Waterproofing for location nearest you. Telephone: (203) 336-7970. For International availability contact International Division (203) 336-7950.

Cost: The installed cost of Five Star Waterproof Topping is competitive with other waterproofing systems designed to withstand heavy duty traffic, weathering, hydrostatic and tire pressures, abrasion, chemicals, salts, and erosion. It requires only one coat with no curing, protection board, primers or bond coats.

For further estimating information, contact U.S. Waterproofing, Inc. (203) 336-7970.

7. WARRANTY

U.S. Waterproofing, Inc. warrants WCM System products to be free from defects in the material shipped. Should a defect be proven in the material within four years from the date of sale, U.S. Waterproofing's sole liability shall not exceed the cost of defective material on a prorated basis. The warranty extends to the original purchaser only, for the waterproofing performance of the material when applied in accordance with U.S. Waterproofing's written instructions. U.S. WATERPROOFING'S WARRANTY SHALL BE EXCLUSIVE AND IN LIEU OF ANY OTHER WARRANTY OR GUARANTEE EXPRESSED OR IMPLIED, INCLUDING THE IMPLIED WARRANTIES OF MERCHANTABILITY AND FITNESS FOR A PARTICULAR PURPOSE AND ALL OTHER WARRANTIES OTHERWISE ARISING BY OPERATION OF LAW, COURSE OF DEALING, CUSTOM OF TRADE OR OTHERWISE. No labor costs or any claims for consequential or other damages of any kind shall be allowed or recognized.

Any question regarding completed installation guarantee or warranty, should be directed to the installer contracting the work.

8. MAINTENANCE

A scheduled normal floor or deck cleaning maintenance program is recommended. Otherwise, no maintenance is required if proper coverage and application instructions have been followed. Exposed, damaged or cracked areas due to unexpected movement or abuse may be easily and readily patched with Five Star Waterproof Topping, Five Star Waterproofing, Five Star Waterproof Plug or an elastomeric sealant (for moving cracks).

9. TECHNICAL SERVICE

U.S. Waterproofing offers consulting services for architects and engineers covering specifications, architectural details, technical field service, and laboratory material testing.

10. FILING SYSTEMS

Sweet's General Building File
Sweet's Civil and Comprehensive
  Engineering File
Spec-Data® II

PROTECTION OF BRIDGE STRUCTURES
AGAINST CHLORIDE PENETRATION
Work Performed by Wiss, Janney, Elstner & Associates, Inc.
All Work Performed in Accordance with
National Cooperative Highway Research Program
Report 244

Report requires 90% chloride reductions for minimum passing standards. Test performed with ponding salt water with 15% chlorides for 24 weeks.

Product	Minimum Passing Test Requirement 90% Chloride Reduction Ponding Salt Water 15% Chloride 24 weeks
PASSING:	
Epoxy 50% Solids 100 sq. ft./gal. 2 coats	92%
Methyl Methacrylate 100 sf/gal. 1st coat 200 sf/gal. 2nd coat	92%
FIVE STAR WATERPROOF TOPPING 1/4" one coat	91%
FAILING:	
Alkyl–Alkoxy Silane 50 sf/gal. one coat	89%
Polyisobutyl Methacrylate 125 sf/gal. 1st coat 125 sf/gal. 2nd coat	77%
Moisture Cured Urethane 150 sf/gal. 1st coat 150 sf/gal. 2nd coat	70%

RECOMMENDATION: For horizontal surfaces such as bridge decks and other horizontal surfaces with salt water exposure, use FIVE STAR WATERPROOF TOPPING 1/4" for effectiveness, economy, wearability, abrasion resistance and long product life.
For vertical surfaces, use FIVE STAR WATERPROOFING.
For new concrete surfaces, use FIVE STAR WATERPROOFING Dry Shake.

FIVE STAR WATERPROOFING PRODUCTS (Div. of Five Star Products, Inc.)
425 Stillson Road, Fairfield, Connecticut 06430 (203) 336–7970

TECHNICAL BULLETIN
FIVE STAR

AASHTO TEST T277–831
Performed by the Federal Highway Administration
Report Dated April 1985
CHLORIDE PERMEABILITY BASED ON ELECTRIC CHARGE

Charge Passed (coulombs)	Chloride Permeability	Thickness	Typical of
Greater than 4,000	High	2"	High water–cement ratio, conventional (greater than or equal to 0.6) PCC
2,000–4,000	Moderate	2"	Moderate water–cement ratio, conventional (0.4–0.5 PCC
1,000–2,000	Low	2"	Low water–cement ratio, conventional (less than 0.4) PCC
100–1,000	Very Low	2"	Latex–modified concrete
		2"	Internally sealed concrete
Less than 100	Negligible	2"	Polymer impregnated concrete
		2"	Polymer concrete

RESULTS

Product	Thickness	Total Charge Passed (coulombs)
FSW Dry Shake	3/32"	612
FSW Topping	1/4"	431
FSW HG	1/8"	580
FSW Topping	2"	0

RECOMMENDATION: For horizontal surfaces such as bridge decks and other horizontal surfaces with salt water exposure, use FIVE STAR WATERPROOF TOPPING 1/4" for effectiveness, economy, wearability, abrasion resistance and long product life.
For vertical surfaces, use FIVE STAR WATERPROOFING.
For new concrete surfaces, use FIVE STAR WATERPROOFING Dry Shake.

29787–1700P2

FIVE STAR WATERPROOFING PRODUCTS (Div. of Five Star Products, Inc.)
425 Stillson Road, Fairfield, Connecticut 06430 (203) 336–7970

TECHNICAL ⭐5⭐ BULLETIN
FIVE STAR

PRESSURE TEST OF 15% SALT SOLUTION
FOR REDUCTION IN CHLORIDE ION CONTENT
VS. CONCRETE SPECIMEN WITH
PERMEABILITY OF 7.1×10^{-10}cm/sec.

U. S. Army Corps of Engineers Test CRD C–48
Performed by Law Engineering, Atlanta, GA

FIVE STAR WATERPROOFING PRODUCT RESULTS
USING 115 FT. HEAD OF PRESSURE

Product	Thickness	Reduction in Chlorides
Five Star Waterproofing (Dryshake)	–	98%
Five Star Waterproofing	1/8"	96%
Five Star Waterproof Topping	1/4"	99.9%

RECOMMENDATION: For horizontal surfaces such as bridge decks and
other horizontal surfaces with salt water exposure,
use FIVE STAR WATERPROOF TOPPING 1/4" for
effectiveness, economy, wearability, abrasion
resistance and long product life.
For vertical surfaces, use FIVE STAR
WATERPROOFING.
For new concrete surfaces, use FIVE STAR
WATERPROOFING Dry Shake.

29787–1700P3

FIVE STAR WATERPROOFING PRODUCTS (Div. of Five Star Products, Inc.)
425 Stillson Road, Fairfield, Connecticut 06430 (203) 336–7970

FUNNEL ABSORPTION & PERMEABILITY TEST

This test is used to determine the initial absorption and permeability over time of waterproof coatings. A sketch of the apparatus and description of the method follows.

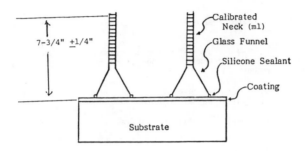

Substrate

1. May be any absorptive and permeable material such as patio block or lean concrete.

2. Surfaces should be prepared as recommended by the manufacturer.

Coating Application

1. Mix coating as recommended by the manufacturer.

2. Apply in the manner and number of coats recommended in the manufacturer's literature.

3. Cure coating in the manner and length of time recommended in the manufacturer's literature.

Apparatus Assembly

1. Place calibrated funnel upside–down on substrate.

2. Adhere and seal funnel to substrate using a silicone sealant. After sealant cures (24 hours minimum) and prior to filling with water, pressure test for leaks using mouth pressure. If assembly holds pressure, proceed to next step.

Test Procedure

1. Fill funnel with water level with top calibration mark. Note and record time and date.

2. Record level of water at 15 minute intervals for the first hour. Thereafter, record water level every hour for the remainder of the day and daily thereafter.

   NOTE: Do not permit water level to fall below lowest calibration mark! Refill as necessary, recording each amount of water added.

3. Run test for a minimum of 14 days, longer if desired.

Report

1. Calculate initial absorption (in ml/cm^2) of wetted surface at 24 hours. Convert to gallons/1,000 sq. ft. and report.

2. Calculate permeability (in ml/cm^2) at two day intervals. Convert to gallons/1,000 sq. ft.

3. Plot graph of permeability, plotting gallons/1,000 sq. ft. vs. time, and report.

The Five Star SYSTEM
FOR
WATERPROOFING

1. Determine waterproofing objectives and proper placement of waterproofing barriers to meet objectives – negative or positive side.

2. Take the necessary steps to reflect and accommodate for the FSW System's rigidity and nonelastomeric properties noting the unit substrate concept.*

3. Select the right Five Star* cementitious membrane, elastomeric sealants and joint compounds for all surfaces, penetrations, joints and cracks to be waterproofed.

4. Follow the concrete waterproofing guidelines to help select where other materials, such as elastomeric membranes should be applied to complete the proper enveloping of the structure.

*Unit Substrate - A unit substrate is defined as any rigid surface that will receive a waterproofing barrier which has been designed to move freely and independently, by proper joint design and crack control so that cracks other than drying shrinkage cracks, do not occur in the surface itself. A series of unit substrates are joined together by expansion/contraction, control and construction joints to make up an entire structure.

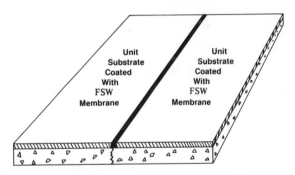

Expansion/contraction, isolation, control, or construction joint

- Moving joints or cracks are sealed with elastomeric sealants or compression seals.
- Nonmoving joints or cracks are sealed with FSW System products.

FIVE STAR WATERPROOFING PRODUCTS, 425 STILLSON ROAD, FAIRFIELD, CONNECTICUT 06430 ● (203) 336-7970

IV.25

WATERPROOFING
NEGATIVE OR POSITIVE SIDE?

Negative Side - Placement of waterproof barrier on side **opposite to applied hydrostatic pressure.**

Positive Side - Placement of waterproof barrier **on side of applied hydrostatic pressure.**

One Coat
Five Star
Waterproofing →

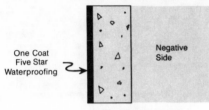

Negative
Side

Positive
Side
Application

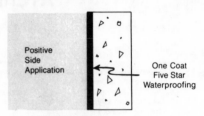

← One Coat
Five Star
Waterproofing

Water enters concrete.
Concrete is saturated and
moist cured.

Water is blocked from
entering concrete.
Concrete dries out.

ADVANTAGES

Negative side membrane

- Concrete remains moist cured
- Elimination of drying shrinkage cracking
- Continued increase in concrete strength
- Inspection and repair after backfill
- No additional excavation costs for application or repair
- No possible damage from backfilling

Positive side membrane

- Water is prevented from entering concrete
- Dried concrete is protected from freeze/thaw damage
- Corrosion protection if harsh chemicals are in water
- Utilize both Five Star Waterproofing or elastomeric barriers

DISADVANTAGES

Negative side membrane

- No freeze/thaw protection on above grade applications
- No corrosion protection if harsh chemicals are in water
- Limited to Five Star Waterproofing - rigid barrier

Positive side membrane

- Concrete dries out
- Drying shrinkage cracking occurs
- Concrete strength development ceases
- Membrane inaccessible if sandwiched or backfilled
- Inspection/repairs difficult and costly
- Damage possible during backfill or earth settlement

If a positive side application is necessary, thereby allowing shrinkage cracking to occur, it is recommended that the concrete be properly cured first, then allowed to dry out, shrink, and crack to nearly its widest point, usually 28 days. Then all cracks subject to further shrinkage and no other movement should be routed out and filled with an application of Five Star Waterproofing. The remaining minor shrinkage cracking will then be compensated for by this special tough, rigid, nonshrink, self-healing barrier.

FIVE STAR WATERPROOFING PRODUCTS, 425 STILLSON ROAD, FAIRFIELD, CONNECTICUT 06430 • (203) 336-7970

WATERPROOFING WITH
Five Star® Waterproofing Products

WATERPROOFING
WITH INORGANIC RIGID MEMBRANES

Since the patented, inorganic waterproofing membranes of the FSW System are rigid and possess no elastomeric properties, the designer should review the following considerations, guidelines and steps to ensure proper specifications, architectural details and field inspection programs.

1. The FSW System is rigid and has no elongation properties. However, FSW System materials will not crack by themselves and will move with the concrete since they are nonshrink and have an equivalent thermal coefficient of expansion.

2. Each surface area to be waterproofed with the FSW System should be broken up into individual **substrate units** with proper expansion/contraction joints, control joints and isolation joints to prevent cracking within each unit substrate.

3. For positive side applications, large unit substrates may undergo drying shrinkage cracking, and therefore, must be allowed to cure and dry out a minimum of 28 days before applying the FSW System.

4. Unit substrates which are undergoing deterioration and cracking must be completely repaired and rendered sound to provide a complete and totally sound unit substrate before applying the FSW System.

5. The FSW System membranes do not span moving cracks or joints, and therefore, are only recommended for use in static joints and cracks.

6. All above grade joints, cracks and penetrations subject to thermal movement must be treated with an elastomeric sealant or compression seal.

7. Below grade joints, cracks and penetrations that are not subjected to thermal movement should be sealed with Five Star Waterproofing.

8. Joints, cracks, penetrations subject to structural movement and hydrostatic pressure require the use of elastomeric sealants backed by a FSW membrane.

9. The FSW System should be applied prior to application of any elastomeric sealant or compression seal to ensure the sealant bonds directly to the cured FSW membrane.

FSW architectural details have been broken up into above grade and below grade and positive and negative side applications for your convenience to reflect the different detailing requirements for each area of your project.

FSW = FIVE STAR WATERPROOFING

IV.27

ARCHITECTS
ENGINEERS
CONTRACTORS
OWNERS

1988
EDITION

PRODUCT SELECTION

STANDARDS

- CEMENTITIOUS GROUTS ■ EPOXY GROUTS
- STRUCTURAL CONCRETE REPAIR
- HIGHWAY REPAIR ■ WATERPROOFING

FIVE STAR
PRODUCTS INC.
425 Stillson Road
Fairfield, CT 06430
(203) 336-7900

V.1

The tables, data, and other information in this book have been obtained from many sources, including professional architects, engineers, contractors, subcontractors, manufacturers, government organizations, trade associations and suppliers of building materials. The publisher has made every reasonable effort to make this reference work accurate and authoritative, but does not warrant, and assumes no liability for, the accuracy or completeness of the text or its fitness for any particular purpose. It is the responsibility of the users to apply their professional knowledge for the use of the information contained in this book, to consult the original source, publisher or manufacturer for additional information when appropriate, and, if they themselves are not professional experts in the field, to consult FIVE STAR PRODUCTS, INC. when appropriate.

Publisher:

FIVE STAR PRODUCTS, INC.
425 Stillson Road
Fairfield, CT 06430

The following are registered trademarks:

FIVE STAR® GROUT and device
FIVE STAR® INSTANT GROUT
FIVE STAR® SPECIAL GROUT 100
FIVE STAR® SPECIAL GROUT 110
FIVE STAR® SPECIAL GROUT 120
FIVE STAR® SPECIAL GROUT 130
FIVE STAR® SPECIAL GROUT 150
FIVE STAR® SPECIAL GROUT 160
FIVE STAR® SPECIAL GROUT 200
FIVE STAR® SPECIAL GROUT 400
FIVE STAR® SPECIAL GROUT 550
FIVE STAR® EPOXY GROUT
FIVE STAR ET® EPOXY GROUT
FIVE STAR® RAPID EPOXY GROUT
FIVE STAR® SPEED EPOXY GROUT
FIVE STAR® HIGHWAY PATCH
FIVE STAR STRUCTURAL CONCRETE™
FIVE STAR STRUCTURAL CONCRETE™ V/O
DEVOIDER®
SUMMERSET®
PostSet™

Printed in the United States of America

PREFACE

Contractors and professionals in the construction industry have been asking, since the early development of the concrete building industry in the early 1900's, for product selection standards which would enable them to determine what products are to be used for particular applications.

The staff of the Engineering and Technical Center of FIVE STAR PRODUCTS, INC. has accumulated this information over many years of experience and believes that this book will be a most useful tool.

We hope you will find this PRODUCT SELECTION STANDARDS useful and time-saving. We would appreciate any additional construction applications that you would like included in the next edition.

Please write to our Engineering and Technical Center on your company letterhead with your suggestions or if you wish additional copies for your office or field staffs.

Construction applications have been arranged alphabetically for easy search procedures.

Each of these products has unique properties for specific purposes. They have all had a long and successful history of service. No other manufacturer has been able to duplicate these superior products or their outstanding properties, although many have tried.

PRODUCT CODES:

DEV	DEVOIDER®
FSG	FIVE STAR® GROUT
FSEG	FIVE STAR® EPOXY GROUT
FSETEG	FIVE STAR ET® EPOXY GROUT (Elevated Temperature)
FSHP	FIVE STAR® HIGHWAY PATCH
FSIG	FIVE STAR® INSTANT GROUT
FSREG	FIVE STAR® RAPID EPOXY GROUT
FSSEG	FIVE STAR® SPEED EPOXY GROUT
FSSC	FIVE STAR STRUCTURAL CONCRETE™
FSSC V/O	FIVE STAR STRUCTURAL CONCRETE™ V/O (Vertical and Overhead)
FSG 100	FIVE STAR® SPECIAL GROUT 100
FSG 110	FIVE STAR® SPECIAL GROUT 110
FSG 120	FIVE STAR® SPECIAL GROUT 120
FSG 130	FIVE STAR® SPECIAL GROUT 130
FSG 150	FIVE STAR® SPECIAL GROUT 150
FSG 160	FIVE STAR® SPECIAL GROUT 160
FSG 200	FIVE STAR® SPECIAL GROUT 200
FSG 400	FIVE STAR® SPECIAL GROUT 400
FSG 550	FIVE STAR® SPECIAL GROUT 550
FSW	FIVE STAR® WATERPROOFING
FSW-HG	FIVE STAR® WATERPROOFING - HG (Horizontal Grade)
PS	PostSet™
SS	SUMMERSET®

Automatic parking meters	FSSC
Balancing machinery	FSG
	FSEG
Bank equipment, setting	FSG
Bank security systems	FSIG
Barricades:	
Emergency	FSIG
Barrier curbs:	
Concrete	FSSC
Barriers:	
Guard rail	FSG
Bathroom waterproofing	FSW
Bleachers:	
Anchoring	FSSC
Blinker lights:	
Anchoring	FSEG
	FSREG
	FSSEG
Blocks:	
Concrete repair	FSSC
Boiler lining:	FSIG
High temperature	FSG 200
Boiler settings	FSSC
Boats, anchoring:	
Critical	FSIG
	FSEG
Fast setting	FSSC
Regular	FSG
Saltwater resistance	FSG 120
Bond:	
High concrete bond	FSSC
	FSHP
	FSIG
	FSEG

Bowstring trusses:	
Bearing	FSG
Brick mortar repair	FSSC
Brick paving mortar	FSSC
Brick vents:	
Grouting	FSG
Bridge anchors	FSSC
Bridge bearing plates:	
Grouting	FSG
Epoxy grouting	FSIG
	FSEG
Bridge piers	FSIG
	FSSC
	FSG 120
	FSG 150
	FSW
Bridge topping:	
Deck	FSW–HG
Saltwater	FSW–HG
Bridgework concrete repair:	
Columns	FSSC
Curbs	FSHP
Potholes	FSHP
Saltwater resistance	FSSC
	FSIG
	FSG 120
	FSG 150
Sidewalks	FSHP
Soffits	FSSC V/O
Walls	FSSC V/O
Wearing surface	FSHP
Bronze signs:	
Anchoring	FSSC

Building door saddles	FSG	Catchbasin castings	FSHP
Building stair treads	FSSC		FSSC
Building, prefabricated:		Caulking:	
Grouting	FSG	Concrete	FSSC
Bulkheads:		Cement block repair	FSSC
Fresh water concrete		Cement admixtures:	
repair	FSSC	Delay set	SS
Saltwater concrete		Eliminate shrinkage	DEV
repair	FSSC	Cement floor coatings:	
	FSG 120	Waterproofing	FSW
	FSG 150	Cement paint:	
Piles	FSSC	Waterproofing	FSW
Burners, heating equipment:		Cement pipe lining	FSW
Grouting	FSIG	Cement pipe repair	FSSC
Cabinets:		Cement sidewalk and curb	
Shower	FSW	repair	FSHP
Cafeteria equipment:		Cesspool lining	FSW
Grouting	FSSC	Chainlink fence anchoring	PS
Cages:			FSHP
Anchoring	FSSC	Chairs:	
Caissons:		Anchoring	FSSC
Repair	FSSC	Channels, precast concrete:	
	FSIG	Repair	FSSC
Canopies:		Grouting	FSG
Anchors	FSIG	Chemical resistant floor	
	FSSC	repairs	FSW
Car bumpers:			FSSC
Curbing	FSHP	Chemical waste disposal	
Castings:		systems	FSW
Roadway	FSHP		FSSC
Castings:		Chimneys and smoke stacks:	
Manhole	FSSC	Mortars	FSIG
Casting facilities	FSG		FSSC
	FSIG	Repairs	FSIG
	FSEG		FSSC
		Chute doors, access:	
		Grouting	FSG

Cinder and concrete block:			Concrete repair (cont.):	
Repair	FSSC		Benches	FSSC
Coating	FSW		Block	FSSC
Clamps for concrete forms:			Chipped or spalled	FSSC
Waterproof plugs	FSSC		Concrete grouts	FSG
Coating, waterproofing:			Concrete panels, precast	FSSC
Walls	FSW		Concrete patching	
Heavy duty floors	FSW–HG		materials	FSSC
Coffer dam repair	FSSC			FSW
	FSW		Concrete pavement	FSHP
Cold room:			Concrete piling	FSSC
Refrigerators	FSW		Concrete pipe	FSSC
	FSSC		Concrete post–tensioned	
Cold storage construction:			members	FSSC
Lining	FSW		Concrete architectural,	
Cold weather applications	*		precast	FSG 130
	FSIG		Concrete precast	
	FSG		sanitary drainage	FSSC
	FSEG		Concrete grout pumping	All FIVE STAR cementitious grouts
	FSHP			
Columns, concrete:				
Masonry repair	FSSC			
Repair	FSSC		Concrete ready mix	*
Compressors:			Concrete restoration	FSSC
Setting	FSEG			FSW
	FSETEG			FSEG
	FSREG			FSG
	FSSEG			FSHP
Concrete repair:	Refer to FIVE STAR PRODUCTS HANDBOOK		Concrete road	
			construction	FSHP
Arches	FSSC		Concrete sidewalks	FSHP
			Concrete slabs	FSSC
			Concrete stanchions	FSIG
			Cribbing:	
			Rail ties	FSSC
			Curbs	FSSC
				FSHP
			Floors	FSSC
				FSW–HG

Concrete repair (cont.):			Cribbing:	
Form tie holes	FSSC		Concrete repair	FSSC
Foundation walls	FSSC		Culverts:	
	FSW		Concrete repair	FSSC
Honeycombed concrete			Curbing:	
repair	FSSC		Concrete repair	FSSC
Lightweight block	FSSC		Granite mortar	FSG 130
Precast or prestressed			Stone mortar	FSIG
conduit	FSSC			FSSC
Reinforced concrete			Curing compounds	FSW (brush coat)
structures	FSSC			
Sidewalks	FSSC		Cut stone, natural:	
Conduit:			Mortar	FSG 130
Concrete repair	FSSC		Dampers:	
Contractor's mixing equipment:			Grouting	FSG
By hand	*		Dampproofing and	
Concrete trucks	*		waterproofing materials	FSW
Jiffy mixers	*		Decking:	
Mortar repairs	*		Bridge gratings	FSHP
Pumping	*		Concrete repair	FSSC
Conveying machinery:				FSHP
Grouting	FSEG		Deep pours:	
	FSG		To prevent high	
Cooling pond linings	FSW		temperature	*
Cooling tower protection	FSW		cracking	Refer to FIVE STAR PRODUCTS HANDBOOK
Corner guards:				
Anchoring	FSIG		Depositories:	
	FSSC		Vaults, safes, etc.	FSIG
Corrosion-proofing	FSW		Detention screens:	
	FSEG		Prison security	FSSC
Crane rails	FSEG		Diesel engines:	
Crane rail pads	FSEG		Setting	FSEG
Crane rail bearing	FSEG			FSG
Creep, extremely low	FSG			
	FSEG			
	FSETEG			

Dock bumpers:		Drain repair	FSSC
Anchoring	FSIG	Drainage castings:	
	FSSC	Bedding	FSSC
Dock levelers	FSG		FSHP
Docks and wharves:		Drains:	
Fresh water areas	FSG	Trench, precast	FSSC
	FSSC	Duct work wall openings	FSG
Piers	FSEG	Electric motors:	
	FSSC	Grouting	FSG
	FSIG	Electric power plants:	*
Saltwater areas	FSSC		All FIVE STAR GROUTS
	FSIG		
	FSG 120	Radiation shielding	FSG 160
	FSG 150	Electric signs:	
Stairs	FSSC	Grouting	FSSC
Walls	FSSC		FSG
Dogs:		Electrical:	
Security fencing	FSIG	Heavy equipment	FSG
	PS	Elevator:	
	FSHP	Door saddles	FSSC
Door closers:		Machinery	FSEG
Recessed	FSSC	Machinery replacement	FSEG
Doors:		Pits	FSW
Aircraft hangar tracks	FSSC	Sidewalk, setting	FSSC
Blast resistant	FSIG	Emergency lighting:	
	FSSC	Anchorages, exterior	FSSC
Clean out	FSG	Enclosures, metal:	
Cold storage, anchorages	FSSC	Anchorages	FSG
Controls, recessed	FSSC	Energy management systems:	
Elevated saddles	FSSC	Resource recovery	FSIG
Metal frames, anchorages	FSSC		FSSC
Rolling steel,			
anchorages	FSIG		
Sidewalk	FSSC		
Vault	FSSC		

Fire coatings	FSSC
	FSW
Fire coatings, high temperature	FSG 200
Fire escapes:	
Anchoring	FSIG
Fire hydrants:	
Grouting	FSSC
Fireplaces, mortars:	
Chimneys	FSSC
Dampers	FSIG
Floors	FSIG
Flue linings	FSSC
Fire resistant masonry wall mortars	FSIG
	FSSC
Fittings:	
Pipe hangars	FSG
Fixtures:	
Drains	FSSC
Light poles	FSG
Flag poles:	
Grouting	FSG
	FSSC
Flagstone:	
Mortars	FSSC
Flashing:	
Exposed roofs, waterproofing	FSW
Spandrels, waterproofing	FSW
Flat plate concrete slabs:	
Repair	FSSC
Flat slab concrete:	
Repair	FSSC
Flat truss:	
Grouting	FSSC
	FSG

Flood, dam coatings	FSW
Floor coatings:	
Waterproofing	FSW
Floor drains:	
Grouting	FSSC
	FSG
Floor leveling	FSSC
Floor joists:	
Grouting	FSG
Flooring systems:	
Chemical resistant	FSW
Precast concrete protection course	FSW
Radiant heating, grouting	FSW
	FSG
Repair	FSSC
Slab on grade and walls	FSW
Waterproofing	FSW
Floors, below grade:	
Waterproofing	FSW
Flower planting boxes	FSW
Flue linings	FSSC
	FSG 200
Folding gates:	
Anchorages	FSG
Food service counters:	
Grouting	FSSC
Footings and foundations, repair of:	
Drains	FSSC
Embedded anchorages	FSSC
Expansion joint corners	FSSC
Honeycombed concrete	FSSC
Snap tie holes	FSSC
Spalled concrete	FSSC
Waterproofing	FSW

Forms for concrete:	
Form tie holes	FSSC
Snap tie holes	FSSC
Forms, concrete repair:	
Beams	FSSC
Columns	FSSC
Girders	FSSC
Precast	FSSC
Prestressed	FSSC
Slabs	FSSC
Walls	FSSC
Foundation repair:	
Footings	FSSC
Piles	FSSC
Pile caps	FSSC
Salt resistant areas	FSSC
	FSW
Waterproofing	FSW
Fountains:	
Plazas	FSW
Waterproofing	FSW
Framed openings:	
Repair	FSSC
Framing steel:	
Fire protection	FSSC
Freezers and refrigerators:	
Ceilings	FSW
Floors	FSW
Walls	FSW
Freezers and refrigerators,	
repair of:	
Ceilings	FSSC
	FSW

Freezers and refrigerators,	
repair of (cont.):	
Floors	FSSC
	FSW
Walls	FSSC
	FSW
Freezing conditions/cold	
weather conditions	Refer to FIVE STAR PRODUCTS HANDBOOK
Freezing highways:	
Road repair	FSHP
Salt protection	FSW–HG
Freight elevators:	
Machinery	FSG
Pits	FSW
Freight hoists:	
Pits	FSW
Sidewalk	FSSC
Furnace flues:	
Linings	FSIG
	FSSC
Linings, high temperature	FSG 200
Mortars	FSIG
Mortars, high temperature	FSG 200
Furniture:	
Auditorium seating,	
anchorages	FSIG
	FSSC
Playground and park	
equipment	FSIG
	FSSC
Stadium seating,	
anchorages	FSSC
Furring:	
Radiation shielding	FSG 160

Games and sports:		Generators	FSG
Accessories	FSSC		FSG 100
Swimming pools	FSW		FSG 110
Gantry crane rails	FSEG		FSIG
	FSREG		FSEG
Garage parking:		Geometric construction	
Deck coatings	FSW–HG	systems:	
Structural repair:		Grouting	FSEG
Beams	FSSC	Repair	FSSC
Columns	FSSC	Girders, precast:	
Floor sections	FSSC	Repair	FSSC
Girders	FSSC	Glass block:	
Precast	FSSC	Mortar	FSG 130
Prestressed	FSSC	Grade beams and wall footings:	
Walls	FSSC	Repair	FSSC
Garbage:		Grandstand and bleachers:	
Rubbish and incinerators	FSIG	Repair	FSSC
	FSSC	Granite, mortars:	
	FSG	Architectural walls	FSG 130
Garden fountains	FSW	Curbs and paving	FSSC
Gas engines:		Gratings and treads:	
Grouting	FSG	Setting	FSSC
	FSEG	Gravity water tank:	
	FSIG	Exterior coating	FSW
	FSETEG	Lining	FSW
Gasoline station equipment:		Grease traps:	
Chemical protective		Setting	FSSC
coating	FSW	Grills:	
Curbing	FSSC	Anchoring	FSSC
Setting	FSSC	Grouting:	Refer to FIVE STAR PRODUCTS HANDBOOK
Gates:			
Anchoring	PS	Architectural stone mortar,	
	FSIG	non–staining	FSG 130
	FSEG		
	FSHP		
	FSREG		

V.14

Grouting (cont.):

Brackish water	FSG 120
	FSG 150
Cable	FSG 400
Chemical Resistance	FSEG
	FSETEG
Deep pours	*
	Refer to FIVE STAR PRODUCTS HANDBOOK
Deep pours and fast machinery start-up	FSIG
	FSREG
	FSEG
	(FSIG + FSEG)
Dynamic loads	FSEG
Fast start-up for compressors, naval and railroad work	FSSEG
Four hour machinery start-up	FSIG
Guniting	FSW
	FSIG
	FSSC
High effective bearing area (EBA)	* All FIVE STAR GROUTS
High operating temperature	FSG 200
High temperature	FSG 550
Impact resistance	FSEG
	FSETEG
Low creep	FSEG
	FSETEG

Grouting (cont.):

Low creep combined with high operating temperatures and fast start-up	FSETEG
Nonshrink	All FIVE STAR GROUTS
Pressure	*
Pumping	FSG 110
Radiation shielding	FSG 160
Saltwater attack	FSG 120
	FSG 150
Small annular space	FSG 400
	FSSEG
Tight clearances	FSG 100
Two hour start-up combined with impact, dynamic loads, and anchor bolts	FSREG
Vibration resistance	FSEG
Guards, wall and corner:	
Anchoring	FSG
Gutters and curbs, concrete:	
Repair	FSSC
	FSHP
Gutters and swimming pools	FSSC
	FSW
Gymnasium equipment:	
Anchoring systems	FSG
Locker and shower room floors	FSW
Handicapped equipment:	
Anchorages	FSSC

Handicapped equipment (cont.):		Highway repair (cont.):	
Hand rails:		Road surfaces	FSHP
Anchorages	FSG	Salt resistance	FSW
	FSIG	Sidewalks	FSSC
	FSSC		FSHP
Fire Escapes	FSIG	Soffits	FSSC
Ladder rails	FSIG	Hoists and cranes:	
Hangars, anchorages	FSSC	Crane rails	FSEG
Harbor improvements:			FSETEG
Repairs	FSG 120	Permanent	FSEG
	FSSC	Hoistway elevators:	
	FSIG	Machinery, grouting	FSG
	FSG 150	Pits	FSW
	FSHP	Hollow metal doors and frames:	
Hardware, anchorages	FSSC	Anchorages	FSG
Heating and heat recovery		Detention doors	FSIG
systems	FSETEG	Fire rated doors	FSIG
	FSG 200	Security doors	FSIG
	FSG	Special doors and frames	FSIG
Heating:		Honeycombed concrete:	
Masonry duct and pipe		Repair	FSSC
hole closures:		Horizontal anchors:	
Floors	FSSC	Cable	FSG 400
Walls	FSSC	Chemical resistance	FSEG
Highway repair:	Refer to FIVE STAR PRODUCTS HANDBOOK	Quick loading	FSIG
		Radiation areas	FSG 160
		Rod	FSG 100
Curbs	FSSC	Saltwater attack	FSG 120
	FSHP	Hot weather applications	*
Expansion gratings	FSIG		(cementitious & epoxy grouts
	FSHP		
Exterior walls	FSSC		
Headers	FSHP		SS
Piers	FSSC	Hot tubs	FSW
	FSW		
Railings.	FSSC		

Hot water construction	SS	Interceptor drains	FSSC
Hot water storage tanks	FSW	Interior materials:	
House drains and sewers	FSSC	Beam repair	FSSC
Humidity controlled rooms	FSW	Column repair	FSSC
Hydrant grouting	FSSC	Floor repair	FSSC
Hydraulic elevators:		Girder repair	FSSC
Anchorages and sleeves	FSSC	Limestone joints	FSG 130
Pits	FSW	Marble joints	FSG 130
Hydraulic pumps	FSG	Soffit repair	FSSC
Hydrolithic coatings	FSW	Travertine joints	FSG 130
Hyperbolic concrete roof		Waterproofing flooring	FSW
coatings	FSW		FSW–HG
Ice skating rinks:		Waterproofing walls	FSW
Floors	FSW	Wet areas:	
Illumination:		Basement floors and	
Flood lighting	FSG	walls	FSW
Light poles	FSG	Entrance vestibules	FSW
Power lines	FSG		FSW–HG
Industrial floors:	FSW–HG	Mechanical rooms	FSW
Gratings	FSSC		FSW–HG
Repairs	FSSC	Showers	FSW
Treads	FSSC	Iron castings	FSSC
Industrial pipe grouting	FSG	Iron fences	PS
Industrial piping:			FSHP
Anchors	FSG	Iron, miscellaneous:	
Wall repair	FSSC	Beam pads	FSG
Industrial steel stairs	FSSC	Channel openings	FSG
Industrial waste disposal	FSG 150	Columns	FSG
	FSW	Lally columns	FSG
Inlets	FSSC	Lintels	FSG
	FSW	Ornamental metals	FSG
Insulation coating:		Railings	FSSC
Cold storage facilities	FSW	Signs	FSSC
Masonry walls	FSW	Stair anchors	FSG
			FSSC

Jamb details:		Letter boxes:	
Vaults	FSSC	Grouting	FSG
X–ray rooms	FSG 160	Posts	PS
Joints:		Letter chutes, anchorages	FSG
Brickwork, waterproofing	FSSC	Leveling, tanks	FSEG
Concrete snap ties	FSSC	Lift–slab construction:	
Cut stone	FSG 130	Grouting	FSG
Expansion covers	FSSC		FSIG
Joints, bearing	FSG	Repair	FSSC
Joists:		Lifts, material handling:	
Bearing	FSG	Grouting	FSG
Precast, repair	FSSC	Light fixtures, exterior:	
Prestressed, repair	FSSC	Grouting	FSG
Steel, bearing	FSG	Lighted hand rails:	
Waterproofing	FSW	Grouting	FSG
Junction boxes:		Lighting, grouting:	
Floor raceways	FSSC	Airport	FSSC
Ladders:		Heliport	FSSC
Manhole rungs	FSIG	Highway	FSG
Pit rungs	FSIG	Street Lamps	FSSC
Landings:		Swimming Pools	FSG
Concrete stairs	FSSC		FSW
Steel stair treads	FSSC	Lighting, tunnels:	
Landscaping:		Grouting	FSG
Pools and fountains	FSW	Limestone mortar	FSG 130
Retaining wall		Linings, tanks & vaults:	
maintenance	FSSC	Concrete	FSW
Walks and paths	FSSC	Chemical Resistance	FSW
Wood and metal fences	PS	Repair	FSSC
Lavatory equipment:		Loading docks	FSSC
Setting	FSSC	Loading dock levelers:	
Lawn & tennis equipment:		Grouting	FSSC
Grouting	FSG		
Lead protection:			
Radiation	FSG 160		

Loads, grouting:	
Bearing	FSG
	FSEG
Centrifugal	FSEG
Columns	FSG
Compressive	FSG
Dams	FSG
Docks	FSG 120
Impact	FSEG
	FSREG
Moving	FSEG
	FSREG
Sea water conditions	FSG 120
	FSG 150
	FSW
Machine room ladders:	
Grouting	FSG
Machinery grouting:	
Cold weather grouting	FSIG
Dynamic loads	FSEG
Fast machine set up	FSIG
Fast turnaround time	FSIG
High impact:	
Dynamic loads	FSREG
Fast set up	FSREG
High operating	
temperatures	FSG 200
Hot climate, high	
sulphate conditions	FSG 550
Impact	FSEG
Impact, vibration,	
dynamic loads at	
high temperatures	FSETEG
Non–vibrating	FSG
Pumping long distances	FSG 110

Machinery grouting (cont.):	
Radiation conditions	FSG 160
Saltwater exposure	FSG 120
Ships:	
Generators	FSREG
	FSSEG
Gunmounts	FSREG
	FSSEG
Hoists	FSREG
	FSSEG
Small annular spaces:	
Cable grouting	FSG 400
Strong sulphate attack	FSG 150
Tight clearance	FSG 100
Vibration	FSEG
Mailbox, anchoring	PS
Manholes, grouting:	
Frames & covers	FSSC
Linings	FSW
Rungs	FSIG
Marine repairs	FSSC
Marine terminals:	
Saltwater resistant	FSW
Masonry mortars:	FSIG
Construction anchorage	FSG
Flue tile joints	FSIG
High bond	FSSC
Non–staining mortar	FSG 130
Material handling equipment:	
Conveyors	FSG
	FSEG
Crane rails	FSEG
	FSETEG
	FSREG

Material handling equipment (cont.):		
Hoists	FSG	
	FSEG	
Mechanical equipment:		
Grouting	FSEG	
Rooms, floors	FSW	
Membrane waterproofing:		
Plaza waterproofing	FSW	
Roof waterproofing	FSW	
Slab on ground		
waterproofing	FSW	
Wall waterproofing	FSW	
Mines:		
Anchorages	FSIG	
	FSSC	
Tunnel walls	FSW	
Walls	FSW	
Mortars, non-staining	FSG 100	
Moving stairways	FSG	
Nosings, stair repair	FSSC	
Nuclear shielding	FSG 160	
Oil & gasoline pumps	FSSC	
Oil bulk tank plants	FSSC	
Oil pumps	FSIG	
Open web joists:		
Grouting	FSG	
Openings:		
Masonry concrete walls	FSG	
	FSSC	
Ornamental metal, working	FSIG	
Outdoor lighting fixtures	FSG	
Overhangs	FSW	
Overhead concrete repairs	FSSC	
Overhead crane rail	FSEG	
Overhead hoists	FSEG	
Overhead monorail	FSEG	
Package conveyor systems	FSSC	
Paint, waterproof, brush coat	FSW	
Panels, concrete repair	FSSC	
Parapet repair	FSSC	
Park bench repair	FSSC	
Parking area repair	FSHP	
Parking curb repair	FSSC	
Parking field lighting	FSG	
Parking garages, repairs:		
Floors	FSW	
Gates	FSW	
Walls	FSSC	
Partitions:		
Repair	FSSC	
Waterproofing	FSW	
Patching Materials	FSSC	
	FSIG	
	FSHP	
	FSGs	
	FSEG	
Paths & walks:		
Repair	FSHP	
Pavement:		
Curb repair	FSSC	
Headers	FSHP	
Pothole repair	FSHP	
Salt resistant coating	FSW–HG	
Saltwater protection	FSW	
Underwater pier repair	FSW	
Permeability stoppage	FSW	

Pier construction:	
Fresh water:	
Coatings	FSW
Concrete repair	FSSC
Pile cap repair	FSSC
Saltwater	FSW
Coatings	FSW
Concrete repair	FSSC
Pile cap repair	FSSC
Pipe hand rails	FSSC
Pit waterproofing	FSW
Planks, concrete	FSSC
Planting boxes	FSW
Plates, expansion	FSSC
Platforms, diving	FSSC
Plaza waterproofing	FSW
Poles, grouting:	
Flag	FSSC
Sign	FSSC
Street lighting	FSSC
Pools:	
Fittings	FSG
Hot tubs/saunas	FSW
Waterproofing	FSW
Post Anchors	PS
	FSG
	FSIG
Post–tensioning	FSG 400
Post & railing anchors	FSG
Posts:	
Chainlink fences	PS
Sports facilities	PS

Power generators	FSG
	FSEG
	FSG 100
	FSG 110
Power plant equipment	FSG
	FSIG
	FSEG
	FSG 160
Power, tower lines	FSG
Precast concrete, grouting:	
Beams & columns	FSG
Copings	FSG
Jointing	FSEG
Lintels	FSG
Long spans	FSG
Short spans	FSG
Tilt Up Joints	FSREG
Wall Panels	FSREG
Precast concrete, repair:	
Beams & columns	FSSC
Copings	FSSC
Jointing	FSSC
Lintels	FSSC
Long spans	FSSC
Short spans	FSSC
Tilt up joints	FSSC
	FSG
	FSREG
Wall panels	FSSC
	FSG
	FSREG
Prepackaged concrete:	* All FIVE STAR PRODUCTS

Prison equipment:			Railroads (cont.):	
Anchorages	FSIG		Monorail anchorages	FSEG
Pretensioned concrete:				FSSEG
Repair	FSSC			FSREG
Pumps	FSIG		Rail scales	FSEG
	FSEG		Rapid transit rail	
	FSETEG		grouting:	FSEG
Quarry tile underlayment	FSW		Repair	FSREG
Quays: see docks & piers				FSSEG
Quick setting:			Rails:	
Cementitious grouts	FSIG		Anchors	FSEG
Concrete repair material	FSSC		Crane	FSEG
Epoxy grouts	FSEG			FSETEG
	FSREG		Fast set-ups	FSREG
	FSETEG			FSSEG
	FSSEG		Ram pack:	
Raceways, electrical:			Grouting	FSG
Grouting	FSG		Rapid transit:	
Radiation shielding	FSG 160		Rails & tracks, repair	FSREG
Radio/TV antenna systems	FSEG			FSSEG
Radio or power towers:			Repair	FSSC
Grouting	FSG		Tunnel walls	FSW
Railings, anchorages	FSG		Reciprocating engines	FSEG
	FSSC		Recreation equipment:	
	FSIG		Grouting	FSEG
	FSEG			FSSC
	PS			PS
	FSREG		Refrigeration equipment:	
Railroads:			Grouting	FSG
Fast turnaround	FSREG		Refrigeration equipment areas	FSW
Grouting, pre-cast			Reinforced concrete repair:	
section joints	FSREG		Floors	FSSC
	FSSEG		Foundations	FSSC
	FSG 100		Honeycomb	FSSC

Reinforced concrete repair (cont.):	
Pits	FSW
Roofs	FSW
Snap tie holes	FSSC
Soffits	FSSC V/O
Spalled	FSSC
Stairs	FSSC
Surfaces	FSSC
Walls:	FSSC
Retaining walls	FSW
Reservoirs:	
Protective coating	FSW
Repair:	
Saltwater conditions	FSW
Spillways	FSSC
Surfaces	FSSC
Water penetration	FSW
Water treatment	FSW
Restaurants:	
Floors	FSW
Retaining walls, concrete:	
Repair	FSSC
Waterproofing	FSW
Riser & tread repair,	
concrete	FSSC
Roads & sidewalks:	
Repair	FSSC
	FSHP
Salt protection	FSW
Rock anchors:	FSG
	FSG 100
	FSG 110
	FSG 400
Roofing	FSW

Runways:	FSHP
Lighting	FSSC
Saddles:	
Exterior doors	FSG
Safety deposit vaults	FSW
	FSG
Saltwater:	
Coatings	FSW
	FSW–HG
Grouts	FSEG
	FSIG
	FSSC
Sanitation systems:	
Grouting	FSG
	FSG 120
Waterproofing	FSW
Sea walls:	
Below water	FSIG
Repair	FSSC
Saltwater protection	FSW
Seating:	
Permanent, outdoor	FSIG
Security fences	PS
	FSHP
Service elevator pits	FSW
Setting beds, waterproofing	FSW
Stone floors	FSW
Terrazzo	FSW
Tile	FSW
Sewage disposal facilities:	
Equipment	FSEG
Grouting	FSG 120
	FSG 150

Sewage disposal facilities (cont.):	
Protective coatings	FSW
Repair	FSSC
Sewer manhole coatings:	FSW
Ladders	FSG 120
Manhole covers	FSSC
Pumping stations	FSEG
Shielding, radiation:	FSG 160
Shell, thin concrete roofs	FSW
Ships:	
Generators	FSREG
	FSSEG
Gunmounts	FSREG
	FSSEG
Hoists	FSREG
	FSSEG
Shopping centers:	
Columns, grouting	FSG
Shoring, anchorage:	FSIG
Shotcrete:	All FIVE STAR cementitious products
Sidewalk elevator:	FSW
Sidewalk framing:	FSG
Silos, concrete, waterproof coating	FSW
Slab & plate floors:	See Reinforced Concrete
Slab-on-grade	FSW
Slab pre-cast repair	FSSC
Spandrel waterproofing	FSW

Spillways:	
Coating	FSW
Gates	FSEG
	FSREG
Repair	FSSC
Sports equipment:	
Anchorage	FSSC
	PS
Stacks:	
Lining	FSW
Mortar	FSIG
Stair treads	FSSC
Stairs:	
Repair	FSSC
Standard floor leveling	FSSC
Steel access doors:	
Grouting	FSG
Joists, bearing	FSG
Ladders, anchoring	FSG
Railings & posts, anchoring	FSSC
Shapes, bearing	FSG
Stair treads	FSSC
Stone:	
Marble joints	FSG 130
Mortars	FSSC
Limestone joints	FSG 130
Travertine	FSG 130
Storage facilities:	
Chemical resistance	FSW
Cold storage	FSW
Concrete catch basins	FSW
Industrial chemical pits	FSW
Water tanks	FSW

Storage facilities (cont.):	
Water towers	FSW
Waterproofing	FSW
Storm drainage	
Inlets & catch basins	FSW
	FSG
Street repair	FSHP
Structural concrete:	
Repairs	Refer to FIVE STAR PRODUCTS HANDBOOK
Structural repair:	
Concrete	FSSC
Floors	FSSC
Roofs	FSSC
Walls	FSSC
Structural steel fireproofing:	
Repair	FSSC
Structural systems precast, concrete:	
Repair	FSSC
Stucco, waterproofing	FSW
Concrete	FSSC
Exposed aggregate	FSSC
Masonry	FSSC
Surface bonding	FSSC
Surfacing materials	FSW
Swimming pools:	
Coatings	FSW
Fittings, grout	FSG
Tanks:	
Chemical resistance	FSW
Exterior	FSW
Ladders	FSSC
Leveling	FSEG

Tanks (cont.):	
Protective lining	FSW
Repair	FSSC
Tee structural shapes:	
Cable grouts	FSG 400
Grouting	FSG
Repair	FSSC
Television antenna systems	FSEG
Tendons:	
Grouting	FSG 400
Tension crack repair	FSREG
	FSSEG
	FSEG
	FSSC
Tiles	FSSC
Tilt–up construction joints	FSSC
Tracks, rail:	
Rapid resetting	FSREG
	FSSEG
	FSEG
Treads, concrete:	FSSC
Repair	FSSC
Trench covers	FSSC
	FSHP
Transformers	FSEG
Transmission poles	FSG
Tunnels, rail:	
Grouting	FSG
Grouting rail fittings	FSEG
Guniting linings	FSSC
Rail slab repair	FSHP
Waterproofing	FSW

Tunnels, structural concrete:	
Instant repair	FSREG
Repair	FSSC
Tunnels, vehicle:	
Grouting	FSG
Guniting, linings	FSSC
Road repair	FSHP
Waterproofing	FSW
Turbines, fixed	FSG 100
	FSG 110
High temperatures	FSETEG
Vibrating	FSEG
Turnpikes, see Highway	
Underground structures:	
Concrete repair	FSSC
Fast setting	FSIG
Grouting, misc.	FSG
Road repair	FSHP
Waterproofing	FSW
Underpinning:	
Fast grout	FSIG
Structural repair	FSSC
Utilities:	
See poles, generators,	
turbines & other	
electrical equipment	
transmissions	
Vapor barriers	FSW
Vapor penetration, low	FSW
Vaults & storage rooms:	
Dry	FSW
Ladders, grouting	FSG
Manhole in road	FSIG
Manholes, grouting	FSG
Structural repair	FSSC

Vehicle control devices in road	FSSC
Waffle plate construction repair	FSSC
Walkway covers, metal	FSG
Walkway surfacing, salt resistant	FSW–HG
Wall pipe chases, closures	FSSC
Walls, pre–cast repair	FSSC
Cavity repair:	FSSC
Anchorages	FSG
Bearing pads	FSG
Form tie – holes	FSSC
Negative pressure waterproofing	FSW
Saltwater exposure	FSW
Saltwater repair	FSIG
Surface coating	FSW
Waste & water treatment:	
Chemical resistance	FSW
	FSEG
Grouting	FSG 120
	FSG 150
Skimming tanks	FSW
Waste disposal system:	
Chemical resistance	FSW
	FSEG
Grouting	FSG 120
	FSG 150
Wastewater tunnel:	
Interior lining	FSW
Water, drinking, potable, EPA approved	FSW
Water, pools & fountains	FSW
Waterproofing	Refer to FIVE STAR PRODUCTS HANDBOOK

Water storage:	
Concrete catch basins	FSW
Elevated concrete tanks	FSW
Water supply, drinking water,	
EPA approved	FSW
Water supply desalinization	
plants:	
Grouting	FSG 120
	FSG 550
Water supply equipment:	
Grouting	FSG 120
Water supply pump	FSEG
Water supply treatment	
facilities	FSW
Water treatment equipment:	FSG 120
Purification tanks	FSW
Water treatment facilities	FSW
Water tunnels:	
Interior lining	FSW
Waterproof materials:	FSW See particular application
Below grade	FSW
Deck drains	FSW
Plazas	FSW
Vaults & pits	FSW
Weather conditions	Refer to FIVE STAR PRODUCTS HANDBOOK
Weathertight curtain walls	FSW
Wells & pumps:	
Grouting	FSG
Wharves – see docks	

Wire fence posts	PS
	FSHP
	FSG
X–ray protection:	FSG 160
Floors, nuclear shield	FSG 160
Overhead nuclear shield	FSG 160
Walls, nuclear shield	FSG 160
Yard drainage, grouting:	
Inlets, catch basins	FSG
Zoning, fire resistance:	All FIVE STAR cementitious products
Potable water coating, EPA approved	FSW